360 Problems for
Mathematical Contests

360 Problems for
Mathematical Contests

Titu Andreescu, Dorin Andrica

LEVANT
Levant Books

360 Problems for Mathematical Contests
by Titu Andreescu, Dorin Andrica

© GIL Publishing House

This Indian Edition Published by
Levant Books
27C, Creek Row
Kolkata - 700 014

By arrangement with
GIL Publishing House

And Exclusively Distributed By
Sarat Book Distributors
18 B Shyama Charan Dey Street
Kolkata - 700 073
orders@saratbookhouse.com

This edition for sale in India, Bangladesh, Pakistan, Sri Lanka and Myanmar only. Not for export elsewhere.

First Indian Edition 2014

ISBN 978-93-80663-96-8

Printed and bound at
Sarat Impressions Pvt. Ltd., 18B Shyama Charan Dey Street, Kolkata.

Contents

FOREWORD

I take great pleasure in recommending to all readers - Romanians or from abroad - the book of professors Titu Andreescu and Dorin Andrica. This book is the fruit of a prodigious activity of the two authors, well-known creators of mathematics questions for Olympiads and other mathematical contests. They have published innumerable original problems in various mathematical journals.

The book is organized in six chapters: algebra, number theory, geometry, trigonometry, analysis and comprehensive problems. In addition, other fields of mathematics found their place in this book, for example, combinatorial problems can be found in the last chapter, and problems involving complex numbers are included in the trigonometry section. Moreover, in all chapters of this book the serious reader can find numerous challenging inequality problems. All featured problems are interesting, with an increased level of difficulty; some of them are real gems that will give great satisfaction to any math lover attempting to solve or even extend them.

Through their outstanding work as jury members of the National Mathematical Olympiad, the Balkan Mathematics Contest (BMO), and the International Mathematical Olympiad (IMO), the authors also supported the excellent results of the Romanian contestants in these competitions. A great effort was given in preparing lectures for summer and winter training camps and also for creating original problems to be used in selection tests to search for truly gifted mathematics students. To support the claim that the Romanian students selected to represent the country were really the ones to deserve such honor, we note that only two mathematicians of Romanian origin, both former IMO gold-medalists, were invited recently to give conferences at the International Mathematical Congress: Dan Voiculescu (Zürich, 1994) and Daniel Tataru (Beijing, 2002). The Romanian mathematical community unanimously recognized this outstanding activity of professors Titu Andreescu and Dorin Andrica. As a consequence, Titu Andreescu, at that time professor at Loga Academy in Timişoara and having students on the team participating in the IMO, was appointed to serve as deputy leader of the national team. Nowadays, Titu's potential, as with other Romanians in different fields, has been fully realized in the United States, leading the USA team in the IMO, coordinating the training and selection of team contestants and serving as member of several national and regional mathematical contest juries.

One more time, I strongly express my belief that the 360 mathematics problems featured in this book will reveal the beauty of mathematics to all students and it will be a guide to their teachers and professors.

Professor Ioan Tomescu
Department of Mathematics and Computer Science
University of Bucharest
Associate member of the Romanian Academy

FROM THE AUTHORS

This book is intended to help students preparing for all rounds of Mathematical Olympiads or any other significant mathematics contest. Teachers will also find this work useful in training young talented students.

Our experience as contestants was a great asset in preparing this book. To this we added our vast personal experience from the other side of the "barricade", as creators of problems and members of numerous contest committees.

All the featured problems are supposed to be original. They are the fruit of our collaboration for the last 30 years with several elementary mathematics journals from all over the world. Many of these problems were used in contests throughout these years, from the first round to the international level. It is possible that some problems are already known, but this is not critical. The important thing is that an educated - to a certain extent - reader will find in this book problems that bring something new and will teach new ways of dealing with key mathematics concepts, a variety of methods, tactics, and strategies.

The problems are divided in chapters, although this division is not firm, for some of the problems require background in several fields of mathematics.

Besides the traditional fields: algebra, geometry, trigonometry and analysis, we devoted an entire chapter to number theory, because many contest problems require knowledge in this field.

The comprehensive problems in the last chapter are also intended to help undergraduate students participating in mathematics contests hone their problem solving skills. Students and teachers can find here ideas and questions that can be interesting topics for mathematics circles.

Due to the difficulty level of the problems contained in this book, we deemed it appropriate to give a very clear and complete presentation of all solutions. In many cases, alternative solutions are provided.

As a piece of advice to all readers, we suggest that they try to find their own solutions to the problems before reading the given ones. Many problems can be solved in multiple ways and pertain to interesting extensions.

This edition is significantly different from the 2002 Romanian edition. It features more recent problems, enhanced solutions, along with references for all published problems.

We wish to extend our gratitude to everyone who influenced in one way or another the final version of this book.

We will gladly receive any observation from the readers.

The authors

Chapter 1
ALGEBRA

PROBLEMS

1. Let C be a set of n characters $\{c_1, c_2, \ldots, c_n\}$. We call **word** a string of at most m characters, $m \leq n$, that does not start nor end with c_1.

How many **words** can be formed with the characters of the set C?

2. The numbers $1, 2, \ldots, 5n$ are divided into two disjoint sets. Prove that these sets contain at least n pairs (x, y), $x > y$, such that the number $x - y$ is also an element of the set which contains the pair.

3. Let $a_1, a_2, \ldots, a_n$ be distinct numbers from the interval $[a, b]$ and let σ be a permutation of $\{1, 2, \ldots, n\}$.

Define the function $f : [a, b] \to [a, b]$ as follows:

$$f(x) = \begin{cases} a_{\sigma(i)} & \text{if } x = a_i, \ i = \overline{1, n} \\ x & \text{otherwise} \end{cases}$$

Prove that there is a positive integer h such that $f^{[h]}(x) = x$, where $f^{[h]} = \underbrace{f \circ f \circ \cdots \circ f}_{h \text{ times}}$.

4. Prove that if x, y, z are nonzero real numbers with $x + y + z = 0$, then

$$\frac{x^2 + y^2}{x + y} + \frac{y^2 + z^2}{y + z} + \frac{z^2 + x^2}{z + x} = \frac{x^3}{yz} + \frac{y^3}{zx} + \frac{z^3}{xy}.$$

5. Let a, b, c, d be complex numbers with $a + b + c + d = 0$. Prove that

$$a^3 + b^3 + c^3 + d^3 = 3(abc + bcd + cda + dab).$$

6. Let a, b, c be nonzero real numbers such that $a + b + c = 0$ and $a^3 + b^3 + c^3 = a^5 + b^5 + c^5$. Prove that

$$a^2 + b^2 + c^2 = \frac{6}{5}.$$

7. Let a, b, c, d be integers. Prove that $a + b + c + d$ divides

$$2(a^4 + b^4 + c^4 + d^4) - (a^2 + b^2 + c^2 + d^2)^2 + 8abcd.$$

8. Solve in complex numbers the equation

$$(x+1)(x+2)(x+3)^2(x+4)(x+5) = 360.$$

9. Solve in real numbers the equation

$$\sqrt{x} + \sqrt{y} + 2\sqrt{z-2} + \sqrt{u} + \sqrt{v} = x + y + z + u + v.$$

10. Find the real solutions to the equation

$$(x+y)^2 = (x+1)(y-1).$$

11. Solve the equation

$$\sqrt{x + \sqrt{4x + \sqrt{16x + \sqrt{\cdots + \sqrt{4^n x + 3}}}}} - \sqrt{x} = 1.$$

12. Solve the equation

$$\sqrt{x+a} + \sqrt{x+b} + \sqrt{x+c} = \sqrt{x+a+b-c},$$

where a, b, c are real parameters. Discuss the equation in terms of the values of the parameters.

13. Let a and b be distinct positive real numbers. Find all pairs of positive real numbers (x, y), solutions to the system of equations

$$\begin{cases} x^4 - y^4 = ax - by \\ x^2 - y^2 = \sqrt[3]{a^2 - b^2}. \end{cases}$$

14. Solve the equation

$$\left[\frac{25x - 2}{4} \right] = \frac{13x + 4}{3},$$

where $[a]$ denotes the integer part of a real number a.

15. Prove that if $a \geq \dfrac{1 + \sqrt{5}}{2}$, then

$$\left[\frac{1 + \left[\dfrac{1 + na^2}{a} \right]}{a} \right] = n, \quad n = 0, 1, 2, \ldots$$

16. Prove that if x, y, z are real numbers such that $x^3 + y^3 + z^3 \neq 0$, then the ratio

$$\frac{2xyz - (x + y + z)}{x^3 + y^3 + z^3}$$

equals $\frac{2}{3}$ if and only if $x + y + z = 0$.

17. Solve in real numbers the equation

$$\sqrt{x_1 - 1} + 2\sqrt{x_2 - 4} + \cdots + n\sqrt{x_n - n^2} = \frac{1}{2}(x_1 + x_2 + \cdots + x_n).$$

18. Find the real solutions to the system of equations

$$\begin{cases} \dfrac{1}{x} + \dfrac{1}{y} = 9 \\ \left(\dfrac{1}{\sqrt[3]{x}} + \dfrac{1}{\sqrt[3]{y}}\right)\left(1 + \dfrac{1}{\sqrt[3]{x}}\right)\left(1 + \dfrac{1}{\sqrt[3]{y}}\right) = 18 \end{cases}$$

19. Solve in real numbers the system of equations

$$\begin{cases} y^2 + u^2 + v^2 + w^2 = 4x - 1 \\ x^2 + u^2 + v^2 + w^2 = 4y - 1 \\ x^2 + y^2 + v^2 + w^2 = 4u - 1 \\ x^2 + y^2 + u^2 + w^2 = 4v - 1 \\ x^2 + y^2 + u^2 + v^2 = 4w - 1 \end{cases}$$

20. Let a_1, a_2, a_3, a_4, a_5 be real numbers such that $a_1 + a_2 + a_3 + a_4 + a_5 = 0$ and $\max\limits_{1 \leq i < j \leq 5} |a_i - a_j| \leq 1$. Prove that $a_1^2 + a_2^2 + a_3^2 + a_4^2 + a_5^2 \leq 10$.

21. Let a, b, c be positive real numbers. Prove that

$$\frac{1}{2a} + \frac{1}{2b} + \frac{1}{2c} \geq \frac{1}{a + b} + \frac{1}{b + c} + \frac{1}{c + a}$$

22. Let a, b, c be real numbers such that the sum of any two of them is not equal to zero. Prove that

$$\frac{a^5 + b^5 + c^5 - (a + b + c)^5}{a^3 + b^3 + c^3 - (a + b + c)^3} \geq \frac{10}{9}(a + b + c)^2$$

23. Let a, b, c be real numbers such that $abc = 1$. Prove that at most two of the numbers

$$2a - \frac{1}{b}, \quad 2b - \frac{1}{c}, \quad 2c - \frac{1}{a}$$

are greater than 1.

24. Let a, b, c, d be real numbers. Prove that

$$\min(a - b^2, b - c^2, c - d^2, d - a^2) \le \frac{1}{4}.$$

25. Let $a_1, a_2, \ldots, a_n$ be numbers in the interval $(0, 1)$ and let $k \ge 2$ be an integer. Find the maximum value of the expression

$$\sum_{i=1}^{n} \sqrt[k]{a_i(1 - a_{i+1})},$$

where $a_{n+1} = a_1$.

26. Let m and n be positive integers. Prove that

$$\frac{x^{mn} - 1}{m} \ge \frac{x^n - 1}{x}$$

for any positive real number x.

27. Prove that $m! \ge (n!)^{\left[\frac{m}{n}\right]}$ for all positive integers m and n.

28. Prove that

$$1 + \frac{1}{\sqrt[2]{2}} + \frac{1}{\sqrt[3]{3}} + \cdots + \frac{1}{\sqrt[n]{n}} > n \sqrt[n]{\frac{2}{n+1}}$$

for any integer $n \ge 2$.

29. Prove that

$$n\left(1 - 1/\sqrt[n]{n}\right) + 1 > 1 + \frac{1}{2} + \frac{1}{3} + \cdots + \frac{1}{n} > n\left(\sqrt[n]{n+1} - 1\right)$$

for any positive integer n.

30. Let $a_1, a_2, \ldots, a_n \in (0, 1)$ and let $t_n = \dfrac{n a_1 a_2 \ldots a_n}{a_1 + a_2 + \cdots + a_n}$. Prove that

$$\sum_{i=1}^{n} \log_{a_i} t_n \ge (n - 1)n.$$

31. Prove that between n and $3n$ there is at least a perfect cube for any integer $n \ge 10$.

32. Compute the sum

$$S_n = \sum_{k=1}^{n} (-1)^{\frac{k(k+1)}{2}} k.$$

33. Compute the sums:

a) $S_n = \displaystyle\sum_{k=0}^{n} \frac{1}{(k+1)(k+2)} \binom{n}{k}$; b) $T_n = \displaystyle\sum_{k=0}^{n} \frac{1}{(k+1)(k+2)(k+3)} \binom{n}{k}$.

34. Show that for any positive integer n the number

$$\binom{2n+1}{0}2^{2n} + \binom{2n+1}{2}2^{2n-2}\cdot 3 + \cdots + \binom{2n+1}{2n}3^n$$

is the sum of two consecutive perfect squares.

35. Evaluate the sums:

$$S_n = \binom{n}{1} - 3\binom{n}{3} + 5\binom{n}{5} - 7\binom{n}{7} + \cdots$$

36. Prove that

$$1^2\binom{n}{1} + 3^2\binom{n}{3} + 5^2\binom{n}{5} + \cdots = n(n+1)2^{n-3}$$

for all integers $n \geq 3$.

37. Prove that

$$\sum_{k=1}^{2^n}[\log_2 k] = (n-2)2^n + n + 2$$

for all positive integers n.

38. Let $x_n = 2^{2^n} + 1$, $n = 1, 2, 3, \ldots$ Prove that

$$\frac{1}{x_1} + \frac{2}{x_2} + \frac{2^2}{x_3} + \cdots + \frac{2^{n-1}}{x_n} < \frac{1}{3}$$

for all positive integers n.

39. Let $f : \mathbb{C} \to \mathbb{C}$ be a function such that $f(z)f(iz) = z^2$ for all $z \in \mathbb{C}$. Prove that

$$f(z) + f(-z) = 0 \text{ for all } z \in \mathbb{C}$$

40. Consider a function $f : (0,\infty) \to \mathbb{R}$ and a real number $a > 0$ such that $f(a) = 1$. Prove that if

$$f(x)f(y) + f\left(\frac{a}{x}\right)f\left(\frac{a}{y}\right) = 2f(xy) \text{ for all } x, y \in (0,\infty),$$

then f is a constant function.

41. Find with proof if the function $f : \mathbb{R} \to [-1,1]$, $f(x) = \sin[x]$ is periodical.

42. For all $i, j = \overline{1,n}$ define $S(i,j) = \sum_{k=1}^{n} k^{i+j}$. Evaluate the determinant $\Delta = |S(i,j)|$.

'43. Let

$$x_{ij} = \begin{cases} a_i & \text{if } i = j \\ 0 & \text{if } i \neq j, \ i + j \neq 2n + 1 \\ b_i & \text{if } i + j = 2n + 1 \end{cases}$$

where a_i, b_i are real numbers.

Evaluate the determinant $\Delta_{2n} = |x_{ij}|$.

44. a) Compute the determinant

$$\begin{vmatrix} x & y & z & v \\ y & x & v & z \\ z & v & x & y \\ v & z & y & x \end{vmatrix}$$

b) Prove that if the numbers $\overline{abcd}, \overline{badc}, \overline{cdab}, \overline{dcba}$ are divisible by a prime p, then at least one of the numbers

$$a + b + c + d, \quad a + b - c - d, \quad a - b + c - d, \quad a - b - c + d,$$

is divisible by p.

45. Consider the quadratic polynomials $t_1(x) = x^2 + p_1 x + q_1^2$ and $t_2(x) = x^2 + p_2 x + q_2^2$, where p_1, p_2, q_1, q_2 are real numbers.

Prove that if polynomials t_1 and t_2 have zeros of the same nature, then the polynomial

$$t(x) = x^2 + (p_1 p_2 + 4 q_1 q_2)x + (p_1 q_2 + p_2 q_1)^2$$

has real zeros.

46. Let a, b, c be real numbers with $a > 0$ such that the quadratic polynomial

$$T(x) = ax^2 + bcx + b^3 + c^3 - 4abc$$

has nonreal zeros.

Prove that exactly one of the polynomials $T_1(x) = ax^2 + bx + c$ and $T_2(x) = ax^2 + cx + b$ has only positive values.

47. Consider the polynomials with complex coefficients

$$P(x) = x^n + a_1 x^{n-1} + \cdots + a_n \text{ and } Q(x) = x^n + b_1 x^{n-1} + \cdots + b_n$$

having zeros $x_1, x_2, \ldots, x_n$ and $x_1^2, x_2^2, \ldots, x_n^2$ respectively.

Prove that if $a_1 + a_3 + a_5 + \ldots$ and $a_2 + a_4 + a_6 + \ldots$ are real numbers, then $b_1 + b_2 + \cdots + b_n$ is also a real number.

48. Let $P(x)$ be a polynomial of degree n. If

$$P(k) = \frac{k}{k+1} \text{ for } k = 0, 1, \ldots, n$$

evaluate $P(m)$, where $m > n$.

49. Find all polynomials $P(x)$ with integral coefficients such that

$$P(P'(x)) = P'(P(x))$$

for all real numbers x.

50. Consider the polynomials p_i, $i = 1, 2, \ldots, n$ with degrees at least 1. Prove that if the polynomial

$$P(x) = p_1(x^{n+1}) + xp_2(x^{n+1}) + \cdots + x^{n-1}p_n(x^{n+1}),$$

is divisible by $x^n + x^{n-1} + \cdots + x + 1$, then all polynomials $p_i(x)$, $i = \overline{1,n}$, are divisible by $x - 1$.

51. Let p be a prime number and let

$$P(x) = a_0 x^n + a_1 x^{n-1} + \cdots + a_n$$

be a polynomial with integral coefficients such that $a_n \not\equiv 0 \pmod{p}$. Prove that if there are $n + 1$ integers $\alpha_1, \alpha_2, \ldots, \alpha_{n+1}$ such that $P(\alpha_r) \equiv 0 \pmod{p}$ for all $r = 1, 2, \ldots, n + 1$, then there exist i, j with $i \neq j$ such that $\alpha_i \equiv \alpha_j \pmod{p}$.

52. Determine all polynomials P with real coefficients such that $P^n(x) = P(x^n)$ for all real numbers x, where $n > 1$ is a given integer.

53. Let

$$P(x) = a_0 x^n + a_1 x^{n-1} + \cdots + a_n, \quad a_n \neq 0,$$

be a polynomial with complex coefficients such that there is an integer m with

$$\left| \frac{a_m}{a_n} \right| > \binom{n}{m}.$$

Prove that the polynomial P has at least a zero with the absolute value less than 1.

54. Find all polynomials P of degree n having only real zeros $x_1, x_2, \ldots, x_n$ such that

$$\sum_{i=1}^{n} \frac{1}{P(x) - x_i} = \frac{n^2}{xP'(x)},$$

for all nonzero real numbers x.

55. Consider the polynomial with real coefficients

$$P(x) = a_0 x^n + a_1 x^{n-1} + \cdots + a_n,$$

and $a_n \neq 0$.

Prove that if the equation $P(x) = 0$ has all of its roots real and distinct, then the equation

$$x^2 P''(x) + 3x P'(x) + P(x) = 0$$

has the same property.

56. Let $R_{[x]}^{(0)}$ and $R_{[x]}^{(n)}$ be the sets of polynomials with real coefficients having no multiple zeros and having multiple zeros of order n respectively. Prove that if $P(x) \in R_{[x]}^{(0)}$ and $P(Q(x)) \in R_{[x]}^{(k)}$, then $Q'(x) \in R_{[x]}^{(k-1)}$.

57. Let $P(x)$ be a polynomial with real coefficients of degree at least 2. Prove that if there is a real number a such that

$$P(a)P''(a) > (P'(a))^2,$$

then P has at least two nonreal zeros.

58. Consider the equation

$$a_0 x^n + a_1 x^{n-1} + \cdots + a_n = 0$$

with real coefficients a_i. Prove that if the equation has all of its roots real, then $(n-1)a_1^2 \geq 2n a_0 a_2$. Is the reciprocal true?

59. Solve the equation

$$x^4 - (2m+1)x^3 + (m-1)x^2 + (2m^2+1)x + m = 0,$$

where m is a real parameter.

60. Solve the equation

$$x^{2n} + a_1 x^{2n-1} + \cdots + a_{2n-2}x^2 - 2nx + 1 = 0,$$

if all of its roots are real.

SOLUTIONS

1. Let N_k be the number of words having exactly k characters from the set C, $1 \leq k \leq m$. Clearly, $N_1 = n - 1$. The number that we seek is $N_1 + N_2 + \cdots + N_m$.

Let $A_k = \{1, 2, \ldots, k\}$, $1 \leq k \leq m$. We need to find out the number of functions $f : A_k \to A$, $k = \overline{2, n}$ with the properties

$$f(1) \neq a_1 \quad \text{and} \quad f(k) \neq a_1$$

For $f(1)$ and $f(k)$ there are $n - 1$ possibilities of choosing a character from $c_2, \ldots, c_n$ and for $f(i)$, $1 < i < k$ there are n such possibilities. Therefore the number of strings $f(1)f(2) \ldots f(k-1)f(k)$ is

$$N_k = (n-1)^2 n^{k-2}$$

It follows that

$$N_1 + N_2 + \cdots + N_m = (n-1) + (n-1)^2 n^0 + (n-1)^2 n^1 + \cdots + (n-1)^2 n^{m-2} =$$

$$= n^m - n^{m-1}$$

(*Dorin Andrica*)

2. Suppose, for the sake of contradiction, that there are two sets A and B such that $A \cup B = \{1, 2, \ldots, 5n\}$, $A \cap B = \emptyset$ and the sets contain together less than n pairs (x, y), $x > y$, with the desired property.

Let k be a given number, $k = \overline{1, n}$. If k and $2k$ are in the same set – A or B – the same can be said about the difference $2k - k = k$. The same argument is applied for $4k$ and $2k$. Consider the case when k and $4k$ are elements of A and $2k$ is an element of B. If $3k$ is an element of A, then $4k - 3k = k \in A$, so let $3k \in B$. Now if $5k \in A$, then $5k - 4k = k \in A$ and if $5k \in B$, then $5k - 3k = 2k \in B$; so among the numbers $k, 2k, 3k, 4k, 5k$ there is at least a pair with the desired property. Because $k = 1, 2, \ldots, n$, it follows that there are at least n pairs with the desired property.

(*Dorin Andrica*, Revista Matematică Timişoara (RMT), No. 2(1978), pp. 75, Problem 3698)

3. Note that

$$f^{[k+1]} = f \circ f^{[k]}, \quad k \geq 1 \tag{1}$$

17

and furthermore

$$f^{[m_1+m_2]} = f^{[m_1]} \circ f^{[m_2]} \tag{2}$$

for all integers $m_1, m_2 \geq 1$.

Suppose that for all integers $k \geq 1$ we have $f^{[k]}(x) \neq x$.

Because there are $n!$ permutations, it follows that for $k > n!$ there are distinct positive integers $n_1 > n_2$ such that

$$f^{[n_1]}(x) = f^{[n_2]}(x) \tag{3}$$

Let $h = n_1 - n_2 > 0$ and observe that for all k the functions $f^{[k]}$ are injective, since numbers a_i, $i = \overline{1,n}$ are distinct. From relation (3) we derive that

$$f^{[n_2+h]}(x) = f^{[n_2]}(x), \quad x \in [a,b],$$

or

$$(f \circ f^{[n_2+h-1]})(x) = (f \circ f^{[n_2-1]})(x), \quad x \in [a,b].$$

Because f is injective, we obtain

$$f^{[n_2+h-1]}(x) = f^{[n_2-1]}(x), \quad x \in [a,b]$$

and in the same manner

$$f^{[h+1]}(x) = f(x), \quad x \in [a,b]$$

or

$$f^{[h]}(x) = x, \quad x \in [a,b].$$

Alternative solution. Let S_n be the symmetric group of order n and H_n the cyclic subgroup generated by σ. It is clear that H_n is a finite group and therefore there is integer h such that $\sigma^{[h]}$ is identical permutation.

Notice that

$$f^{[k]}(x) = \begin{cases} a_{\sigma^{[k]}(i)} & \text{if } x = a_i, \ i = \overline{1,n} \\ x & \text{otherwise} \end{cases}$$

Then $f^{[h]}(x) = x$ and the solution is complete.

(*Dorin Andrica*, Revista Matematică Timişoara (RMT), No. 2(1978), pp. 53, Problem 3540)

4. Because $x + y + z = 0$, we obtain

$$x + y = -z, \quad y + z = -x, \quad z + x = -y,$$

or, by squaring and rearranging,

$$x^2 + y^2 = z^2 - 2xy, \quad y^2 + z^2 = x^2 - 2yz, \quad z^2 + x^2 = y^2 - 2zx.$$

The given equality is equivalent to

$$\frac{z^2 - 2xy}{-z} + \frac{x^2 - 2yz}{-x} + \frac{y^2 - 2zx}{-y} = \frac{x^3}{yz} + \frac{y^3}{zx} + \frac{z^3}{xy},$$

and consequently to

$$-(x+y+z)+2\left(\frac{xy}{z}+\frac{yz}{x}+\frac{zx}{y}\right)=\frac{x^3}{yz}+\frac{y^3}{zx}+\frac{z^3}{xy}.$$

The last equality is equivalent to

$$2(x^2y^2+y^2z^2+z^2x^2)=x^4+y^4+z^4.$$

On the other side, from $x+y+z=0$ we obtain $(x+y+z)^2=0$ or

$$x^2+y^2+z^2=-2(xy+yz+zx).$$

Squaring yields

$$x^4+y^4+z^4+2(x^2y^2+y^2z^2+z^2x^2)=4(x^2y^2+y^2z^2+z^2x^2)+8xyz(x+y+z)$$

or

$$x^4+y^4+z^4=2(x^2y^2+y^2z^2+z^2x^2),$$

as desired.

(*Titu Andreescu*, Revista Matematică Timişoara (RMT), No. 3(1971), pp. 25, Problem 483; Gazeta Matematică (GM-B), No. 12(1977), pp. 501, Problem 6090)

5. We assume that numbers a,b,c,d are different from zero. Consider the equation

$$x^4-\left(\sum a\right)x^3+\left(\sum ab\right)x^2-\left(\sum abc\right)x+abcd=0$$

with roots a,b,c,d. Substituting x with a,b,c and d and simplifying by $a,b,c,d\neq 0$, after summing up we obtain

$$\sum a^3-\left(\sum a\right)\left(\sum a^2\right)+\left(\sum ab\right)\left(\sum a\right)-3\sum abc=0.$$

Because $\sum a=0$, it follows that

$$\sum a^3=3\sum abc.$$

If one of the numbers is zero, say a, then

$$b+c+d=0,$$

or $b+c=-d$. It is left to prove that $b^3+c^3+d^3=3bcd$. Now

$$b^3+c^3+d^3=b^3+c^3-(b+c)^3=-3bc(b+c)=3bcd$$

as desired.

(*Dorin Andrica*, Revista Matematică Timişoara (RMT), No. 1-2(1979), pp. 47, Problem 3803)

6. Because $a+b+c=0$, we obtain

$$a^3+b^3+c^3=3abc \quad\text{and}\quad a^5+b^5+c^5=5abc(a^2+b^2+c^2+ab+bc+ca)$$

The given relation becomes

$$3abc = 5abc(a^2 + b^2 + c^2 + ab + bc + ca)$$

or

$$a^2 + b^2 + c^2 + ab + bc + ca = \frac{3}{5},$$

since a, b, c are nonzero numbers. It follows that

$$\frac{1}{2}[(a + b + c)^2 + a^2 + b^2 + c^2] = \frac{3}{5}$$

and, using again the relation $a + b + c = 0$, we obtain

$$a^2 + b^2 + c^2 = \frac{6}{5},$$

as desired.

(*Titu Andreescu*, Revista Matematică Timişoara (RMT), No. 2(1977), pp. 59, Problem 3016)

7. Consider the equation

$$x^4 - \left(\sum a\right) x^3 + \left(\sum ab\right) x^2 - \left(\sum abc\right) x + abcd = 0,$$

with roots a, b, c, d. Substituting x with a, b, c and d, respectively, we obtain after summation that

$$\sum a^4 + \left(\sum ab\right) \sum a^2 + 4abcd$$

is divisible by $\sum a$. Taking into account that

$$\sum ab = \frac{\left(\sum a\right)^2 - \sum a^2}{2},$$

we deduce that

$$2\sum a^4 + \left[\left(\sum a\right)^2 - \sum a^2\right] \sum a^2 + 8abcd,$$

is divisible by $\sum a$. Hence

$$2(a^4 + b^4 + c^4 + d^4) - (a^2 + b^2 + c^2 + d^2)^2 + 8abcd$$

is divisible by $a + b + c + d$, as desired.

(*Dorin Andrica*)

8. The equation is equivalent to

$$(x^2 + 6x + 5)(x^2 + 6x + 8)(x^2 + 6x + 9) = 360.$$

Setting $x^2 + 6x = y$ yields

$$(y + 5)(y + 8)(y + 9) = 360,$$

or

$$y^3 + 22y^2 + 157y = 0,$$

with solutions

$$y_1 = 0, \quad y_2 = -11 + 6i, \quad y_3 = -11 - 6i.$$

Turning back to the substitution, we obtain a first equation, $x^2 + 6x = 0$, with solutions $x_1 = 0$, $x_2 = -6$.

The equation $x^2 + 6x = -11 + 6i$ is equivalent to $(x+3)^2 = -2 + 6i$. Setting $x + 3 = u + iv$, $u, v \in \mathbb{R}$, we obtain the system

$$\begin{cases} u^2 - v^2 = -2 \\ 2uv = 6 \end{cases}$$

It follows that $(u^2 + v^2)^2 = (u^2 - v^2)^2 + (2uv)^2 = 4 + 36 = 40$. Therefore

$$\begin{cases} u^2 - v^2 = -2 \\ u^2 + v^2 = 2\sqrt{10} \end{cases}$$

and $u^2 = \sqrt{10} - 1$, $v^2 = \sqrt{10} + 1$, yielding the solutions

$$x_{3,4} = -3 \pm \sqrt{\sqrt{10} - 1} \pm i\sqrt{\sqrt{10} + 1}$$

where the signs $+$ and $-$ correspond.

The equation $x^2 + 6x = -11 - 6i$ can be solved in a similar way and it has the solutions

$$x_5 = -3 + \sqrt{\sqrt{10} - 1} - i\sqrt{\sqrt{10} + 1}, \quad x_6 = -3 - \sqrt{\sqrt{10} - 1} + i\sqrt{\sqrt{10} + 1}.$$

(*Titu Andreescu*, Revista Matematică Timişoara (RMT), No. 3(1972), pp. 26, Problem 1255)

9. The equation is equivalent to

$$x - \sqrt{x} + y - \sqrt{y} + z - 2\sqrt{z-2} + u - \sqrt{u} + v - \sqrt{v} = 0,$$

or

$$\left(\sqrt{x} - \frac{1}{2}\right)^2 + \left(\sqrt{y} - \frac{1}{2}\right)^2 + \left(\sqrt{z-2} - 1\right)^2 +$$

$$+ \left(\sqrt{u} - \frac{1}{2}\right)^2 + \left(\sqrt{v} - \frac{1}{2}\right)^2 = 0$$

Because x, y, z, u, v are real numbers, it follows that

$$\sqrt{x} = \sqrt{y} = \sqrt{u} = \sqrt{v} = \frac{1}{2} \quad \text{and} \quad \sqrt{z-2} = 1.$$

Hence

$$x = y = u = v = \frac{1}{4}, \quad z = 3.$$

(*Titu Andreescu*, Revista Matematică Timişoara (RMT), No. 2(1974), pp. 47, Problem 2002; Gazeta Matematică (GM-B), No. 10(1974), pp. 560, Problem 14536)

10. Setting $X = x + 1$ and $Y = y - 1$ yields

$$(X + Y)^2 = XY$$

or

$$\frac{1}{2}[X^2 + Y^2 + (X + Y)^2] = 0.$$

Hence $X = Y = 0$, so the solution is $x = -1$ and $y = 1$.

(*Titu Andreescu*, Revista Matematică Timişoara (RMT), No. 1(1977), pp. 40, Problem 2811)

11. The equation is equivalent to

$$\sqrt{x + \sqrt{4x + \sqrt{16x + \sqrt{\cdots + \sqrt{4^n x + 3}}}}} = \sqrt{x} + 1$$

Squaring the equation yields

$$\sqrt{4x + \sqrt{16x + \sqrt{\cdots + \sqrt{4^n x + 3}}}} = 2\sqrt{x} + 1$$

Squaring again implies

$$\sqrt{16x + \sqrt{\cdots + \sqrt{4^n x + 3}}} = 4\sqrt{x} + 1$$

Continuing this procedure yields

$$4^n x + 3 = 4^n x + 2 \cdot 2^n \sqrt{x} + 1$$

and $2 \cdot 2^n \sqrt{x} = 2$. Hence $x = \dfrac{1}{4^n}$.

(*Titu Andreescu*, Revista Matematică Timişoara (RMT), No. 4-5(1972), pp. 43, Problem 1385)

12. We distinguish two cases:

1) $b = c$. The equation becomes

$$\sqrt{x + a} + \sqrt{x + b} = \sqrt{x + a},$$

so $x = -b$.

2) $b \neq c$. The equation is equivalent to

$$\sqrt{x + b} + \sqrt{x + c} = \sqrt{x + a + b - c} - \sqrt{x + a}, \qquad (1)$$

or

$$\frac{b - c}{\sqrt{x + b} - \sqrt{x + c}} = \frac{b - c}{\sqrt{x + a + b - c} + \sqrt{x + a}},$$

so

$$\sqrt{x + b} - \sqrt{x + c} = \sqrt{x + a + b - c} + \sqrt{x + a}. \qquad (2)$$

Summing up relations (1) and (2) we obtain

$$\sqrt{x+b} = \sqrt{x+a+b-c},$$

and then $a = c$.

To conclude, we have found that

(i) If $b = c$, then the equation has the solution $x = -b$.

(ii) If $b \neq c$ and $a \neq c$, there is no solution.

(iii) If $b \neq c$ and $a = c$, then $x = -a$ is the only solution.

$\langle$*Titu Andreescu*, Revista Matematică Timişoara (RMT), No. 2(1978), pp. 26, Problem 3017)

13. Because a and b are distinct numbers, x and y are distinct as well. The second equation could be written as

$$a^2 - b^2 = (x^2 - y^2)^3$$

and the system could be solved in terms of a and b. We have

$$a^2 b^2 = b^2 y^2 + 2by(x^4 - y^4) + (x^4 - y^4)^2$$
$$a^2 x^2 = b^2 x^2 + x^2 (x^2 - y^2)^3.$$

Subtracting the first equation from the second yields

$$b^2(x^2 - y^2) - 2by(x^2 - y^2)(x^2 + y^2) + x^2(x^2 - y^2)^3 - (x^2 - y^2)^2(x^2 + y^2)^2 = 0$$

which reduces to

$$b^2 - 2by(x^2 + y^2) - y^2(x^2 - y^2)(3x^2 + y^2) = 0.$$

Solving the quadratic equation in b yields $b = y^3 + 3x^2 y$ (and $a = x^3 + 3xy^2$) or $b = y^3 - x^2 y$ (and $a = x^3 - xy^2$). The second alternative is not possible because $a = x(x^2 - y^2)$ and $b = y(y^2 - x^2)$ cannot be both positive. It follows that $a = x^3 + 3xy^2$ and $b = 3x^2 y + y^3$. Hence $a + b = (x + y)^3$ and $a - b = (x - y)^3$. The system now becomes

$$x + y = \sqrt[3]{a+b}$$
$$x - y = \sqrt[3]{a-b}$$

and its unique solution is $x = (\sqrt[3]{a+b} + \sqrt[3]{a-b})/2$, $y = (\sqrt[3]{a+b} - \sqrt[3]{a-b})/2$.

(*Titu Andreescu*, Korean Mathematics Competitions, 2001)

14. Let $\dfrac{13x + 4}{3} = y$, $y \in \mathbb{Z}$. It follows that

$$x = \frac{3y - 4}{13}$$

and the equation is equivalent to

$$\left[\dfrac{\dfrac{25}{13}(3y-4)-2}{4}\right] = y,$$

or

$$\left[\dfrac{75y-126}{52}\right] = y$$

Using that for any real number a, $[a] \leq a < [a]+1$, we obtain

$$y \leq \dfrac{75y-126}{52} < y+1,$$

or $126 \leq 23y < 178$, so $\dfrac{126}{23} \leq y < \dfrac{178}{23}$.

Note that $y \in \mathbb{Z}$, therefore $y = 6$ or $y = 7$, thus

$$x_1 = \dfrac{14}{13} \quad \text{and} \quad x_2 = \dfrac{17}{13},$$

are the desired solutions.

(*Titu Andreescu*, Revista Matematică Timişoara (RMT), No. 3(1972), pp. 25, Problem 1552)

15. From $a \geq \dfrac{1+\sqrt{5}}{2}$ we obtain $a^2 - a - 1 \geq 0$, or $a \geq \dfrac{1}{a}+1$. We have

$$\left[\dfrac{1+na^2}{a}\right] = \dfrac{1}{a} + na - \alpha, \quad 0 \leq \alpha < 1.$$

Hence

$$\left[\dfrac{1+\left[\dfrac{1+na^2}{a}\right]}{a}\right] = \left[\dfrac{1+\dfrac{1}{a}+na-\alpha}{a}\right] =$$

$$= \left[\left(1+\dfrac{1}{a}-\alpha\right)\dfrac{1}{a}+n\right] = n, \quad n \geq 0.$$

That is because

$$\left(1+\dfrac{1}{a}-\alpha\right)\dfrac{1}{a} \leq (a-\alpha)\dfrac{1}{a} = 1-\dfrac{\alpha}{a} < 1$$

and

$$\left(1+\dfrac{1}{a}-\alpha\right)\dfrac{1}{a} > \dfrac{1}{a^2} > 0.$$

(*Titu Andreescu*, Revista Matematică Timişoara (RMT), No. 2(1978), pp. 45, Problem 3479)

16. First we consider the case when $x+y+z = 0$. Then $x^3+y^3+z^3 = 3xyz$ and the ratio equals $\dfrac{2}{3}$, as desired.

Conversely, if

$$\frac{2xyz - (x + y + z)}{x^3 + y^3 + z^3} = \frac{2}{3},$$

then

$$6xyz - 3(x + y + z) = 2(x^3 + y^3 + z^3)$$

and so

$$2(x^3 + y^3 + z^3 - 3xyz) + 3(x + y + z) = 0.$$

Using the formula

$$x^3 + y^3 + z^3 - 3xyz = (x + y + z)(x^2 + y^2 + z^2 - xy - yz - zx),$$

we obtain by factorization that

$$(x + y + z)[2(x^2 + y^2 + z^2 - xy - yz - zx) + 3] = 0$$

and so

$$(x + y + z)[(x - y)^2 + (y - z)^2 + (z - x)^2 + 3] = 0.$$

Because the second factor is positive, it follows that $x + y + z = 0$, as desired.

(*Titu Andreescu*, Revista Matematică Timişoara (RMT), No. 1(1973), pp. 30, Problem 1513)

17. We write the equation as

$$x_1 - 2\sqrt{x_1 - 1} + x_2 - 2 \cdot 2\sqrt{x_2 - 2^2} + \cdots + x_n - 2n\sqrt{x_n - n^2} = 0,$$

or

$$\left(\sqrt{x_1 - 1} - 1\right)^2 + \left(\sqrt{x_2 - 2^2} - 2\right)^2 + \cdots + \left(\sqrt{x_n - n^2} - n\right)^2 = 0.$$

Because the numbers x_i, $i = \overline{1, n}$ are real, it follows that

$$x_1 = 2, \quad x_2 = 2 \cdot 2^2, \ldots, x_n = 2n^2$$

(*Titu Andreescu*, Revista Matematică Timişoara (RMT), No. 1(1977), pp. 14, Problem 2243)

18. Using the identity

$$(a + b + c)^3 = a^3 + b^3 + c^3 + 3(a + b)(b + c)(c + a)$$

we obtain

$$\left(\frac{1}{\sqrt[3]{x}} + \frac{1}{\sqrt[3]{y}} + 1\right)^3 = \frac{1}{x} + \frac{1}{y} + 1 + 3\left(\frac{1}{\sqrt[3]{x}} + \frac{1}{\sqrt[3]{y}}\right)\left(1 + \frac{1}{\sqrt[3]{x}}\right)\left(1 + \frac{1}{\sqrt[3]{y}}\right) =$$

$$= 9 + 1 + 54 = 64$$

Hence

$$\frac{1}{\sqrt[3]{x}} + \frac{1}{\sqrt[3]{y}} + 1 = 4,$$

and so

$$\frac{1}{\sqrt[3]{x}} + \frac{1}{\sqrt[3]{y}} = 3.$$

The system is now reduced to

$$\begin{cases} \dfrac{1}{x} + \dfrac{1}{y} = 9 \\[2mm] \dfrac{1}{\sqrt[3]{x}} + \dfrac{1}{\sqrt[3]{y}} = 3, \end{cases}$$

which is a symmetric system, having the solution

$$x = \frac{1}{8},\ y = 1 \quad \text{and} \quad x = 1,\ y = \frac{1}{8}.$$

(*Titu Andreescu*, Revista Matematică Timişoara (RMT), No. 4-5(1972), pp. 43, Problem 1386)

19. By summing up the equations of the system we obtain

$$(4x^2 - 4x + 1) + (4y^2 - 4y + 1) + (4u^2 - 4u + 1) +$$

$$+ (4v^2 - 4v + 1) + (4w^2 - 4w + 1) = 0.$$

It follows that

$$(2x - 1)^2 + (2y - 1)^2 + (2u - 1)^2 + (2v - 1)^2 + (2w - 1)^2 = 0$$

Due to the fact that x, y, u, v, w are real numbers, we obtain

$$x = y = u = v = w = \frac{1}{2}$$

(*Dorin Andrica*, Gazeta Matematică (GM-B), No. 8(1977), pp. 321, Problem 16782)

20. From the triangle inequality we deduce

$$|a_i - a_j| \le |a_i - a_{i+1}| + \cdots + |a_{j-1} - a_j| \le$$

$$\le (j - i) \max_{1 \le i < j \le 5} |a_i - a_j| \le j - i, \quad 1 \le i < j \le 5$$

Hence

$$\sum_{1 \le i < j \le 5} (a_i - a_j)^2 \le \sum_{1 \le i < j \le 5} (i - j)^2 =$$

$$= (1^2 + 2^2 + 3^2 + 4^2) + (1^2 + 2^2 + 3^2) + (1^2 + 2^2) + 1^2 = 50$$

So

$$4 \sum_{i=1}^{5} a_i^2 - 2 \sum_{\substack{i,j=1 \\ i \ne j}}^{5} a_i a_j \le 50$$

and consequently

$$5\sum_{i=1}^{5} a_i^2 - \left(\sum_{i=1}^{5} a_i\right)^2 \le 50$$

Note that $\sum_{i=1}^{5} a_i = 0$ and so $\sum_{i=1}^{5} a_i^2 \le 10$, as claimed.

(*Titu Andreescu*, Romanian Mathematica Olympiad - second round 1979; Revista Matematică Timişoara (RMT), No. 1-2(1980), pp. 61, Problem 4094)

21. The inequality $(a+b)^2 \ge 4ab$ yields

$$\frac{1}{a} + \frac{1}{b} \ge \frac{4}{a+b}$$

and, similarly, $\dfrac{1}{b} + \dfrac{1}{c} \ge \dfrac{4}{b+c}$, $\dfrac{1}{c} + \dfrac{1}{a} \ge \dfrac{4}{c+a}$.

Summing up these inequalities yields

$$\frac{1}{2a} + \frac{1}{2b} + \frac{1}{2c} \ge \frac{1}{a+b} + \frac{1}{b+c} + \frac{1}{c+a},$$

as desired.

(*Dorin Andrica*, Gazeta Matematică (GM-B), No. 8(1977), Problem 5966)

22. Using the identities

$$a^5 + b^5 + c^5 = (a+b+c)^5 - 5(a+b)(b+c)(c+a)(a^2+b^2+c^2+ab+bc+ca)$$

and

$$a^3 + b^3 + c^3 = (a+b+c)^3 - 3(a+b)(b+c)(c+a)$$

we obtain

$$\frac{a^5+b^5+c^5-(a+b+c)^5}{a^3+b^3+c^3-(a+b+c)^3} = \frac{5}{3}(a^2+b^2+c^2+ab+bc+ca)$$

It suffices now to prove that

$$\frac{5}{3}(a^2+b^2+c^2+ab+bc+ca) \ge \frac{10}{9}(a+b+c)^2$$

or

$$3(a^2+b^2+c^2+ab+bc+ca) \ge 2(a^2+b^2+c^2+2ab+2bc+2ca).$$

The last inequality is equivalent to

$$a^2 + b^2 + c^2 \ge ab + bc + ca,$$

which is clearly true.

(*Titu Andreescu*, Revista Matematică Timişoara (RMT), No. 1(1981), pp. 49, Problem 4295; Gazeta Matematică (GM-B), No. 6(1980), pp. 280, Problem O-148; No. 11(1982), pp. 422, Problem 19450)

23. Assume by contradiction that all numbers $2a - \dfrac{1}{b}$, $2b - \dfrac{1}{c}$, $2c - \dfrac{1}{a}$ are greater than 1. Then

$$\left(2a - \frac{1}{b}\right)\left(2b - \frac{1}{c}\right)\left(2c - \frac{1}{a}\right) > 1 \tag{1}$$

and

$$\left(2a - \frac{1}{b}\right) + \left(2b - \frac{1}{c}\right) + \left(2c - \frac{1}{a}\right) > 3. \tag{2}$$

From the relation (1) and using $abc = 1$ we obtain

$$3 > 2(a + b + c) - \left(\frac{1}{a} + \frac{1}{b} + \frac{1}{c}\right). \tag{3}$$

On the other hand, relation (2) gives

$$2(a + b + c) - \left(\frac{1}{a} + \frac{1}{b} + \frac{1}{c}\right) > 3$$

which is a contradiction.

The proof is complete.

(*Titu Andreescu*, Revista Matematică Timişoara (RMT), No. 2(1986), pp. 72, Problem 5982)

24. Assume by contradiction that all numbers are greater than 1/4. Then

$$a - b^2 + b - c^2 + c - d^2 + d - a^2 > \frac{1}{4} + \frac{1}{4} + \frac{1}{4} + \frac{1}{4}$$

hence

$$0 > \left(\frac{1}{2} - a\right)^2 + \left(\frac{1}{2} - b\right)^2 + \left(\frac{1}{2} - c\right)^2 + \left(\frac{1}{2} - d\right)^2.$$

This is a contradiction so the claim holds.

(*Titu Andreescu*, Revista Matematică Timişoara (RMT), No. 1(1985), pp. 59, Problem 5479)

25. Setting $a_i = \sin^2 \alpha_i$ for $i = \overline{1, n}$, where $\alpha_1, \alpha_2, \ldots, \alpha_n$ are real numbers, the expression becomes

$$E = \sum_{i=1}^{n} \sqrt[k]{\sin^2 \alpha_i \cos^2 \alpha_{i+1}}, \quad \alpha_{n+1} = \alpha_1.$$

Using the AM-GM inequality yields

$$\frac{1}{k} \sum_{i=1}^{k} b_i^k \geq b_1 b_2 \ldots b_k, \quad b_i > 0, \quad i = \overline{1, k}.$$

For $b_1 = \sin^{\frac{2}{k}} \alpha_i$, $b_2 = \cos^{\frac{2}{k}} \alpha_{i+1}$ and $b_3 = b_4 = \cdots = b_k = \dfrac{1}{\sqrt{2}}$ we obtain

$$\frac{1}{k}\left(\sin^2 \alpha_i + \cos^2 \alpha_{i+1} + \frac{k - 2}{2}\right) \geq \frac{1}{2^{\frac{k-2}{k}}} \sqrt[k]{\sin^2 \alpha_i \cos^2 \alpha_{i+1}}.$$

Summing up these relations for $k = 1, 2, \ldots, n$ yields

$$\frac{1}{k}\left(n + \frac{n(k-2)}{2}\right) \geq \frac{1}{2^{\frac{k-2}{k}}} E,$$

and so

$$E \leq \frac{n \cdot 2^{\frac{k-2}{k}}}{2} = \frac{n \cdot 2^{1-\frac{2}{k}}}{2} = \frac{n}{\sqrt[k]{4}}.$$

Hence the maximum value of E is $\dfrac{n}{\sqrt[k]{4}}$ and it is reached if and only if

$$a_1 = a_2 = \cdots = a_n = \frac{1}{2}.$$

(*Dorin Andrica*, Revista Matematică Timişoara (RMT), No. 1(1978), pp. 63, Problem 3266)

26. Because x and m are positive, we have to prove that

$$x(x^{mn} - 1) - m(x^n - 1) \geq 0,$$

or

$$(x^n - 1)[(x^n)^{m-1}x + (x^n)^{m-2}x + \cdots + x - m] \geq 0.$$

Define $E(x) = (x^n)^{m-1}x + (x^n)^{m-2}x + \cdots + x - m$ and note that if $x \geq 1$, then $x^n \geq 1$ and $E(x) \geq 0$, so the inequality holds. In the other case, when $x < 1$, we have $x^n < 1$ and $E(x) < 0$ and again the inequality holds, as claimed.

(*Titu Andreescu*, Revista Matematică Timişoara (RMT), No. 2(1978), pp. 45, Problem 3480)

27. For $m \leq n$ the inequality is clearly true, so consider $m > n$ and define $p = \left[\dfrac{m}{n}\right]$. This implies that $m = pn + q$ with $q \in \{0, 1, \ldots, n-1\}$ and the inequality can be written as

$$(pn + q)! \geq (n!)^p.$$

We have

$$(pn + q)! \geq (pn)! =$$

$$= (1 \cdot 2 \ldots n)(n+1) \ldots (2n) \ldots ((p-1)n+1) \ldots (pn) \geq (n!)^p,$$

and we are done.

(*Titu Andreescu*, Revista Matematică Timişoara (RMT), No. 2(1977), pp. 61, Problem 3034)

28. We will use the inequality

$$x_1^m + x_2^m + \cdots + x_n^m \geq \frac{1}{n^{m-1}}(x_1 + x_2 + \cdots + x_n)^m,$$

which holds for all positive real numbers $x_1, x_2, \ldots, x_n$ and all $m \in (-\infty, 0] \cup [1, \infty)$.

Now set $x_1 = 1, x_2 = 2, \ldots, x_n = n$ and $m = -\dfrac{1}{n}$. We obtain

$$1 + \frac{1}{\sqrt[n]{2}} + \frac{1}{\sqrt[n]{3}} + \cdots + \frac{1}{\sqrt[n]{n}} > \frac{1}{n^{-\frac{1}{n}-1}} \left[\frac{n(n+1)}{2} \right]^{-\frac{1}{n}} = n\sqrt[n]{\frac{2}{n+1}},$$

as desired.

(*Titu Andreescu*, Revista Matematică Timişoara (RMT), No. 2(1974), pp. 52, Problem 2035)

29. From the AM-GM inequality we deduce

$$\frac{1}{n} \sum_{i=1}^{n} \frac{i+1}{i} \geq \sqrt[n]{\prod_{i=1}^{n} \frac{i+1}{i}} = \sqrt[n]{n+1},$$

or

$$1 + \frac{1}{n} \sum_{i=1}^{n} \frac{1}{i} \geq \sqrt[n]{n+1},$$

and so

$$1 + \frac{1}{2} + \frac{1}{3} + \cdots + \frac{1}{n} > n\left(\sqrt[n]{n+1} - 1\right),$$

as desired.

Observe that the inequality is strict because the numbers $\dfrac{i+1}{i}$, $i = \overline{1,n}$, are distinct.

In order to prove the first inequality we apply the AM-GM inequality in the form

$$\frac{1 + \frac{1}{2} + \frac{2}{3} + \cdots + \frac{n-1}{n}}{n} > \sqrt[n]{\frac{1}{n}} = \frac{1}{\sqrt[n]{n}}.$$

Therefore

$$\frac{1 + \left(1 - \frac{1}{2}\right) + \left(1 - \frac{1}{3}\right) + \cdots + \left(1 - \frac{1}{n}\right)}{n} > \frac{1}{\sqrt[n]{n}}$$

or

$$n\left(1 - \frac{1}{\sqrt[n]{n}}\right) + 1 > 1 + \frac{1}{2} + \cdots + \frac{1}{n}.$$

(*Dorin Andrica*, Revista Matematică Timişoara (RMT), No. 2(1977), pp. 62, Problem 3037)

30. Because the numbers $a_1, a_2, \ldots, a_n$ are positive, from the AM-GM inequality

$$\frac{a_1 + a_2 + \cdots + a_n}{n} \geq \sqrt[n]{a_1 a_2 \ldots a_n}$$

we deduce that $t_n \leq (a_1 a_2 \ldots a_n)^{\frac{n-1}{n}}$. Using that numbers a_i are less than 1 we obtain

$$\log_{a_i} t_n \geq \frac{n-1}{n} \log_{a_i}(a_1 a_2 \ldots a_n).$$

Summing up these inequalities yields

$$\sum_{i=1}^{n} \log_{a_i} t_n \geq \frac{n-1}{n} \sum_{i=1}^{n} \log_{a_i}(a_1 a_2 \ldots a_n) =$$

$$= \frac{n-1}{n}[n + (\log_{a_1} a_2 + \log_{a_2} a_1) + \cdots + (\log_{a_1} a_n + \log_{a_n} a_1) + \cdots +$$

$$+ (\log_{a_n} a_{n-1} + \log_{a_{n-1}} a_n)].$$

Note that $a + \dfrac{1}{a} \geq 2$ for all $a > 0$, so

$$\sum_{i=1}^{n} \log_{a_i} t_n \geq \frac{n-1}{n}[n + 2(n-1) + 2(n-2) + \cdots + 2] = (n-1)n,$$

as claimed.

(*Dorin Andrica*, Revista Matematică Timişoara (RMT), No. 2(1977), pp. 62, Problem 3038)

31. We begin with the following lemma.

Lemma. *Let $a > b$ be two positive integers such that*

$$\sqrt[3]{a} - \sqrt[3]{b} > 1.$$

Then between numbers a and b there is at least a perfect cube.

Proof. Suppose, for the sake of contradiction, that there is no perfect cube between a and b. Then there is an integer c such that

$$c^3 \leq b < a \leq (c+1)^3.$$

This means

$$c \leq \sqrt[3]{b} < \sqrt[3]{a} \leq c+1,$$

so

$$\sqrt[3]{a} - \sqrt[3]{b} \leq 1,$$

which is false. $\square$

Now we can easily check that for $n = 10, 11, 12, 13, 14, 15$ the statement holds. If $n \geq 16$, then

$$n > (2,5)^3 = \frac{1}{(1,4-1)^3} > \frac{1}{\left(\sqrt[3]{3}-1\right)^3},$$

or

$$\sqrt[3]{n} > \frac{1}{\sqrt[3]{3}-1}.$$

Hence

$$\sqrt[3]{3n} - \sqrt[3]{n} > 1,$$

and using the above lemma the problem is solved.

(*Titu Andreescu*, Revista Matematică Timişoara (RMT), No. 1-2(1990), pp. 59, Problem 4080)

32. Note that the number $\dfrac{k(k+1)}{2}$ is odd for $k = 4p + 1$ or $k = 4p + 2$ and is even for $k = 4p + 3$ or $k = 4p$, where p is a positive integer.

We have the following cases:

i) if $n = 4m$, then

$$S_n = \sum_{k=1}^{n} (-1)^{\frac{k(k+1)}{2}} k = \sum_{p=0}^{m-1} (-4p - 1 - 4p - 2 + 4p + 3 + 4p + 4) = 4m.$$

ii) if $n = 4m + 1$, then

$$S_n = 4m - (4m + 1) = -1.$$

iii) if $n = 4m + 2$, then

$$S_n = 4m - (4m + 1) - (4m + 2) = -(4m + 3).$$

iv) if $n = 4m + 3$ then

$$S_n = 4m - (4m + 1) - (4m + 2) + (4m + 3) = 0.$$

Hence

$$S_n = \begin{cases} 4m & \text{if } n = 4m \\ -1 & \text{if } n = 4m + 1 \\ -(4m + 3) & \text{if } n = 4m + 2 \\ 0 & \text{if } n = 4m + 3. \end{cases}$$

(*Dorin Andrica*, Revista Matematică Timişoara (RMT), No. 1(1981), pp. 50, Problem 4303)

33. a) Summing up the identities

$$\binom{n+2}{k} = \frac{(n+2)(n+1)}{(n+2-k)(n+1-k)} \binom{n}{k}$$

for $k = 0$ to $k = n$ yields

$$S_n = \frac{1}{(n+2)(n+1)} \left(\sum_{k=0}^{n+2} \binom{n+2}{k} - \binom{n+2}{n+1} - \binom{n+2}{n+2} \right) =$$

$$= \frac{1}{(n+2)(n+1)} [2^{n+2} - (n+2) - 1] = \frac{2^{n+2} - (n+3)}{(n+2)(n+1)}.$$

b) Summing up the identities

$$\binom{n+3}{k} = \frac{(n+3)(n+2)(n+1)}{(n+3-k)(n+2-k)(n+1-k)} \binom{n}{k}$$

for $k = 0$ to $k = n$ yields

$$T_n = \frac{1}{(n+3)(n+2)(n+1)}.$$

$$\cdot \left(\sum_{k=0}^{n+3} \binom{n+3}{k} - \binom{n+3}{n+1} - \binom{n+3}{n+2} - \binom{n+3}{n+3} \right) =$$

$$= \frac{1}{(n+3)(n+2)(n+1)} \left(2^{n+3} - \frac{1}{2}(n^2 + 3n + 2) \right) =$$

$$= \frac{2^{n+4} - (n^2 + 3n + 2)}{2(n+3)(n+2)(n+1)}.$$

(*Dorin Andrica*, Revista Matematică Timişoara (RMT), No. 2(1975), pp. 43, Problem 2116)

34. Let S_n be the number in the statement.
It is not difficult to see that

$$S_n = \frac{1}{4} \left[\left(2 + \sqrt{3} \right)^{2n+1} + \left(2 - \sqrt{3} \right)^{2n+1} \right].$$

The required property says: there exists $k > 0$ such that $S_n = (k-1)^2 + k^2$, or, equivalently,

$$2k^2 - 2k + 1 - S_n = 0.$$

The discriminant of this equation is $\Delta = 4(2S_n - 1)$, and, after usual computations, we obtain

$$\Delta = \left(\frac{\left(1 + \sqrt{3} \right)^{2n+1} + \left(1 - \sqrt{3} \right)^{2n+1}}{2^n} \right)^2.$$

Solving the equation, we find

$$k = \frac{2^{n+1} + \left(1 + \sqrt{3} \right)^{2n+1} + \left(1 - \sqrt{3} \right)^{2n+1}}{2^{n+2}}.$$

Therefore, it is sufficient to prove that k is an integer. Let us denote $E_m = \left(1 + \sqrt{3} \right)^m + \left(1 - \sqrt{3} \right)^m$, where m is a positive integer. Clearly, E_m is an integer for all m. We will prove that $2^{\left[\frac{m}{2} \right]}$ divides E_m, $m = 1, 2, 3, \ldots$ Moreover, the numbers E_m satisfy the relation

$$E_m = 2E_{m-1} + 2E_{m-2}.$$

The property now follows by induction.
(*Dorin Andrica*, Romanian IMO Selection Test, 1999)

35. Differentiating the identity

$$\sin nx = \sin^n x \left(\binom{n}{1} \cot^{n-1} x - \binom{n}{3} \cot^{n-3} x + \binom{n}{5} \cot^{n-5} x - \ldots \right)$$

yields

$$n \cos nx = n \sin^{n-1} x \cos x P(\cot x) - \sin^n x \frac{1}{\sin^2 x} P'(\cot x),$$

where

$$P(y) = \binom{n}{1} y^{n-1} - \binom{n}{3} y^{n-3} + \binom{n}{5} y^{n-5} - \ldots$$

For $x = \dfrac{\pi}{4}$ we obtain

$$n \cos n \frac{\pi}{4} = \left(\frac{\sqrt{2}}{2} \right)^n (nP(1) - 2P'(1)).$$

Because

$$nP(1) = n\binom{n}{1} - n\binom{n}{3} + n\binom{n}{5} - \ldots$$

and

$$-2P'(1) = -2(n-1)\binom{n}{1} + 2(n-3)\binom{n}{3} - 2(n-5)\binom{n}{5} + \ldots,$$

we have

$$nP(1) - 2P'(1) = -\left[(n-2)\binom{n}{1} - (n-6)\binom{n}{3} + (n-10)\binom{n}{5} - \ldots \right] =$$

$$= -n\left(\binom{n}{1} - \binom{n}{3} + \binom{n}{5} - \ldots \right) + 2S_n.$$

To conclude, use that

$$\binom{n}{1} - \binom{n}{3} + \binom{n}{5} - \cdots = \left(\sqrt{2} \right)^n \sin \frac{n\pi}{4},$$

hence

$$S_n = \frac{n \left(\sqrt{2} \right)^n}{2} \left(\cos \frac{n\pi}{4} + \sin \frac{n\pi}{4} \right)$$

(*Dorin Andrica*, Revista Matematică Timişoara (RMT), No. 2(1977), pp. 89, Problem 3200)

36. Differentiating with respect to x the identities

$$(x+1)^n = \binom{n}{0} + \binom{n}{1}x + \cdots + \binom{n}{n}x^n$$

and

$$(x-1)^n = \binom{n}{n}x^n - \binom{n}{n-1}x^{n-1} + \cdots + (-1)^n \binom{n}{0}$$

yields

$$n(x+1)^{n-1} = \binom{n}{1} + 2\binom{n}{2}x + \cdots + n\binom{n}{n}x^{n-1}$$

and

$$n(x-1)^{n-1} = n\binom{n}{n}x^{n-1} - (n-1)\binom{n}{n-1}x^{n-2} + \cdots + (-1)^{n-1}\binom{n}{1}.$$

Multiplying by x gives

$$nx(x+1)^{n-1} = \binom{n}{1}x + 2\binom{n}{2}x^2 + \cdots + n\binom{n}{n}x^n$$

and

$$nx(x-1)^{n-1} = n\binom{n}{n}x^n - (n-1)\binom{n}{n-1}x^{n-1} + \cdots + (-1)^{n-1}\binom{n}{1}x.$$

Differentiating again we obtain

$$n(x+1)^{n-1} + n(n-1)x(x+1)^{n-2} = \binom{n}{1} + 2^2\binom{n}{2}x + \cdots + n^2\binom{n}{n}x^{n-1}$$

$$n(x-1)^{n-1} + n(n-1)x(x-1)^{n-2} = n^2\binom{n}{n}x^{n-1} - (n-1)^2\binom{n}{n-1}x^{n-2} +$$

$$+ \cdots + (-1)^{n-1}\binom{n}{1}$$

Setting $x = 1$ yields

$$1^2\binom{n}{1} + 2^2\binom{n}{2} + \cdots + n^2\binom{n}{n} = n(n+1)2^{n-2}$$

and

$$1^2\binom{n}{1} - 2^2\binom{n}{2} + 3^2\binom{n}{3} - \cdots = 0.$$

Summing up the last two identities gives

$$S_n = 1^2\binom{n}{1} + 3^2\binom{n}{3} + \cdots = n(n+1)2^{n-3},$$

as desired.

(*Dorin Andrica*, Revista Matematică Timișoara (RMT), No. 1(1978), pp. 90, Problem 3438)

37. Note that

$$\sum_{k=1}^{2^n}[\log_2 k] = \sum_{i=0}^{n-1}\sum_{k=2^i}^{2^{i+1}-1}[\log_2 k] + [\log_2 2^n],$$

and $[\log_2 k] = i$ for $2^i \le k < 2^{i+1}$.

Hence

$$\sum_{k=1}^{2^n}[\log_2 k] = \sum_{i=0}^{n-1}i\cdot 2^i + [\log_2 2^n] = (n-2)2^n + n + 2$$

as claimed.

(*Dorin Andrica*, Revista Matematică Timișoara (RMT), No. 2(1981), pp. 63, Problem 4585; Gazeta Matematică (GM-B), No. 2-3(1982), pp. 83, Problem 19113)

38. Let $y_n = 2^{2^n} - 1$ for all positive integers n. Then

$$\frac{1}{y_n} - \frac{2}{y_{n+1}} = \frac{1}{2^{2^n}-1} - \frac{2}{2^{2^{n+1}}-1} = \frac{(2^{2^n})^2 - 2\cdot 2^{2^n} + 1}{(2^{2^n}-1)(2^{2^{n+1}}-1)} =$$

$$= \frac{(2^{2^n}-1)^2}{(2^{2^n}-1)(2^{2^{n+1}}-1)} = \frac{2^{2^n}-1}{(2^{2^n})^2-1} = \frac{1}{2^{2^n}+1} = \frac{1}{x_n}$$

and therefore

$$\frac{1}{x_1} = \frac{1}{y_1} - \frac{2}{y_2}$$

$$\frac{2}{x_2} = \frac{2}{y_2} - \frac{2^2}{y_3}$$

$$\cdots$$

$$\frac{2^{n-1}}{x_n} = \frac{2^{n-1}}{y_n} - \frac{2^n}{y_{n+1}}$$

Summing up these relations yields

$$\frac{1}{x_1} + \frac{2}{x_2} + \frac{2^2}{x_3} + \cdots + \frac{2^{n-1}}{x_n} = \frac{1}{y_1} - \frac{2^n}{y_{n+1}} < \frac{1}{y_1}$$

for all positive integers n, as desired.

(*Dorin Andrica*, Revista Matematică Timişoara (RMT), No. 1-2(1980), pp. 67, Problem 4135)

39. Substituting z with iz in the relation

$$f(z)f(iz) = z^2$$

yields

$$f(iz)f(-z) = -z^2.$$

Summing up gives

$$f(iz)(f(z) + f(-z)) = 0,$$

so $f(iz) = 0$ or $f(z) + f(-z) = 0$.

From the relation $f(z)f(iz) = z^2$ we deduce that $f(z) = 0$ if and only if $z = 0$. Hence if $z \neq 0$, then $f(iz) \neq 0$ and so $f(z) + f(-z) = 0$ and, if $z = 0$, then $f(z) + f(-z) = 2f(0) = 0$. Clearly, $f(z) + f(-z) = 0$ for all numbers $z \in \mathbb{C}$, as desired.

Remark. A function $f : \mathbb{C} \to \mathbb{C}$ satisfying the relation $f(z)f(iz) = z^2$ is $f(z) = \left(-\frac{\sqrt{2}}{2} + i\frac{\sqrt{2}}{2}\right) z$.

(*Titu Andreescu*, Revista Matematică Timişoara (RMT), No. 2(1976), pp. 56, Problem 2583)

40. Setting $x = y = 1$ yields

$$f^2(1) + f^2(a) = 2f(1)$$

and $(f(1) - 1)^2 = 0$ so $f(1) = 1$. Substituting $y = 1$ gives

$$f(x)f(1) + f\left(\frac{a}{x}\right) f(a) = 2f(x)$$

or

$$f(x) = f\left(\frac{a}{x}\right), \quad x > 0.$$

Take now $y = \frac{a}{x}$ and observe that

$$f(x)f\left(\frac{a}{x}\right) + f\left(\frac{a}{x}\right) f(x) = 2f(a).$$

Consequently,

$$f(x)f\left(\frac{a}{x}\right) = 1,$$

therefore $f^2(x) = 1$, $x > 0$.

Now set $x = y = \sqrt{t}$, that gives

$$f^2(\sqrt{t}) + f^2\left(\frac{a}{\sqrt{t}}\right) = 2f(t)$$

and because the left-hand side is positive, it follows that f is positive and $f(x) = 1$ for all x. Then f is a constant function, as claimed.

(*Titu Andreescu*, Revista Matematică Timişoara (RMT), No. 12(1977), pp. 45, Problem 2849; Gazeta Matematică (GM-B), No. 10(1980), pp. 439, Problem 18455)

41. The function is not periodical. Suppose, by way of contradiction, that there is a number $T > 0$ such that

$$f(x+T) = f(x) \text{ or } \sin[x+T] = \sin[x], \text{ for all } x \in \mathbb{R}.$$

It follows that

$$[x+T] - [x] = 2k(x)\pi, \quad x \in \mathbb{R},$$

where $k : \mathbb{R} \to \mathbb{Z}$ is a function. Because π is irrational, we deduce that $k(x) = 0$ for all $x \in \mathbb{R}$ and therefore

$$[x] = [x+T] \text{ for all } x \in \mathbb{R}$$

which is false, since the greatest integer function is not periodical.

(*Dorin Andrica*, Revista Matematică Timişoara (RMT), No. 1(1978), pp. 89, Problem 3430)

42. Considering the determinant

$$\delta = \begin{vmatrix} 1 & 2 & 3 & \dots & n \\ 1^2 & 2^2 & 3^2 & \dots & n^2 \\ \dots & \dots & \dots & \dots & \dots \\ 1^n & 2^n & 3^n & \dots & n^n \end{vmatrix}$$

we have

$$\Delta = |S(i,j)| = \delta \cdot \begin{vmatrix} 1 & 1^2 & 1^3 & \dots & 1^n \\ 2^1 & 2^2 & 2^3 & \dots & 2^n \\ \dots & \dots & \dots & \dots & \dots \\ n^1 & n^2 & n^3 & \dots & n^n \end{vmatrix} = \delta^2,$$

because the second determinant is obtained from δ by interchanging rows and columns.

On the other hand,

$$\delta = n! \begin{vmatrix} 1 & 1 & 1 & \ldots & 1 \\ 1 & 2 & 3 & \ldots & n \\ \ldots & \ldots & \ldots & \ldots & \ldots \\ 1^{n-1} & 2^{n-1} & 3^{n-1} & \ldots & n^{n-1} \end{vmatrix} = n!(1^{n-1} \cdot 2^{n-2} \ldots (n-1)^1)$$

(here we used the known result on Vandermonde determinants). Therefore

$$|S(i,j)| = \delta^2 = (1^n \cdot 2^{n-1} \ldots (n-1)^2 n)^2$$

(*Dorin Andrica*, Revista Matematică Timişoara (RMT), No. 1(1982), pp. 52, Problem 3862)

43. The determinant is

$$\Delta_{2n} = \begin{vmatrix} a_1 & 0 & 0 & \ldots & 0 & 0 & b_1 \\ 0 & a_2 & 0 & \ldots & 0 & b_2 & 0 \\ 0 & 0 & a_3 & \ldots & b_3 & 0 & 0 \\ \ldots & \ldots & \ldots & \ldots & \ldots & \ldots & \ldots \\ 0 & 0 & b_{2n-2} & \ldots & a_{2n-2} & 0 & 0 \\ 0 & b_{2n-1} & 0 & \ldots & 0 & a_{2n-1} & 0 \\ b_{2n} & 0 & 0 & \ldots & 0 & 0 & a_{2n} \end{vmatrix}$$

Expanding along the first and then the last row we obtain

$$\Delta_{2n} = (a_1 a_{2n} - b_1 b_{2n})\Delta_{2n-2},$$

which gives

$$\Delta_{2n} = \prod_{k=1}^{n}(a_k a_{2n-k+1} - b_k b_{2n-k+1})$$

(*Dorin Andrica*, Revista Matematică Timişoara (RMT), No. 2(1977), pp. 90, Problem 3201; Gazeta Matematică (GM-B), No. 8(1977), pp. 325, Problem 16808)

44. a) Adding the last three columns to the first one yields that $x + y + z + v$ divides the determinant.

Adding the first and second columns and subtracting the last two columns implies that $x + y - z - v$ divides the determinant.

Analogously we can check that $x-y+z-v$ and $x-y-z+v$ divide the determinant, and taking into account that it has degree 4 in each of the variables, the determinant equals

$$\lambda(x + y + z + v)(x + y - z - v)(x - y + z - v)(x - y - z + v),$$

where λ is a constant.

Because the coefficient of x^4 is equal to 1, we have $\lambda = 1$ and so

$$\begin{vmatrix} x & y & z & w \\ y & x & v & z \\ z & v & x & y \\ v & z & y & x \end{vmatrix} = (x+y+z+v)(x+y-z-v)(x-y+z-v)(x-y-z+v)$$

b) As shown above, we have

$$\Delta = \begin{vmatrix} a & b & c & d \\ b & a & d & c \\ c & d & a & b \\ d & c & b & a \end{vmatrix} = (a+b+c+d)(a+b-c-d)(a-b+c-d)(a-b-c+d)$$

On the other hand, multiplying the first column by 1000, the second by 100, the third by 10 and adding all these to the fourth, we obtain on the last column the numbers $\overline{abcd}$, $\overline{badc}$, $\overline{cdab}$, $\overline{dcba}$. Because all those numbers are divisible by the prime number p, it follows that p divides Δ and therefore p divides at least one of the numbers $a+b+c+d$, $a+b-c-d$, $a-b+c-d$, $a-b-c+d$.

(*Titu Andreescu*)

45. Because the quadratic polynomials $t_1(x)$ and $t_2(x)$ have zeros of the same nature, it follows that their discriminants have the same sign, hence

$$(p_1^2 - 4q_1^2)(p_2^2 - 4q_2^2) \geq 0.$$

Consequently,

$$(p_1 p_2 + 4q_1 q_2)^2 - 4(p_1 q_2 + p_2 q_1)^2 \geq 0.$$

Note now that the left-hand side of the inequality is the discriminant of the quadratic polynomial t and the conclusion follows.

(*Titu Andreescu*, Revista Matematică Timişoara (RMT), No. 1(1978), pp. 63, Problem 3267; Gazeta Matematică (GM-B), No. 5(1979), pp. 191, Problem 17740)

46. Because the quadratic polynomial T has nonreal zeros, the discriminant

$$\Delta = b^2 c^2 - 4a(b^3 + c^3 - 4abc)$$

is negative.

Observe that

$$\Delta = (b^2 - 4ac)(c^2 - 4ab) < 0,$$

where $\Delta_1 = b^2 - 4ac$ and $\Delta_2 = c^2 - 4ab$ are the discriminants of the quadratic polynomials T_1 and T_2. Hence exactly one of the numbers Δ_1 and Δ_2 is negative and since $a > 0$, the conclusion follows.

(*Titu Andreescu*, Revista Matematică Timişoara (RMT), No. 1(1977), pp. 40, Problem 2810)

47. Observe that $a_1 + a_2 + \cdots + a_n$ and $a_1 - a_2 + \cdots + (-1)^{n-1}a_n$ are real numbers, that is $P(1)$ and $P(-1)$ are real numbers. Hence

$$P(1) = \overline{P(1)} \text{ and } P(-1) = \overline{P(-1)} \tag{1}$$

Because $P(x) = (x - x_1) \ldots (x - x_n)$, the relations (1) become

$$(1 - x_1) \ldots (1 - x_n) = (1 - \overline{x}_1) \ldots (1 - \overline{x}_n)$$

and

$$(1 + x_1) \ldots (1 + x_n) = (1 + \overline{x}_1) \ldots (1 + \overline{x}_n)$$

Multiplying these relations yields

$$(1 - x_1^2) \ldots (1 - x_n^2) = (1 - \overline{x}_1^2) \ldots (1 - \overline{x}_n^2),$$

or $Q(1) = \overline{Q(1)}$. Therefore $b_1 + b_2 + \cdots + b_n$ is a real number.

(*Titu Andreescu*, Revista Matematică Timişoara (RMT), No. 1(1977), pp. 47, Problem 2864)

48. Because $P(0) = 0$, there is a polynomial Q with $P(x) = xQ(x)$. Then

$$Q(k) = \frac{1}{k+1}, \quad k = \overline{1,n}.$$

Define $H(x) = (x + 1)Q(x) - 1$. It is clear that $degH(x) = n$ and $H(k) = 0$ for all $k = \overline{1,n}$, hence

$$H(x) = (x + 1)Q(x) - 1 = a_0(x - 1)(x - 2) \ldots (x - n) \tag{1}$$

Setting $x = m$, $m > n$ in relation (1) yields

$$Q(m) = \frac{a_0(m - 1)(m - 2) \ldots (m - n) + 1}{m + 1}.$$

On the other hand, setting $x = -1$ in the same relation implies

$$a_0 = \frac{(-1)^{n+1}}{(n + 1)!}$$

Therefore

$$Q(m) = \frac{(-1)^{n+1}(m - 1)(m - 2) \ldots (m - n)}{(n + 1)!(m + 1)} + \frac{1}{m + 1}$$

and then

$$P(m) = \frac{(-1)^{n+1}m(m - 1) \ldots (m - n)}{(n + 1)!(m + 1)} + \frac{m}{m + 1}.$$

(*Dorin Andrica*, Gazeta Matematică (GM-B), No. 8(1977), pp. 329, Problem 16833; Revista Matematică Timişoara (RMT), No. 1-2(1980), p. 67, Problem 4133)

49. We are looking for a polynomial with integral coefficients

$$P(x) = a_0x^n + a_1x^{n-1} + \cdots + a_n, \quad a_0 \neq 0.$$

We have

$$P'(x) = na_0 x^{n-1} + (n-1)a_1 x^{n-2} + \cdots + a_{n-1}$$

and by identifying the coefficient of $x^{(n-1)n}$ in the relation $P(P'(x)) = P'(P(x))$, we obtain

$$a_0^{n+1} \cdot n^n = a_0^n \cdot n,$$

or $a_0 n^{n-1} = 1$. Hence

$$a_0 = \frac{1}{n^{n-1}}$$

and since a_0 is an integer, we deduce that $n = 1$ and $a_0 = 1$. Then $P(x) = x + a_1$, $P'(x) = 1$ and $P(P'(x)) = P'(P(x))$ yields $1 + a_1 = 1$ or $a_1 = 0$.

Therefore $P(x) = x$ is the only polynomial with the desired property.

(*Titu Andreescu*, Revista Matematică Timişoara (RMT), No. 1-2(1979), Problem 3902)

50. Let $\theta_1, \theta_2, \ldots, \theta_n$ be the roots of the equation

$$x^n + x^{n-1} + \cdots + x + 1 = 0.$$

They are all distinct and $\theta_i^{n+1} = 1$, $i = \overline{1, n}$.

Because $P(x)$ is divisible by $x^n + x^{n-1} + \cdots + x + 1$, it follows that $P(\theta_i) = 0$, $i = \overline{1, n}$, hence

$$p_1(1) + \theta_1 p_2(1) + \cdots + \theta_1^{n-1} p_n(1) = 0$$

$$p_1(1) + \theta_2 p_2(1) + \cdots + \theta_2^{n-1} p_n(1) = 0$$

$$\cdots$$

$$p_1(1) + \theta_n p_2(1) + \cdots + \theta_n^{n-1} p_n(1) = 0.$$

The above system of equations has the determinant

$$V = \begin{vmatrix} 1 & \theta_1 & \ldots & \theta_1^{n-1} \\ 1 & \theta_2 & \ldots & \theta_2^{n-1} \\ \cdots & \cdots & \cdots & \cdots \\ 1 & \theta_n & \ldots & \theta_n^{n-1} \end{vmatrix}.$$

Because all of the numbers $\theta_1, \theta_2, \ldots, \theta_n$ are distinct, it follows that $V \neq 0$ and so the system has only the trivial solution $p_1(1) = p_2(1) = \cdots = p_n(1) = 0$. This is just another way of saying that $x - 1$ divides $p_i(x)$ for all $i = \overline{1, n}$.

(*Dorin Andrica*, Revista Matematică Timişoara (RMT), No. 2(1977), pp. 75, Problem 3120; Gazeta Matematică (GM-B), No. 8(1977), pp. 329, Problem 16834)

51. Consider the determinant

$$V = \begin{vmatrix} a_n & a_n & \cdots & a_n \\ \alpha_1 & \alpha_2 & \cdots & \alpha_{n+1} \\ \alpha_1^2 & \alpha_2^2 & \cdots & \alpha_{n+1}^2 \\ \cdots & \cdots & \cdots & \cdots \\ \alpha_1^n & \alpha_2^n & \cdots & \alpha_{n+1}^n \end{vmatrix} = a_n \prod_{\substack{k,l=1 \\ k>l}}^{n+1} (\alpha_k - \alpha_l)$$

Multiplying the second row by a_{n-1}, the third by $a_{n-2}, \ldots$, the last by a_0 and adding all to the first yields

$$V = \begin{vmatrix} P(\alpha_1) & P(\alpha_2) & \cdots & P(\alpha_{n+1}) \\ \alpha_1 & \alpha_2 & \cdots & \alpha_{n+1} \\ \alpha_1^2 & \alpha_2^2 & \cdots & \alpha_{n+1}^2 \\ \cdots & \cdots & \cdots & \cdots \\ \alpha_1^n & \alpha_2^n & \cdots & \alpha_{n+1}^n \end{vmatrix} = a_n \prod_{\substack{k,l=1 \\ k>l}}^{n+1} (\alpha_k - \alpha_l)$$

On the other hand, $P(\alpha_r) \equiv 0 \pmod p$, for all $r = \overline{1, n+1}$ and $a_n \not\equiv 0 \pmod p$ implies $\displaystyle\prod_{1 \le l < k \le n+1} (\alpha_k - \alpha_l) \equiv 0 \pmod p$. Therefore there are at least two numbers $\alpha_i, \alpha_j, i \ne j$ such that $\alpha_i - \alpha_j \equiv 0 \pmod p$ and so $\alpha_i \equiv \alpha_j \pmod p$, as desired.

(*Dorin Andrica*, Gazeta Matematică (GM-B), No. 8(1977), pp. 329, Problem 16835)

52. Let $m = deg P(x)$ and let

$$P(x) = a_0 x^m + Q(x), \quad a_0 \ne 0$$

If follows that $deg Q(x) = r \le m - 1$.

From $P^n(x) = P(x^n)$ we obtain

$$a_0^n x^{mn} + \binom{n}{1} a_0^{n-1} x^{m(n-1)} Q(x) + \cdots + Q^n(x) = a_0 x^{mn} + Q(x^n),$$

or

$$a_0^n x^{mn} + R(x) = a_0 x^{mn} + S(x),$$

where

$$deg R(x) = m(n-1) + r \text{ and } deg S(x) = nr.$$

Because $a_0 \ne 0$, it follows that $a_0 = 1$ if n is even and $a_0 = 1$ or $a_0 = -1$ if n is odd. Moreover,

$$deg R(x) = deg S(x)$$

or

$$m(n-1) + r = nr$$

and so

$$(n-1)(m-r) = 0.$$

This is impossible if $Q(x) \neq 0$, because $n > 1$ and $m > r$, therefore $Q(x) = 0$ and the polynomials are

$$P(x) = x^m, \text{ for } n \text{ even and}$$
$$P(x) = \pm x^m, \text{ for } n \text{ odd}.$$

Alternative solution. Let $deg P(x) = m$ and let

$$P(x) = a_0 x^m + a_1 x^{m-1} + \cdots + a_m.$$

If $P(x) = x^k Q(x)$ with k a positive integer, then

$$x^{kn} Q^n(x) = x^{kn} Q(x^n) \text{ or } Q^n(x) = Q(x^n)$$

Note that Q satisfies the same condition as P. Assume that $P(0) \neq 0$.

Setting $x = 0$ in the initial condition yields $a_m^n = a_m$. Then $a_m = 1$ if n is even and $a_m = \pm 1$ if n is odd. Differentiating the relations implies

$$n P^{n-1}(x) P'(x) = n P'(x^n) x^{n-1}. \tag{1}$$

Setting now $x = 0$ gives $P'(0) = 0$ and so $a_{m-1} = 0$.

Differentiating again in relation (1) yields analogously $a_{m-2} = 0$ and then

$$a_{m-3} = a_{m-4} = \cdots = a_0 = 0.$$

The polynomials are

$$P(x) = x^m, \text{ if } n \text{ is even and}$$
$$P(x) = \pm x^m, \text{ if } n \text{ is odd}.$$

(*Titu Andreescu*, Revista Matematică Timişoara (RMT), No. 1-2(1979), pp. 59, Problem 3884)

53. From the relations between the zeros and the coefficients we obtain

$$\frac{a_m}{a_0} = (-1)^m \sum x_1 x_2 \ldots x_m$$

and

$$\frac{a_n}{a_0} = (-1)^n x_1 x_2 \ldots x_n.$$

It follows that

$$\left| \sum \frac{1}{x_1 x_2 \ldots x_{n-m}} \right| = \left| \frac{a_m}{a_n} \right| > \binom{n}{m},$$

and by applying the triangle's inequality for complex numbers, we deduce that

$$\sum \frac{1}{|x_1||x_2| \ldots |x_{n-m}|} > \binom{n}{m}.$$

Consider $x_0 = \min\{|x_1|, |x_2|, \ldots, |x_{n-m}|\}$. Then

$$\binom{n}{n-m} \frac{1}{x_0^{n-m}} > \binom{n}{m}$$

so $x_0 < 1$, as claimed.

(*Titu Andreescu*, Revista Matematică Timişoara (RMT), No. 2(1978), pp. 52, Problem 3531)

54. We have

$$\sum_{i=1}^{n} \frac{P'(x)}{P(x) - x_i} = \frac{n^2}{x}.$$

Integrating the equation yields

$$\sum_{i=1}^{n} \ln |P(x) - x_i| = n^2 \ln C|x|, \quad C > 0$$

or

$$\ln \prod_{i=1}^{n} |P(x) - x_i| = \ln C^{n^2} |x|^{n^2}$$

Hence

$$\left| \prod_{i=1}^{n} (P(x) - x_i) \right| = k|x|^{n^2}, \quad k > 0$$

or

$$|P(P(x))| = k|x|^{n^2}.$$

Eliminating the modules gives

$$P(P(x)) = \lambda x^{n^2}, \quad \lambda \in \mathbb{R}.$$

Therefore $P(x) = ax^n$ with $a \in \mathbb{R}$.

(*Titu Andreescu*, Revista Matematică Timişoara (RMT), No. 1(1977), pp. 47, Problem 2863; Gazeta Matematică (GM-B), No. 1(1977), pp. 22, Problem 17034)

55. Define $Q(x) = xP(x)$. Because $a_n \neq 0$, the polynomial Q has distinct real zeros, so the polynomial Q' has distinct real zeros as well.

Consider $H(x) = xQ'(x)$. Again, we deduce that H' has distinct real zeros, and since

$$H'(x) = x^2 P''(x) + 3xP'(x) + P(x)$$

the conclusion follows.

(*Dorin Andrica*, Revista Matematică Timişoara (RMT), No. 2(1978), pp. 52, Problem 3530)

56. Let $m = \deg P(x)$ and let

$$P(x) = a_0 (x - x_1)(x - x_2) \ldots (x - x_m).$$

Because $P(x) \in R[x]$, $x_1, x_2, \ldots, x_m$ are distinct zeros.
Now

$$P(Q(x)) = (Q(x) - x_1)(Q(x) - x_2) \ldots (Q(x) - x_m)$$

has a multiple zero α of order k. Since $P(Q(\alpha)) = 0$, we have

$$a_0 \prod_{i=1}^{m} (Q(\alpha) - x_i) = 0,$$

and so there is an integer p, $1 \le p \le m$, such that $Q(\alpha) - x_p = 0$. Observe that $Q(\alpha) - x_p \ne 0$, for all $j \ne p$, otherwise $x_j = x_p$, which is false. Hence $Q(x) - x_j$ has the multiple zero α of order k and so $Q'(x) = (Q(x) - x_p)' = Q'(x)$ has a multiple zero of order $k - 1$. This concludes the proof.

(*Dorin Andrica*, Romanian Mathematical Olympiad - final round, 1978; Revista Matematică Timișoara (RMT), No. 2(1978), pp. 67, Problem 3614)

57. Assume by way of contradiction that $P(x)$ has less than two nonreal zeros. As a polynomial with real coefficients $P(x)$ cannot have only one nonreal zero, hence all of its are real. Let $x_1, x_2, \ldots, x_n$ be the zeros of $P(x)$.
Then

$$\frac{P'(x)}{P(x)} = \sum_{i=1}^{n} \frac{1}{x - x_i}$$

and differentiating we obtain

$$\frac{P''(x)P(x) - [P'(x)]^2}{P^2(x)} = -\sum_{i=1}^{n} \frac{1}{(x - x_i)^2}$$

Setting $x = a$ we reach a contradiction, therefore $P(x)$ has at least two nonreal zeros, as claimed.

(*Titu Andreescu*, Revista Matematică Timișoara (RMT), No. 1-2(1979), pp. 59, Problem 3883)

58. Let $P(x) = a_0 x^n + a_1 x^{n-1} + \cdots + a_n$ be a polynomial with real coefficients.
If all of its zeros are real, then the same is true for the polynomials P', $P'', \ldots, P^{(n-2)}$.
Because

$$P^{(n-2)}(x) = \frac{(n-2)!}{2} [n(n-1)a_0 x^2 + 2(n-1)a_1 x + 2a_2]$$

is a quadratic polynomial with real zeros, we have

$$\Delta = (n-1)^2 a_1^2 - 2n(n-1)a_0 a_2 \ge 0,$$

or

$$(n-1)a_1^2 \ge 2n a_0 a_2.$$

The reciprocal is not always true, as we can see from the following example:

$$P(x) = x^3 + (a+1)x^2 + (a+1)x + a,$$

with $a \in (-\infty, -1] \cup [2, \infty)$.

Observe that $2(a+1)^2 \geq 2 \cdot 3(a+1)$, or $(a+1)(a-2) \geq 0$, so the inequality holds. On the other hand, $P(x) = (x+a)(x^2+x+1)$ does not have all zeros real.

(*Dorin Andrica*)

59. For $m = 0$ the equation becomes

$$x^4 - x^3 - x^2 + x = 0$$

and has roots $x_1 = 0$, $x_2 = -1$, $x_3 = x_4 = 1$.

If $m \neq 0$, we will solve the equation in terms of m. We have

$$2xm^2 + (x^2 - 2x^3 + 1)m + x^4 - x^3 - x^2 + x = 0$$

and

$$\Delta = (x^2 - 2x^3 + 1)^2 - 8x^2(x^3 - x^2 - x + 1) = (2x^3 - 3x^2 + 1)^2.$$

It follows that

$$m_1 = x^2 - x \quad \text{and} \quad m_2 = \frac{x^2 - 1}{2x}.$$

The initial equation becomes

$$[m - (x^2 - x)]\left[m - \frac{x^2 - 1}{2x}\right] = 0.$$

Hence

$$x^2 - x - m = 0, \quad \text{with solutions} \quad x_{1,2} = \frac{1 \pm \sqrt{1+4m}}{2}$$

and

$$x^2 - 2mx - 1 = 0, \quad \text{with solutions} \quad x_{3,4} = m \pm \sqrt{1+m^2}.$$

(*Dorin Andrica*, Revista Matematică Timişoara (RMT), No. 2(1977), pp. 75, Problem 3121)

60. From the relations between the zeros and the coefficients we obtain

$$\sum x_1 x_2 \ldots x_{2n-1} = 2n \quad \text{and} \quad x_1 x_2 \ldots x_{2n} = 1.$$

Hence

$$\sum_{k=1}^{2n} \frac{1}{x_k} = 2n,$$

so we have the equality case in the AM-GM inequality. Therefore $x_1 = x_2 = \cdots = x_{2n}$. Since $x_1 x_2 \ldots x_{2n} = 1$ and

$$\sum_{k=1}^{2n} \frac{1}{x_k} > 0,$$

we have $x_1 = x_2 = \cdots = x_{2n} = 1$.

(*Titu Andreescu*, Revista Matematică Timişoara (RMT), No. 2(1977), pp. 52, Problem 2299)

Chapter 2
NUMBER THEORY

PROBLEMS

1. How many 7-digit numbers that do not start nor end with 1 are there?

2. How many integers are among the numbers

$$\frac{1 \cdot m}{n}, \frac{2 \cdot m}{n}, \ldots, \frac{p \cdot m}{n}$$

where p, m, n are given positive integers?

3. Let $p > 2$ be a prime number and let n be a positive integer. Prove that p divides $1^{p^n} + 2^{p^n} + \cdots + (p-1)^{p^n}$.

4. Prove that for any integer n the number

$$5^{5^{n+1}} + 5^{5^n} + 1$$

is not prime.

5. Let n be an odd integer greater than or equal to 5. Prove that

$$\binom{n}{1} - 5\binom{n}{2} + 5^2\binom{n}{3} - \cdots + 5^{n-1}\binom{n}{n}$$

is not a prime number.

6. Prove that

$$3^{4^5} + 4^{5^6}$$

is a product of two integers, each of which is larger than 10^{2002}.

7. Find all positive integers n such that $\left[\sqrt[n]{111}\right]$ divides 111.

8. Prove that for any distinct positive integers a and b the number $2a(a^2 + 3b^2)$ is not a perfect cube.

9. Let p be a prime greater than 5. Prove that $p - 4$ cannot be the fourth power of an integer.

10. Find all pairs (x, y) of nonnegative integers such that $x^2 + 3y$ and $y^2 + 3x$ are simultaneously perfect squares.

11. Prove that for any positive integer n the number
$$\frac{\left(17 + 12\sqrt{2}\right)^n - \left(17 - 12\sqrt{2}\right)^n}{4\sqrt{2}}$$
is an integer but not a perfect square.

12. Let $(u_n)_{n \geq 1}$ be the Fibonacci sequence:
$$u_{n+2} = u_{n+1} + u_n, \quad u_1 = u_2 = 1.$$
Prove that for all integers $n \geq 6$ between u_n and u_{n+1} there is a perfect square.

13. Prove that for all positive integers n the number $n! + 5$ is not a perfect square.

14. Prove that if n is a perfect cube then $n^2 + 3n + 3$ cannot be a perfect cube.

15. Let p be a prime. Prove that a product of $2p+1$ positive consecutive numbers cannot be the $2p + 1$-power of an integer.

16. Let p be a prime and let α be a positive real number such that $p\alpha^2 < \frac{1}{4}$. Prove that
$$\left[n\sqrt{p} - \frac{\alpha}{n}\right] = \left[n\sqrt{p} + \frac{\alpha}{n}\right]$$
for all integers $n \geq \left[\dfrac{\alpha}{\sqrt{1 - 2\alpha\sqrt{p}}}\right] + 1$.

17. Let n be an odd positive integer. Prove that the set
$$\left\{ \binom{n}{1}, \binom{n}{2}, \ldots, \binom{n}{\frac{n-1}{2}} \right\}$$
contains an odd number of odd numbers.

18. Find all positive integers m and n such that $\binom{m}{n} = 1984$.

19. Solve in nonnegative integers the equation
$$x^2 + 8y^2 + 6xy - 3x - 6y = 3$$

20. Solve in integers the equation
$$(x^2 + 1)(y^2 + 1) + 2(x - y)(1 - xy) = 4(1 + xy)$$

21. Let p and q be prime numbers. Find all positive integers x and y such that
$$\frac{1}{x} + \frac{1}{y} = \frac{1}{pq}.$$

22. Prove that the equation

$$x^2 - y^2 = u^v,$$

has infinitely many solutions in positive integers such that u and v are both primes.

23. Find all triples (x, y, z) of integers such that

$$x^2(y - z) + y^2(z - x) + z^2(x - y) = 2.$$

24. Solve in nonnegative integers the equation

$$x + y + z + xyz = xy + yz + zx + 2$$

25. Solve in integers the equation

$$xy(x^2 + y^2) = 2z^*.$$

26. Prove that for all positive integers n the equation

$$x^2 + y^2 + z^2 = 59^n$$

has integral solutions.

27. Let n be a positive integer. Prove that the equations

$$x^n + y^n + z^n + u^n = v^{n-1}$$

and

$$x^n + y^n + z^n + u^n = v^{n+1}$$

have infinitely many solutions in distinct positive integers.

28. Let n be a positive integer. Solve in rational numbers the equation

$$x^n + y^n = x^{n-1} + y^{n-1}.$$

29. Find all nonnegative integers x and y such that

$$x(x + 2)(x + 8) = 3^y.$$

30. Solve in nonnegative integers the equation

$$(1 + x!)(1 + y!) = (x + y)!.$$

31. Solve the equation

$$x! + y! + z! = 2^{v!}$$

32. Find all distinct positive integers $x_1, x_2, \ldots, x_n$ such that

$$1 + x_1 + 2x_1x_2 + \cdots + (n-1)x_1x_2 \ldots x_{n-1} = x_1x_2 \ldots x_n.$$

33. Prove that for all positive integers n and all integers $a_1, a_2, \ldots, a_n, b_1, b_2, \ldots,$ b_n the number

$$\prod_{k=1}^{n}(a_k^2 - b_k^2)$$

can be written as a difference of two squares.

34. Find all integers x, y, z, v, t such that

$$x + y + z + v + t = xyvt + (x+y)(v+t)$$
$$xy + z + vt = xy(v+t) + vt(x+y).$$

35. Prove that for all nonnegative integers a, b, c, d such that a and b are relatively prime, the system

$$ax - yz - c = 0$$
$$bx - yt + d = 0$$

has at least a solution in nonnegative integers.

36. Let p be a prime and let $x_1, x_2, \ldots, x_p$ be nonnegative integers.
Prove that if

$$x_1 + x_2 + \cdots + x_p \equiv 0 \pmod{p}$$
$$x_1^2 + x_2^2 + \cdots + x_p^2 \equiv 0 \pmod{p}$$
$$\ldots$$
$$x_1^{p-1} + x_2^{p-1} + \cdots + x_p^{p-1} \equiv 0 \pmod{p}$$

then there are $k, l \in \{1, 2, \ldots, p\}$, $k \neq l$, such that $x_k - x_l \equiv 0 \pmod{p}$.

37. Prove that for any odd integers $n, a_1, a_2, \ldots, a_n$, the greatest common divisor of numbers $a_1, a_2, \ldots, a_n$ is equal to the greatest common divisor of $\dfrac{a_1 + a_2}{2}, \dfrac{a_2 + a_3}{2}, \ldots, \dfrac{a_n + a_1}{2}$.

38. Let $\varphi(n)$ be the number of numbers less than n and relatively prime with n. Prove that there are infinitely many positive integers n such that

$$\varphi(n) = \frac{n}{3}.$$

39. Let $\pi(x)$ the number of primes less than or equal to x. Prove that

$$\pi(n) < \frac{n}{3} + 2$$

for all positive integers n.

40. Let p_k denote the k-th prime number. Prove that

$$p_1^m + p_2^m + \cdots + p_n^m > n^{m+1}$$

for all positive integers m and n.

41. Let n be a positive integer. Find the sum of all positive integers less than $2n$ and relatively prime with n.

42. Prove that any number between 1 and $n!$ can be written as a sum of at most n distinct divisors of $n!$.

43. Find the largest value of n such that the complementary set of any subset with n elements of $\{1, 2, \ldots, 1984\}$ contains at least two elements that are relatively prime.

44. Find all positive integers n such that for all odd integers a, if $a^2 \leq n$ then $a \mid n$.

45. Consider the sequences $(u_n)_{n\geq 1}$, $(v_n)_{n\geq 1}$ defined by $u_1 = 3$, $v_1 = 2$ and $u_{n+1} = 3u_n + 4v_n$, $v_{n+1} = 2u_n + 3v_n$, $n \geq 1$. Define $x_n = u_n + v_n$, $y_n = u_n + 2v_n$, $n \geq 1$. Prove that $y_n = [x_n\sqrt{2}]$ for all $n \geq 1$.

46. Define $x_n = 2^{2^{n-1}} + 1$ for all positive integers. Prove that
(i) $x_n = x_1 x_2 \ldots x_{n-1} + 2$, $n \in \mathbb{N}$
(ii) $(x_k, x_l) = 1$, $k, l \in \mathbb{N}$, $k \neq l$
(iii) x_n ends in 7 for all $n \geq 3$.

47. Define the sequence $(a_n)_{n\geq 1}$ by $a_1 = 1$ and

$$a_{n+1} = 2a_n + \sqrt{3a_n^2 - 2}$$

for all integers $n \geq 1$. Prove that a_n is an integer for all n.

48. Define the sequences $(a_n)_{n\geq 0}$ and $(b_n)_{n\geq 0}$, by $a_0 = 1$,

$$a_n = \frac{2a_{n-1}}{1 + 2a_{n-1}^2} \quad \text{and} \quad b_n = \frac{1}{1 - 2a_{n-1}^2}$$

for all positive integers n. Prove that all terms of the sequence $(a_n)_{n\geq 0}$ are irreducible fractions and all terms of the sequence $(b_n)_{n\geq 0}$ are squares.

49. Define the sequences $(x_n)_{n\geq 0}$ and $(y_n)_{n\geq 0}$ by $x_0 = 3$, $y_0 = 2$,

$$x_n = 3x_{n-1} + 4y_{n-1} \quad \text{and} \quad y_n = 2x_{n-1} + 3y_{n-1}$$

for all positive integers n. Prove that the sequence $(z_n)_{n\geq 0}$, where $z_n = 1 + 4x_n^2 y_n^2$, contains no prime numbers.

50. Let p be a positive integer and let x_1 be a positive real number. Define the sequence $(x_n)_{n \geq 1}$ by

$$x_{n+1} = \sqrt{p^2 + 1}\, x_n + p\sqrt{x_n^2 + 1}$$

for all positive integers n. Prove that among the first m terms of the sequence there are at least $\left[\dfrac{m}{3}\right]$ irrational numbers.

51. Define the sequence $(x_n)_{n \geq 0}$ by
1) $x_n = 0$ if and only if $n = 0$ and
2) $x_{n+1} = x_{\left[\frac{n+3}{2}\right]}^2 + (-1)^n x_{\left[\frac{n}{2}\right]}^2$ for all $n \geq 0$.
Find x_n in closed form.

52. Define the sequence $(a_n)_{n \geq 0}$ by $a_0 = 0$, $a_1 = 1$, $a_2 = 2$, $a_3 = 6$ and

$$a_{n+4} = 2a_{n+3} + a_{n+2} - 2a_{n+1} - a_n, \quad n \geq 0.$$

Prove that n divides a_n for all $n > 0$.

53. Let $x_1 = x_2 = x_3 = 1$ and $x_{n+3} = x_n + x_{n+1} x_{n+2}$ for all positive integers n. Prove that for any positive integer m there is an integer $k > 0$ such that m divides x_k.

54. Let $(a_n)_{n \geq 0}$ be the sequence defined by $a_0 = 0$, $a_1 = 1$ and

$$\frac{a_{n+1} - 3a_n + a_{n-1}}{2} = (-1)^n$$

for all integers $n > 0$. Prove that a_n is a perfect square for all $n \geq 0$.

55. Let $a_1 = a_2 = 97$ and

$$a_{n+1} = a_n a_{n-1} + \sqrt{(a_n^2 - 1)(a_{n-1}^2 - 1)}, \quad n > 1.$$

Prove that
   a) $2 + 2a_n$ is a perfect square.
   b) $2 + \sqrt{2 + 2a_n}$ is a perfect square.

56. Let $k \geq 2$ be an integer. Find in closed form for the general term a_n of the sequence defined by $a_0 = 0$ and $a_n - a_{\left[\frac{n}{k}\right]} = 1$ for all $n > 0$.

57. Let $a_0 = a_1 = 3$ and $a_{n+1} = 7a_n - a_{n-1}$ for $n \geq 1$. Prove that $a_n - 2$ is a perfect square for all $n \geq 1$.

58. Let α and β be nonnegative integers such that $\alpha^2 + 4\beta$ is not a perfect square. Define the sequence $(x_n)_{n \geq 0}$ by

$$x_{n+2} = \alpha x_{n+1} + \beta x_n$$

for all integers $n \geq 0$, where x_1 and x_2 are positive integers.

Prove that there is no positive integer n_0 such that

$$x_{n_0}^2 = x_{n_0-1} x_{n_0+1}.$$

59. Let $n > 1$ be an integer. Prove that there is no irrational number a such that $\sqrt[n]{a + \sqrt{a^2 - 1}} + \sqrt[n]{a - \sqrt{a^2 - 1}}$ is rational.

60. Prove that for different choices of signs $+$ and $-$ the expression

$$\pm 1 \pm 2 \pm 3 \pm \cdots \pm (4n + 1),$$

yields all odd positive integers less than or equal to $(2n + 1)(4n + 1)$.

SOLUTIONS

1. The problem is equivalent to finding the number of functions

$$f : \{1,2,3,4,5,6,7\} \to \{0,1,2,\ldots,9\}$$

such that

$$f(1) \neq 0, \quad f(1) \neq 1 \text{ and } f(7) \neq 1.$$

Because $f(1) \in \{2,3,\ldots,9\}$, there are 8 possibilities to define $f(1)$. For $f(7)$ there are 9 possibilities and for $f(2), f(3), f(4), f(5), f(6)$ there are 10.

To conclude, there are $8 \cdot 9 \cdot 10^5 = 72 \cdot 10^5$ numbers with the desired property.

(*Dorin Andrica*, Gazeta Matematică (GM-B), No. 11(1979), pp. 421, Problem 17999)

2. Let d be the greatest common divisor of m and n. Hence $m = m_1 d$ and $n = n_1 d$ for some integers m_1 and n_1.

The numbers are

$$\frac{1 \cdot m_1}{n_1}, \frac{2 \cdot m_1}{n_1}, \ldots, \frac{p \cdot m_1}{n_1}$$

and, since m_1, n_1 are relatively prime, there are $\left[\dfrac{p}{n_1}\right]$ integers among them. Because $n_1 = \dfrac{n}{d} = \dfrac{n}{gcd(m,n)}$ it follows that there are $\left[\dfrac{gcd(m,n)p}{n}\right]$ integers.

(*Dorin Andrica*, Gazeta Matematică (GM-B), No. 11(1979), pp. 429, Problem O:89)

3. Define $k = p^n$ and note that k is odd. Then

$$d^k + (p-d)^k = p[d^{k-1} - d^{k-2}(p-d) + \cdots + (p-d)^{k-1}]$$

Summing up the equalities from $d = 1$ to $d = \left[\dfrac{p}{2}\right]$ implies that p divides $1^k + 2^k + \cdots + (p-1)^k$, as claimed.

(*Dorin Andrica*, Revista Matematică Timişoara (RMT), No. 1-2(1979), pp. 49, Problem 3813)

4. Define $m = 5^{5^n}$. Then

$$5^{5^{n+1}} + 5^{5^n} + 1 = m^5 + m + 1 = (m^2 + m + 1)(m^3 - m^2 + 1)$$

57

and, since both factors are greater than 1, the conclusion follows.

(*Titu Andreescu*, Korean Mathematics Competition, 2001)

5. Let $N = \binom{n}{1} - 5\binom{n}{2} + 5^2\binom{n}{3} - \cdots + 5^{n-1}\binom{n}{n}$. Then

$$5N = 1 - 1 + 5\binom{n}{1} - 5^2\binom{n}{2} + 5^3\binom{n}{3} - \cdots + 5^n\binom{n}{n} = 1 + (-1+5)^n.$$

Hence

$$N = \frac{1}{5}(4^n + 1) = \frac{1}{5}\left[(2^n + 1)^2 - \left(2^{\frac{n+1}{2}}\right)^2\right] =$$

$$= \frac{1}{5}\left[2^n - 2^{\frac{n+1}{2}} + 1\right]\left[2^n + 2^{\frac{n+1}{2}} + 1\right] =$$

$$= \frac{1}{5}\left[\left(2^{\frac{n-1}{2}} - 1\right)^2 + 2^{n-1}\right]\left[\left(2^{\frac{n-1}{2}} + 1\right)^2 + 2^{n-1}\right].$$

Because n is greater than or equal to 5, both factors of the numerator are greater than 5. One of them is divisible by 5, call it $5N_1$, $N_1 > 1$, the other being N_2. Then $N = N_1 N_2$, where N_1 and N_2 are both integers greater than 1, and we are done.

(*Titu Andreescu*, Korean Mathematics Competition, 2001)

6. The given number is of the form $m^4 + \frac{1}{4}n^4$, where $m = 3^{4^4}$ and

$$n = 4^{\frac{5^6+1}{4}} = 2^{\frac{5^6+1}{2}}.$$

The conclusion follows from the identity

$$m^4 + \frac{n^4}{4} = m^4 + m^2 n^2 + \frac{1}{4}n^4 - m^2 n^2 = \left(m^2 + \frac{1}{2}n^2\right)^2 - m^2 n^2 =$$

$$= \left(m^2 + mn + \frac{1}{2}n^2\right)\left(m^2 - mn + \frac{1}{2}n^2\right)$$

and the inequalities

$$m^2 - mn + \frac{1}{2}n^2 > n\left(\frac{1}{2}n - m\right) = 2^{\frac{5^6+1}{2}}\left(2^{\frac{5^6-1}{2}} - 3^{4^4}\right) >$$

$$> 2^{\frac{5^6+1}{2}}\left(2^{\frac{5^6-1}{2}} - 2^{2\cdot4^4}\right) > 2^{\frac{5^6+1}{2}}\cdot 2^{512}\left(2^{\frac{5^6-1}{2}-512} - 1\right) >$$

$$> 2^{10\cdot\frac{5^6+1}{20}}\cdot 2^{512} > 2^{10\cdot5^4}\cdot 2^{10\cdot50} > 10^{3\cdot5^4}\cdot 10^{3\cdot50} > 10^{2002}$$

(*Titu Andreescu*, Korean Mathematics Competition, 2002)

7. The positive divisors of 111 are 1, 3, 37, 111. So we have the following cases:

1) $\left[\sqrt[n]{111}\right] = 1$ or $1 \le 111 < 2^n$, hence $n \ge 7$.

2) $\left[\sqrt[n]{111}\right] = 3$, or $3^n \le 111 < 4^n$, so $n = 4$.

3) $\left[\sqrt[n]{111}\right] = 37$, or $37^n \le 111 < 38^n$, impossible.

4) $\left[\sqrt[n]{111}\right] = 111$, or $111^n \le 111 < 112^n$, and so $n = 1$.

Therefore $n = 1$, $n = 4$ or $n \ge 7$.

(*Titu Andreescu*)

8. Note that

$$2a(a^2 + 3b^2) = (a + b)^3 + (a - b)^3$$

The Fermat equation for $n = 3$

$$x^3 + y^3 = z^3$$

has no solution in positive integers (see T. Andreescu, D. Andrica, "An Introduction to Diophantine Equations", GIL Publishing House, 2002, pp. 87-93).

Hence there is no integer c such that

$$(a + b)^3 + (a - b)^3 = c^3$$

if $a > b$.

On the other hand, if $b > a$ then there is no integer c such that

$$(b - a)^3 + c^3 = (a + b)^3.$$

This concludes the proof.

(*Titu Andreescu*, Revista Matematică Timişoara (RMT), No. 1(1974), pp. 24, Problem 1911)

9. Assume that $p - 4 = q^4$ for some positive integer q. Then $p = q^4 + 4$ and $q > 1$. We obtain

$$p = (q^2 - 2q + 2)(q^2 + 2q + 2),$$

a product of two integers greater than 1, contradicting the fact that p is a prime.

(*Titu Andreescu*, Math Path Qualifying Quiz, 2003)

10. The inequalities

$$x^2 + 3y \geq (x + 2)^2, \quad y^2 + 3x \geq (y + 2)^2$$

cannot hold simultaneously because summing them up yields $0 \geq x + y + 8$, which is false. Hence at least one of $x^2 + 3y < (x + 2)^2$ or $y^2 + 3x < (y + 2)^2$ is true. Without loss of generality assume that $x^2 + 3y < (x + 2)^2$.

From $x^2 < x^2 + 3y < (x + 2)^2$ we derive $x^2 + 3y = (x + 1)^2$, hence $3y = 2x + 1$. Then $x = 3k + 1$ and $y = 2k + 1$ for some integer $k \geq 0$ and so $y^2 + 3x = 4k^2 + 13k + 4$. If $k > 5$, then

$$(2k + 3)^2 < 4k^2 + 13k + 4 < (2k + 4)^2$$

so $y^2 + 3x$ cannot be a square. It is easy to check that for $k \in \{0, 1, 2, 3, 4\}$, $y^2 + 3x$ is not a square but for $k = 0$, $y^2 + 3x = 4 = 2^2$. Therefore the only solution is $(x, y) = (1, 1)$.

(*Titu Andreescu*)

11. Note that $17 + 12\sqrt{2} = \left(\sqrt{2} + 1\right)^4$ and $17 - 12\sqrt{2} = \left(\sqrt{2} - 1\right)^4$, so

$$\frac{\left(17 + 12\sqrt{2}\right)^n - \left(17 - 12\sqrt{2}\right)^n}{4\sqrt{2}} = \frac{\left(\sqrt{2} + 1\right)^{4n} - \left(\sqrt{2} - 1\right)^{4n}}{4\sqrt{2}} =$$

$$= \frac{\left(\sqrt{2} + 1\right)^{2n} + \left(\sqrt{2} - 1\right)^{2n}}{2} \cdot \frac{\left(\sqrt{2} + 1\right)^{2n} - \left(\sqrt{2} - 1\right)^{2n}}{2\sqrt{2}}$$

Define

$$A = \frac{\left(\sqrt{2} + 1\right)^{2n} + \left(\sqrt{2} - 1\right)^{2n}}{2} \quad \text{and} \quad B = \frac{\left(\sqrt{2} + 1\right)^{2n} - \left(\sqrt{2} - 1\right)^{2n}}{2\sqrt{2}}$$

Using the binomial expansion formula we obtain positive integers x and y such that

$$\left(\sqrt{2} + 1\right)^{2n} = x + y\sqrt{2}, \quad \left(\sqrt{2} - 1\right)^{2n} = x - y\sqrt{2}$$

Then

$$x = \frac{\left(\sqrt{2} + 1\right)^{2n} + \left(\sqrt{2} - 1\right)^{2n}}{2} \quad \text{and} \quad y = \frac{\left(\sqrt{2} + 1\right)^{2n} - \left(\sqrt{2} - 1\right)^{2n}}{2\sqrt{2}}$$

and so AB is as integer, as claimed.

Observe that

$$A^2 - 2B^2 = (A + \sqrt{2}B)(A - \sqrt{2}B) = (\sqrt{2} + 1)^{2n}(\sqrt{2} - 1)^{2n} = 1$$

so A and B are relatively prime. It is sufficient to prove that at least one of them is not a perfect square.

We have

$$A = \frac{\left(\sqrt{2} + 1\right)^{2n} + \left(\sqrt{2} - 1\right)^{2n}}{2} = \left[\frac{\left(\sqrt{2} + 1\right)^n + \left(\sqrt{2} - 1\right)^n}{\sqrt{2}}\right]^2 - 1 \qquad (1)$$

and

$$A = \frac{\left(\sqrt{2} + 1\right)^{2n} + \left(\sqrt{2} - 1\right)^{2n}}{2} = \left[\frac{\left(\sqrt{2} + 1\right)^n - \left(\sqrt{2} - 1\right)^n}{\sqrt{2}}\right]^2 + 1 \qquad (2)$$

Since only one of the numbers

$$\frac{\left(\sqrt{2} + 1\right)^n + \left(\sqrt{2} - 1\right)^n}{\sqrt{2}}, \quad \frac{\left(\sqrt{2} + 1\right)^n - \left(\sqrt{2} - 1\right)^n}{\sqrt{2}}$$

is an integer – depending on the parity of n – from the relations (1) and (2) we derive that A is not a square. This completes the proof.

(*Dorin Andrica*, Revista Matematică Timişoara (RMT), No. 1(1981), pp. 48, Problem 4285)

12. The claim is true for $n = 6$ and $n = 7$, because $u_6 = 8 < 9 < u_7 = 13 < 16 < u_8 = 21$.

If $n \geq 8$, then

$$\sqrt{u_{n+1}} - \sqrt{u_n} = \frac{u_{n+1} - u_n}{\sqrt{u_{n+1}} + \sqrt{u_n}} \geq \frac{u_{n-1}}{2\sqrt{u_{n+1}}} \geq$$

$$\geq \frac{u_{n-1}}{2\sqrt{3u_{n-1}}} = \frac{1}{2\sqrt{3}}\sqrt{u_{n-1}} > 1$$

and so between u_n and u_{n+1} there is a perfect square.

(*Dorin Andrica*)

13. If $n = 1, 2, 3$ or 4 then $n! + 5 = 6, 7, 11$ or 29, so it is not a square. If $n \geq 5$, then $n! + 5 = 5(5k + 1)$ for some integer k and therefore is not a perfect square, as desired.

(*Dorin Andrica*, Gazeta Matematică (GM-B), No. 8(1977), pp. 321, Problem 16781; Revista Matematică Timişoara (RMT), No. 1(1978), pp. 61, Problem 3254)

14. Suppose by way of contradiction that $n^2 + 3n + 3$ is a cube. Hence $n(n^2 + 3n + 3)$ is a cube. Note that

$$n(n^2 + 3n + 3) = n^3 + 3n^2 + 3n = (n + 1)^3 - 1$$

and since $(n + 1)^3 - 1$ is not a cube, we obtain a contradiction.

(*Dorin Andrica*, Gazeta Matematică (GM-B), No. 8(1977), pp. 312, Problem E5965; Revista Matematică Timişoara (RMT), No. 1-2(1979), pp. 28, Problem 3253)

15. Consider the product of $2p + 1$ consecutive numbers

$$P(n) = (n + 1)(n + 2) \ldots (n + 2p + 1)$$

Observe that $P(n) > (n + 1)^{2p+1}$. On the other hand,

$$P(n) < \left[\frac{(n + 1) + (n + 2) + \cdots + (n + 2p + 1)}{2p + 1} \right]^{2p+1} = (n + p + 1)^{2p+1}$$

from the AM-GM inequality.

If $P(n) = m^{2p+1}$, then $m \in \{n + 2, \ldots, n + p\}$. Assume by way of contradiction that there is $k \in \{2, 3, \ldots, p\}$ such that $P(n) = (n + k)^{2p+1}$. Then

$$(n + 1)(n + 2) \ldots (n + k - 1)(n + k + 1) \ldots (n + 2p + 1) = (n + k)^{2p}. \qquad (1)$$

We have two cases:

I. $k = p$

1) If $n \equiv 0 \pmod{p}$, then $(n + k)^{2p}$ is divisible by p^{2p}. The left-hand side of the equality (1) is clearly not divisible by p^{2p}, hence we reach a contradiction.

2) If $n \equiv r \pmod{p}$, $r \neq 0$, then the left-hand side of the equality (1) is divisible by p^2, because of the factors $n + p - r$ and $n + 2p - r$, while the right-hand side is not, since $(n + k)^{2p} \equiv r^{2p}$. This is a contradiction.

II. $k \in \{2, 3, \ldots, p - 1\}$

1) If $n \equiv -k \pmod{p}$, then the right-hand side of (1) is divisible by p^{2p}, but the left-hand side is not.

2) If $n \equiv -q \pmod{p}$, $q \neq k$ and $q \in \{0, 1, \ldots, p-1\}$, then the left-hand side of (1) is divisible by p. On the other hand

$$(n+k)^{2p} \equiv (q-k)^2 \pmod{p} \not\equiv 0 \pmod{p},$$

because $0 < |q - k| < p$.

Both cases end up in contradictions, so the problem is solved.

(*Dorin Andrica*)

16. It suffices to prove that there are no integers in the interval $\left(n\sqrt{p} - \dfrac{\alpha}{n}, n\sqrt{p} + \dfrac{\alpha}{n} \right]$ for $n \geq \left[\dfrac{\alpha}{\sqrt{1 - 2\alpha\sqrt{p}}} \right] + 1$.

Assume by way of contradiction that there is integer k such that

$$n\sqrt{p} - \frac{\alpha}{n} < k \leq n\sqrt{p} + \frac{\alpha}{n}.$$

Hence

$$n^2 p + \frac{\alpha^2}{n^2} - 2\alpha\sqrt{p} < k^2 \leq n^2 p + \frac{\alpha^2}{n^2} + 2\alpha\sqrt{p}.$$

Observe that $\dfrac{\alpha^2}{n^2} - 2\alpha\sqrt{p} > -1$. If $n \geq \left[\dfrac{\alpha}{\sqrt{1 - 2\alpha\sqrt{p}}} \right] + 1$, then $\dfrac{\alpha^2}{n^2} + 2\alpha\sqrt{p} < 1$ so

$$n^2 p - 1 < k^2 < n^2 p + 1.$$

It follows that $k^2 = pn^2$ or $\sqrt{p} = \dfrac{k}{n}$, which is false, since p is prime.

(*Dorin Andrica*, Gazeta Matematică (GM-B), No. 8(1977), pp. 324, Problem 16804)

17. For $n = 1$ the claim is clear, so let $n \geq 3$.

Define $S_n = \dbinom{n}{1} + \dbinom{n}{2} + \cdots + \dbinom{n}{\frac{n-1}{2}}$. Then

$$2S_n = \binom{n}{1} + \binom{n}{2} + \cdots + \binom{n}{n-1} = 2^n - 2$$

or $S_n = 2^{n-1} - 1$. Because S_n is odd it follows that the sum S_n contains an odd number of odd terms, as desired.

(*Titu Andreescu*, Revista Matematică Timişoara (RMT), No. 2(1984), pp. 71, Problem 5346)

18. Because $\dbinom{m}{n} = \dbinom{m}{m-n}$, we can assume that $m \leq \left[\dfrac{n}{2} \right]$.

If $n = 0$, then $1 = 1984$, false.

If $n = 1$, then $m = 1984$.

If $n = 2$, then $\dfrac{m(m-1)}{2} = 1984$, with no integral solutions.

If $n \geq 3$, then $\binom{m}{n} \geq \binom{m}{3}$, so $1984 \geq \dfrac{m(m-1)(m-2)}{6}$. Hence $11904 \geq m^3 - 3m^2 + 2m$ or $(m-30)(m^2 + 27m + 812) \leq -12456 < 0$, and so $m < 30$. This implies that $\binom{m}{n} \neq 1984$, because $\dfrac{m(m-1)\dots(m-n+1)}{n!}$ does not contain the factor 31 of 1984.

To conclude, the solutions are $m = 1984$, $n = 1$ and $m = 1984$, $n = 1983$.

(*Titu Andreescu*, Revista Matematică Timişoara (RMT), No. 1(1985), pp. 80, Problem 5)

19. The equation is equivalent to

$$(x + 2y)(x + 4y) - 3(x + 2y) = 3,$$

or

$$(x + 2y)(x + 4y - 3) = 3.$$

We have

(i) $\begin{cases} x + 2y = 3 \\ x + 4y - 3 = 1 \end{cases}$, with solution $(x, y) = \left(2, \dfrac{1}{2}\right)$

or

(ii) $\begin{cases} x + 2y = 1 \\ x + 4y - 3 = 3 \end{cases}$, with solution $(x, y) = \left(-4, \dfrac{5}{2}\right)$.

Note that there are no solutions in integers, as claimed.

(*Titu Andreescu*, Revista Matematică Timişoara (RMT), No. 1(1971), pp. 20, Problem 312)

20. The equation is equivalent to

$$x^2 y^2 - 2xy + 1 + x^2 + y^2 - 2xy + 2(x - y)(1 - xy) = 4,$$

or

$$(xy - 1)^2 + (x - y)^2 + 2(x - y)(1 - xy) = 4.$$

Hence $(1 - xy + x - y)^2 = 4$ and, consequently, $|(1 + x)(1 - y)| = 2$.

We have two cases:

I. $(1 + x)(1 - y) = 2$. Then

a) $1 + x = 2$, $1 - y = 1$, so $x = 1$, $y = 0$.

b) $1 + x = -2$, $1 - y = -1$, so $x = -3$, $y = 2$.

c) $1 + x = 1$, $1 - y = 2$, so $x = 0$, $y = -1$.

d) $1 + x = -1$, $1 - y = -2$, so $x = -2$, $y = 3$.

II. $(1 + x)(1 - y) = -2$. Then

a) $1 + x = 2$, $1 - y = -1$, so $x = 1$, $y = 2$.

b) $1 + x = -2$, $1 - y = 1$, so $x = -3$, $y = 0$.

c) $1 + x = 1$, $1 - y = -2$, so $x = 0$, $y = 3$.

d) $1 + x = -1$, $1 - y = 2$, so $x = -2$, $y = -1$.

(*Titu Andreescu*, Revista Matematică Timişoara (RMT), No. 4-5(1972), pp. 43, Problem 1383)

21. The equation is equivalent to

$$(x - pq)(y - pq) = p^2 q^2.$$

We have the cases:

1) $x - pq = 1$, $y - pq = p^2 q^2$, so $x = 1 + pq$, $y = pq(1 + pq)$.

2) $x - pq = p$, $y - pq = pq^2$, so $x = p(1 + q)$, $y = pq(1 + q)$.

3) $x - pq = q$, $y - pq = p^2 q$, so $x = q(1 + p)$, $y = pq(1 + p)$.

4) $x - pq = p^2$, $y - pq = q^2$, so $x = p(p + q)$, $y = q(p + q)$.

5) $x - pq = pq$, $y - pq = pq$, so $x = 2pq$, $y = 2pq$.

The equation is symmetric, so we have also:

6) $x = pq(1 + pq)$, $y = 1 + pq$.

7) $x = pq(1 + q)$, $y = p(1 + q)$.

8) $x = pq(1 + p)$, $y = q(1 + p)$.

9) $x = q(1 + q)$, $y = p(p + q)$.

(*Titu Andreescu*, Revista Matematică Timişoara (RMT), No. 2(1978), pp. 45, Problem 3486)

22. Define the sequences $(x_n)_{n \geq 1}$ and $(y_n)_{n \geq 1}$ by $x_1 = 2$, $y_1 = 1$,

$$x_{n+1} = 2x_n + y_n \quad \text{and} \quad y_{n+1} = x_n + 2y_n$$

for all $n \geq 1$.

By induction we obtain that

$$3^n = x_n^2 - y_n^2, \quad n \geq 1$$

Denote by p_k the k-th prime number. Then $x = x_{p_k}$, $y = y_{p_k}$, $u = 3$, $v = p_k$ is a solution of equation $x^2 - y^2 = u^v$ for any integer $k > 0$.

Alternative solution. Let p and q be two arbitrary primes, $p \geq 3$. Then $p^q = 2k+1$, for some positive integer k. Because $2k+1 = (k+1)^2 - k^2$, it follows that all quadruples $(x, y, u, v) = \left(\dfrac{p^q + 1}{2}, \dfrac{p^q - 1}{2}, p, q \right)$ satisfy the equation.

(*Dorin Andrica*)

23. The equation is equivalent to

$$(x - y)(x - z)(y - z) = 2.$$

Observe that $(x - y) + (y - z) = x - z$. On the other hand, 2 can be written as a product of three distinct integers in the following ways

   i) $2 = (-1) \cdot (-1) \cdot 2$,

   ii) $2 = 1 \cdot 1 \cdot 2$,

   iii) $2 = (-1) \cdot 1 \cdot (-2)$.

Since in the first case any two factors do not add up to the third, we only have three possibilities:

a) $\begin{cases} x - y = 1 \\ x - z = 2 \\ y - z = 1 \end{cases}$ so $(x, y, z) = (k + 1, k, k - 1)$ for some integer k;

b) $\begin{cases} x - y = -2 \\ x - z = -1 \\ y - z = 1 \end{cases}$ so $(x, y, z) = (k - 1, k + 1, k)$ for some integer k;

c) $\begin{cases} x - y = 1 \\ x - z = -1 \\ y - z = -2. \end{cases}$ so $(x, y, z) = (k, k - 1, k + 1)$ for some integer k.

(*Titu Andreescu*, Revista Matematică Timişoara (RMT), No. 1-2(1989), pp. 97, Problem 2)

24. We have
$$xyz - (xy + yz + zx) + x + y + z - 1 = 1,$$
and, consequently,
$$(x - 1)(y - 1)(z - 1) = 1.$$

Because x, y, z are integers, we obtain
$$x - 1 = y - 1 = z - 1 = 1,$$
so $x = y = z = 2$.

(*Titu Andreescu*, Revista Matematică Timişoara (RMT), No. 3(1971), pp. 26, Problem 487)

25. Multiplying by 8 yields
$$8xy(x^2 + y^2) = 16z^4$$
or
$$(x + y)^4 - (x - y)^4 = (2z)^4,$$
and so
$$(x - y)^4 + (2z)^4 = (x + y)^4.$$

This is Fermat's equation for the case $n = 4$ and it is known that this equation has solutions only if $x - y = 0$ or $2z = 0$ (see T. Andreescu, D. Andrica, "An Introduction to Diophantine Equations", GIL Publishing House, 2002, pp. 85-87).

Case I. If $x - y = 0$, then $x = y$ and $z = \pm x$. The solutions are

$$x = y = m, \quad z = \pm m$$

for any integer m.

Case II. If $z = 0$, then $(x - y)^4 = (x + y)^4$ and so $x = 0$ or $y = 0$. The solutions are

$$x = 0, \quad y = m, \quad z = 0$$

and

$$x = m, \quad y = 0, \quad z = 0$$

for any integer m.

(*Titu Andreescu*, Revista Matematică Timişoara (RMT), No. 1(1978), Problem 2813; Gazeta Matematică (GM-B), No. 11(1981), pp. 424, Problem O:264)

26. Consider the sequences $(x_n)_{n\geq 1}$, $(y_n)_{n\geq 1}$, $(z_n)_{n\geq 1}$, defined by

$$x_{n+2} = 59^2 x_n, \quad x_1 = 1, \quad x_2 = 14$$

$$y_{n+2} = 59^2 y_n, \quad y_1 = 3, \quad y_2 = 39$$

$$z_{n+2} = 59^2 z_n, \quad z_1 = 7, \quad z_2 = 42$$

for all $n \geq 1$.

It is easy to check that $x_n^2 + y_n^2 + z_n^2 = 59^n$, for all integers $n \geq 1$.

(*Dorin Andrica*, Romanian Mathematical Olympiad - second round, 1979, Revista Matematică Timişoara (RMT), No. 1-2(1980), pp. 58, Problem 4075)

27. Observe that the equation

$$x^n + y^n = z^{n-1} \tag{1}$$

has infinitely many solutions in distinct nonnegative integers, for example

$$x_k = (1 + k^n)^{n-2}, \quad y_k = k(1 + k^n)^{n-2}, \quad z_k = (1 + k^n)^{n-1},$$

for any integer $k \geq 0$.

Let $(x_{k_1}, y_{k_1}, z_{k_1})$ and $(x_{k_2}, y_{k_2}, z_{k_2})$ be two solutions of equation (1) with $k_1 \neq k_2$. Then

$$x_{k_1}^n + y_{k_1}^n = z_{k_1}^{n-1}, \quad x_{k_2}^n + y_{k_2}^n = z_{k_2}^{n-1}$$

and multiplying yields

$$(x_{k_1} x_{k_2})^n + (x_{k_1} y_{k_2})^n + (y_{k_1} x_{k_2})^n + (y_{k_1} y_{k_2})^n = (z_{k_1} z_{k_2})^{n-1}$$

This means that

$$(x, y, z, u, v) = (x_{k_1} x_{k_2}, x_{k_1} y_{k_2}, y_{k_1} x_{k_2}, y_{k_1} y_{k_2}, z_{k_1} z_{k_2})$$

is a solution to the equation

$$x^n + y^n + z^n + u^n = v^{n-1}$$

Since $k_1 \neq k_2$ are arbitrary positive integers, the conclusion follows.

For the second equation, the proof is similar, based on the fact that the equation

$$x^n + y^n = z^{n+1} \qquad (2)$$

has infinitely many solutions in distinct nonnegative integers, for example

$$x_k = 1 + k^n, \quad y_k = k(1 + k^n), \quad z_k = 1 + k^n,$$

for any integer $k \geq 0$.

(*Dorin Andrica*)

28. It is clear that $x = 0$, $y = 0$ is a solution to the equation

$$x^n + y^n = x^{n-1} + y^{n-1}$$

Let $\alpha \neq -1$ be a rational number such that $y = \alpha x$. Hence

$$x^n + \alpha^n x^n = x^{n-1} + \alpha^{n-1} x^{n-1},$$

so

$$x = \frac{1 + \alpha^{n-1}}{1 + \alpha^n}, \quad y = \alpha \frac{1 + \alpha^{n-1}}{1 + \alpha^n}$$

Using the symmetry of the equation, we also have the solution

$$x = \alpha \frac{1 + \alpha^{n-1}}{1 + \alpha^n}, \quad y = \frac{1 + \alpha^{n-1}}{1 + \alpha^n}$$

with $\alpha \neq -1$ rational.

If $\alpha = -1$ and $n > 1$, then again $x = y = 0$. This concludes the solution.

(*Dorin Andrica*, Revista Matematică Timişoara (RMT), No. 2(1981), pp. 62, Problem 4578)

29. Let $x = 3^u$, $x + 2 = 3^v$, $x + 8 = 3^t$ so $u + v + t = y$. Then

$$3^v - 3^u = 2 \quad \text{and} \quad 3^t - 3^u = 8.$$

It follows that

$$3^u(3^{v-u} - 1) = 2 \quad \text{and} \quad 3^u(3^{t-u} - 1) = 8.$$

Hence $u = 0$ and $3^v - 1 = 2$, $3^t - 1 = 8$, therefore $v = 1$, $t = 2$.

The solution is $x = 1$, $y = 3$.

(*Titu Andreescu*, Revista Matematică Timişoara (RMT), No. 2(1978), pp. 47, Problem 2812; Gazeta Matematică (GM-B), No. 12(1980), pp. 496, Problem 18541)

30. If $x, y \geq 2$ then $1 + x!$ and $1 + y!$ are both odd and $(x + y)!$ is even. Hence the equation has no solutions.

Consider the case $x = 1$. The equation becomes

$$2(1 + y!) = (1 + y)!$$

and it is not difficult to notice the solution $y = 2$. If $y \geq 3$, then 3 divides $(1 + y)!$ but not $2(1 + y!)$ and $y = 1$ does not satisfy the equality.

Hence $x = 1$, $y = 2$ or $x = 2$, $y = 1$ due to the symmetry of the equation.

(*Titu Andreescu*, Revista Matematică Timişoara (RMT), No. 2(1977), pp. 60, Problem 3028; Gazeta Matematică (GM-B), No. 2(1980), pp. 75, Problem O:118)

31. Without loss of generality we may assume that $x \geq y \geq z$. The equation is equivalent to

$$z![x(x - 1) \ldots (z + 1) + y(y - 1) \ldots (z + 1) + 1] = 2^{v!}.$$

If $z \geq 3$, then the right-hand side is divisible by 3 but the left-hand side is not, so $z \leq 2$. We have two cases.

I. $z = 1$. Then we have

$$x! + y! = 2^{v!} - 1,$$

or

$$y![x(x - 1) \ldots (y + 1) + 1] = 2^{v!} - 1.$$

If $y \geq 2$, then the right-hand side is an even number but the left-hand side is odd, so $y = 1$. Then

$$x! = 2(2^{v!-1} - 1).$$

If $x \geq 4$, then $2(2^{v!-1} - 1) \equiv 0 \pmod 8$, false.

It remains to examine the cases $x = 1$, $x = 2$, and $x = 3$.

If $x = 1$, then $1 = 2(2^{v!-1} - 1)$, impossible.

If $x = 2$, then $2 = 2(2^{v!-1} - 1)$ or $v! = 2$, so $v = 2$.

If $x = 3$, then $2^{v!-1} - 1 = 3$ or $v! = 3$, false.

Hence the only solution in this case is

$$x = 2, \quad y = 1, \quad z = 1, \quad v = 2$$

II. $z = 2$. Now we have

$$x! + y! = 2^{v!} - 2,$$

or

$$y![x(x - 1) \ldots (y + 1) + 1] = 2(2^{v!-1} - 1).$$

If $y \geq 4$, the $2(2^{v!-1} - 1) \equiv 0 \pmod 8$, false.

It follows that $y = 1$, $y = 2$, or $y = 3$.

If $y = 1$, then $x! = 2^{v!} - 3$. Since $x \geq 2$ implies $2^{v!} - 3 \equiv 0 \pmod 2$ false, then $x = 1$, $v = 2$.

If $y = 2$, then $x! = 2^{v!} - 4$. We must have $v \geq 3$ so $x! = 4(2^{v!-2} - 1)$.

If $x \geq 3$, then $4(2^{v!-2} - 1) \equiv 0 \pmod 8$, false.

Hence $x = 1$, $x = 2$ or $x = 3$ and all those cases lead to a contradiction.

If $y = 3$, then $x! = 2^{v!} - 8$. Then $v \geq 3$ and $x! = 2^3(2^{v!-3} - 1) \geq 2^3 \cdot 7$. It follows that $x \geq 5$ and because $x = 5$ does not yield a solution and $x \geq 6$ implies $2^3(2^{v!-3} - 1) \equiv 0 \pmod{16}$, which is false, we do not obtain a solution here.

In case II we have found only

$$x = 1, \quad y = 1, \quad z = 2, \quad v = 2,$$

which does not satisfy the condition $x \geq y \geq z$.

To conclude, we have the solution – from case I –

$$x = 2, \quad y = 1, \quad z = 1, \quad v = 2$$

and, due to the symmetry of the equation, we also have

$$x = 1, \quad y = 2, \quad z = 1, \quad v = 2$$

and

$$x = 1, \quad y = 1, \quad z = 2, \quad v = 2.$$

(*Titu Andreescu*, Revista Matematică Timişoara (RMT), No. 2(1981), pp. 62, Problem 4576)

32. The equation is equivalent to

$$x_1 x_2 \ldots x_n - (n-1)x_1 x_2 \ldots x_{n-1} - \cdots - 2x_1 x_2 - x_1 = 1,$$

or

$$x_1[x_2 \ldots x_n - (n-1)x_2 \ldots x_{n-1} - \cdots - 2x_2 - 1] = 1.$$

Hence $x_1 = 1$ and

$$x_2[x_3 \ldots x_n - (n-1)x_3 \ldots x_{n-1} - \cdots - 3x_3 - 2] = 2.$$

Since $x_2 \neq x_1$, it follows that $x_2 = 2$ and

$$x_3[x_4 \ldots x_n - (n-1)x_4 \ldots x_{n-1} - \cdots - 4x_4 - 3] = 3.$$

Because $x_3 \neq x_2$ and $x_3 \neq x_1$, we obtain $x_3 = 3$.

Continuing with the same procedure we deduce that $x_k = k$ for all k.

Remark. Turning back to the equation we find the identity

$$1 + 1! \cdot 1 + 2! \cdot 2 + \cdots + (n-1)!(n-1) = n!n.$$

(*Titu Andreescu*, Revista Matematică Timişoara (RMT), No. 3(1973), pp. 23, Problem 1509)

33. We proceed by induction on n. For $n = 1$ the claim is true. Using the identity

$$(x^2 - y^2)(u^2 - v^2) = (xu + yv)^2 - (xv + yu)^2$$

and the fact that the claim holds for n we deduce that the property is valid for $n + 1$, as desired.

Alternative solution. We have

$$P_n = \prod_{k=1}^{n}(a_k^2 - b_k^2) = \prod_{k=1}^{n}(a_k - b_k) \prod_{k=1}^{n}(a_k + b_k) =$$

$$= (A_n - B_n)(A_n + B_n),$$

where A_n, B_n are integers.

Hence

$$P_n = A_n^2 - B_n^2,$$

as claimed.

(*Dorin Andrica*, Revista Matematică Timişoara (RMT), No. 2(1975), pp. 45, Problem 2239; Gazeta Matematică (GM-B), No. 7(1975), pp. 268, Problem 15212)

34. Subtracting the equalities yields

$$(x + y - xy) + (v + y - vt) = (x + y - xy)(v + t - vt),$$

or

$$[(x + y - xy) - 1][(v + t - vt) - 1] = 1,$$

so

$$(1 - x)(1 - y)(1 - v)(1 - t) = 1. \tag{1}$$

It follows that

$$|1 - x| = |1 - y| = |1 - v| = |1 - t| = 1,$$

and using (1) we obtain

$$(x, y, z, t) = (0, 0, 0, 0), \ (0, 0, 2, 2), \ (0, 2, 0, 2),$$

$$(0, 2, 2, 0), \ (2, 0, 0, 2), \ (2, 0, 2, 0), \ (2, 2, 0, 0) \text{ and } (2, 2, 2, 2).$$

Turning back to the system we obtain

$$(x, y, z, v, t) = (0, 0, 0, 0, 0), \ (0, 0, -4, 2, 2), \ (0, 2, 0, 0, 2),$$

$$(0, 2, 0, 2, 0), \ (2, 0, 0, 0, 2), \ (2, 0, 0, 2, 0), \ (2, 2, -4, 0, 0) \text{ and } (2, 2, 24, 2, 2)$$

(*Titu Andreescu*, Revista Matematică Timişoara (RMT), No. 2(1978), pp. 46, Problem 3431; Gazeta Matematică (GM-B), No. 5(1981), pp. 216, Problem 18740)

35. We start with a useful lemma.

Lemma. *If a and b are relatively prime positive integers, then there are positive integers u and v such that*

$$au - bv = 1.$$

Proof. Consider the numbers

$$1 \cdot 2, \ 2 \cdot a, \ldots, (b-1) \cdot a \qquad (\Gamma)$$

When divided by b the remainders of these numbers are distinct. Indeed, otherwise we have $k_1 \neq k_2 \in \{1, 2, \ldots, b-1\}$ such that

$$k_1 a = p_1 b + r, \quad k_2 a = p_2 b + r$$

for some integers p_1, p_2. Hence

$$(k_1 - k_2)a = (p_1 - p_2)b \equiv 0 \pmod{b}.$$

Since a and b are relatively prime it follows that $|k_1 - k_2| \equiv 0 \pmod{b}$, which is false because $1 \leq |k_1 - k_2| < b$.

On the other hand, none of the numbers listed in (1) is divisible by b. Indeed, if so, then there is $k \in \{1, 2, \ldots, n-1\}$ such that

$$k \cdot a = p \cdot b \text{ for some integer } p.$$

Let d be the greatest common divisor of k and p. Hence $k = k_1 d$, $p = p_1 d$, for some integers p_1, k_1 with $gcd(p_1, k_1) = 1$. Then $k_1 a = p_1 b$ and since $gcd(a, b) = 1$, we have $k_1 = b$, $p_1 = a$. This is false, because $k_1 < b$.

It follows that one of the numbers from (1) has the remainder 1 when divided by b so there is $u \in \{1, 2, \ldots, b-1\}$ such that $au = bv + 1$ and the lemma is proved.

We prove now that the system

$$\begin{cases} ax - yz - c = 0 \\ bx - yt + d = 0 \end{cases}$$

with a, b, c, d nonnegative integers and $gcd(a, b) = 1$ has at least a solution in nonnegative integers.

Because $gcd(a, b) = 1$ using the lemma, there are positive integers u and v such that $au - bv = 1$. Hence

$$x = cu + dv, \quad y = ad + bc, \quad z = v, \quad t = u,$$

is a solution to the system.

(*Titu Andreescu*, Revista Matematică Timişoara (RMT), No. 2(1977), pp. 60, Problem 3029)

36. Consider the determinant

$$\Delta = \begin{vmatrix} 1 & 1 & \cdots & 1 \\ x_1 & x_2 & \cdots & x_p \\ \cdots & \cdots & \cdots & \cdots \\ x_1^{p-1} & x_2^{p-1} & \cdots & x_p^{p-1} \end{vmatrix} = \prod_{\substack{i,j=1 \\ i>j}}^{p} (x_i - x_j)$$

Summing up all columns to the first one and applying the hypothesis yields $\Delta \equiv 0$ (mod p), hence $\prod\limits_{\substack{i,j=1 \\ i>j}}^{p} (x_i - x_j) \equiv 0$ (mod p).

Because p is a prime number, it follows that there are distinct positive integers $k, l \in \{1, 2, \ldots, p\}$ such that $x_k - x_l \equiv 0$ (mod p).

(*Dorin Andrica*)

37. Let

$$a = gcd(a_1, a_2, \ldots, a_n) \quad \text{and} \quad b = gcd\left(\frac{a_1 + a_2}{2}, \frac{a_2 + a_3}{2}, \ldots, \frac{a_n + a_1}{2}\right)$$

Then $a_k = \alpha_k a$, for some integers α_k, $k = 1, 2, \ldots, n$. It follows that

$$\frac{a_k + a_{k+1}}{2} = \frac{\alpha_k + \alpha_{k+1}}{2} a, \tag{1}$$

where $a_{n+1} = a_1$ and $\alpha_{n+1} = \alpha_1$. Since a_k are odd numbers, α_k are also odd, so $\frac{\alpha_k + \alpha_{k+1}}{2}$ are integers.

From relation (1) it follows that a divides $\frac{a_k + a_{k+1}}{2}$ for all so a divides b.

On the other hand, $\frac{a_k + a_{k+1}}{2} = \beta_k b$, for some integers β_k. Then

$$a_k + a_{k+1} \equiv 0 \quad (\text{mod } 2b)$$

for all $k \in \{1, 2, \ldots, n\}$. Summing up from $k = 1$ to $k = n$ yields

$$2(a_1 + a_2 + \cdots + a_n) \equiv 0 \quad (\text{mod } 2b)$$

Since $n, a_1, a_2, \ldots, a_n$ are all odd $a_1 + a_2 + \cdots + a_n \not\equiv 0$ (mod 2), hence

$$a_1 + a_2 + \cdots + a_n \equiv 0 \quad (\text{mod } b). \tag{3}$$

Summing up for $k = 1, 3, \ldots, n - 2$ implies

$$a_1 + a_2 + \cdots + a_{n-1} \equiv 0 \quad (\text{mod } 2b)$$

and furthermore

$$a_1 + a_2 + \cdots + a_{n-1} \equiv 0 \quad (\text{mod } b). \tag{4}$$

Subtracting (4) from (3) implies $a_n \equiv 0$ (mod b), then using relation (2) we obtain $a_k \equiv 0$ (mod b) for all k. Hence $b|a$ and the proof is complete.

(*Titu Andreescu*, Revista Matematică Timişoara (RMT), No. 1(1978), pp. 47, Problem 2814)

38. It is known that

$$\varphi(kl) = \varphi(k)\varphi(l)$$

for any relatively prime positive integers k and l.

On the other hand, it is easy to see that if p is a prime number, then

$$\varphi(p^l) = p^l - p^{l-1}$$

for all positive integers l.

Let $n = 2 \cdot 3^m$, where m is a positive integer. Then

$$\varphi(n) = \varphi(2 \cdot 3^m) = \varphi(2)\varphi(3^m) = 3^m - 3^{m-1} = 2 \cdot 3^{m-1} = \frac{n}{3}$$

for infinitely many values of n, as desired.

(*Dorin Andrica*, Revista Matematică Timişoara (RMT), No. 1(1978), pp. 61, Problem 3255)

39. For $n = 1$ to $n = 6$ it is easy to check the claim. For $n \geq 7$ note that the number of even positive integers less than n is $\left[\frac{n}{2}\right]$. Moreover, the number of positive multiples of 3 less than n which are odd is $\left[\frac{n}{3}\right] - \left[\frac{n}{6}\right]$. Then

$$\pi(n) < n - \left[\frac{n}{2}\right] - \left(\left[\frac{n}{3}\right] - \left[\frac{n}{6}\right]\right), \quad n \geq 7.$$

Since $x - 1 < [x] \leq x$, it follows that

$$\pi(n) < n - \left(\frac{n}{2} - 1\right) - \left(\frac{n}{3} - 1\right) + \frac{n}{6} = \frac{n}{3} + 2,$$

as desired.

(*Dorin Andrica*, Revista Matematică Timişoara (RMT), No. 1(1978), pp. 61, Problem 3256)

40. Summing the inequalities $p_{k+1} - p_k \geq 2$ from $k = 1$ to $k = n-1$ yields $p_n - 2 \geq 2(n-1)$ and so $p_n > 2n - 1$, $n \geq 1$.

Then

$$p_1 + p_2 + \cdots + p_n > 2\frac{n(n+1)}{2} - n = n^2.$$

The inequality

$$\frac{a_1^m + a_2^m + \cdots + a_n^m}{n} \geq \left(\frac{a_1 + a_2 + \cdots + a_n}{n}\right)^m$$

holds for any positive real numbers $a_1, a_2, \ldots, a_n$. Hence

$$p_1^m + p_2^m + \cdots + p_n^m \geq n\left(\frac{p_1 + p_2 + \cdots + p_n}{n}\right)^m > n\left(\frac{n^2}{n}\right)^m = n^{m+1},$$

as desired.

(*Dorin Andrica*, Revista Matematică Timişoara (RMT), No. 2(1978), pp. 45, Problem 3483)

41. Let $S = \sum_{\substack{d < 2n \\ gcd(d,n)=1}} d$ and let $\varphi(n)$ be the number of numbers less than n and relatively prime with n.

Note that

$$gcd(n, d) = 1 \Leftrightarrow gcd(n, n - d) = 1 \Leftrightarrow gcd(n, n + d) = 1 \qquad (1)$$

Let $d_1, d_2, \ldots, d_{\varphi(n)}$ be the numbers less than n and relatively prime with n. From (1) we deduce that

$$d_1 + d_{\varphi(n)} = n$$

$$d_2 + d_{\varphi(n)-1} = n$$

$$\cdots$$

$$d_{\varphi(n)} + d_1 = n$$

hence

$$\sum_{\substack{d < n \\ gcd(d,n)=1}} d = \frac{n\varphi(n)}{2}.$$

On the other hand,

$$\sum_{\substack{n < d < 2n \\ gcd(d,n)=1}} d = \sum_{\substack{d < n \\ gcd(d,n)=1}} (n + d) = n\varphi(n) + \sum_{\substack{d < n \\ gcd(d,n)=1}} d =$$

$$= n\varphi(n) + \frac{n\varphi(n)}{2} = \frac{3n\varphi(n)}{2}.$$

Therefore

$$S = \frac{n\varphi(n)}{2} + \frac{3n\varphi(n)}{2} = 2n\varphi(n).$$

(*Dorin Andrica*, Revista Matematică Timişoara (RMT), No. 2(1981), pp. 61, Problem 4574)

42. We proceed by induction. For $n = 3$ the claim is true. Assume that the hypothesis holds for $n - 1$. Let $1 < k < n!$ and let k', q be the quotient and the remainder when k is divided by n. Hence $k = k'n + q$, $0 \leq q < n$ and $0 \leq k' < \frac{k}{n} < \frac{n!}{n} = (n - 1)!$.

From the inductive hypothesis, there are integers $d_1' < d_2' < \cdots < d_s'$, $s \leq n - 1$, such that $d_i'|(n - 1)!$, $i = 1, 2, \ldots, s$ and $k' = d_1' + d_2' + \cdots + d_s'$. Hence $k = nd_1' + nd_2' + \cdots + nd_s' + q$. If $q = 0$, then $k = d_1 + d_2 + \cdots + d_s$, where $d_i = nd_i'$, $i = 1, 2, \ldots, s$, are distinct divisors of $n!$.

If $q \neq 0$, then $k = d_1 + d_2 + \cdots + d_{s+1}$, where $d_i = nd_i'$, $i1, 2, \ldots, s$, and $d_{s+1} = q$. It is clear that $d_i|n!$, $i = 1, 2, \ldots, s$ and $d_{s+1}|n!$, since $q < n$. On the other hand, $d_{s+1} < d_1 < d_2 < \cdots < d_s$, because $d_{s+1} = q < n \leq nd_1' = d_1$. Therefore k can be written as a sum of at most n distinct divisors of $n!$, as claimed.

(*Titu Andreescu*, Revista Matematică Timişoara (RMT), No. 2(1983), pp. 88, Problem C4:10)

43. If $n \geq 992$, take the set with all 992 odd numbers from $\{1, 2, \ldots, 1984\}$. Its complementary set has only even numbers, any two of them not being relatively prime. Hence $n \leq 991$. Let c be the complementary set of a subset with 991 elements of the set $\{1, 2, \ldots, 1984\}$. Define $D = \{c + 1 \mid c \in C\}$. If $C \cap D = \emptyset$, then $C \cup D$ has $2 \cdot 993 = 1986$ elements but $C \cup D \subset \{1, 2, \ldots, 1985\}$, which is false.

Hence $C \cap D \neq \emptyset$, so there is an element $a \in C \cap D$. It follows that $a \in C$ and $a + 1 \in C$ and since a and $a + 1$ are relatively prime we are done.

(*Titu Andreescu*, Revista Matematică Timişoara (RMT), No. 1(1984), pp. 102, Problem C4:7)

44. Let a be the greatest odd integer such that $a^2 < n$, hence $n < (a + 2)^2$. If $a \geq 7$, then $a - 4, a - 2, a$ are odd integers which divide n. Note that any two of these numbers are relatively prime, so $(a - 4)(a - 2)a$ divides n. It follows that $(a - 4)(a - 2)a < (a + 2)^2$ so $a^3 - 6a^2 + 8a < a^2 + 4a + 4$. Then $a^3 - 7a^2 + 4a - 4 \leq 0$ or $a^2(a - 7) + 4(a - 1) \leq 0$. This is false, because $a \geq 7$, hence $a = 1, 3$ or 5.

If $a = 1$, then $1^2 \leq n < 3^2$, so $n \in \{1, 2, \ldots, 8\}$.

If $a = 3$, then $3^2 \leq n < 5^2$ and $1 \cdot 3 \mid n$, so $n \in \{9, 12, 15, 18, 21, 24\}$.

If $a = 5$, then $5^2 \leq n < 7^2$ and $1 \cdot 3 \cdot 5 \mid n$ so $n \in \{30, 45\}$. Therefore $n \in \{2, 3, 4, 5, 6, 7, 8, 9, 12, 15, 18, 21, 24, 30, 35\}$.

(*Dorin Andrica* and *Adrian P. Ghioca*, Romanian Winter Camp 1984; Revista Matematică Timişoara (RMT), No. 1(1985), pp. 78, Problem T.21)

45. We prove by induction that

$$u_n^2 - 2v_n^2 = 1, \quad n \geq 1. \tag{1}$$

For $n = 1$ the claim is true. Assuming that the equality is true for some n, we have

$$u_{n+1}^2 - 2v_{n+1}^2 = (3u_n + 4v_n)^2 - 2(2u_n + 3v_n)^2 = u_n^2 - 2v_n^2 = 1$$

hence (1) is true for all $n \geq 1$.

We prove now that

$$2x_n^2 - y_n^2 = 1, \quad n \geq 1 \tag{2}$$

Indeed,

$$2x_n^2 - y_n^2 = 2(u_n + v_n)^2 - (u_n + 2v_n)^2 = u_n^2 - 2v_n^2 = 1,$$

as claimed. It follows that

$$\left(x_n\sqrt{2} - y_n\right)\left(x_n\sqrt{2} + y_n\right) = 1, \quad n \geq 1.$$

Notice that $x_n\sqrt{2} + y_n > 1$ so

$$0 < x_n\sqrt{2} - y_n < 1, \quad n \geq 1.$$

Hence $y_n = \left[x_n\sqrt{2}\right]$, as claimed.

(*Dorin Andrica*, Gazeta Matematică (GM-B), No. 11(1979), pp. 430, Problem O:97)

46. (i) We have

$$x_k = 2^{2^{k-1}} + 1 = 2^{2^{k-2} \cdot 2} + 1 = (x_{k-1} - 1)^2 + 1 = x_{k-1}^2 - 2x_{k-1} + 2,$$

hence

$$x_k - 2 = x_{k-1}(x_{k-1} - 2).\qquad\qquad(1)$$

Multiplying the relations (1) from $k = 2$ to $k = n$ yields

$$x_n - 2 = x_{n-1} \dots x_2 x_1 (x_1 - 2),$$

and since $x_1 = 3$, we obtain

$$x_n = x_1 x_2 \dots x_{n-1} + 2\qquad\qquad(2)$$

for all $n \geq 2$.

For a different proof use the identity

$$\frac{x^{2^{n-1}} - 1}{x - 1} = \prod_{k=1}^{n-1} (x^{2^{k-1}} + 1).$$

(ii) From relation (2) we obtain $gcd(x_n, x_1) = gcd(x_n, x_2) = \cdots = gcd(x_n, x_{n-1}) = 1$ for all n, hence $gcd(x_k, x_l) = 1$ for all distinct positive integers k and l.

(iii) Since $x_2 = 5$ and $x_1 x_2 \dots x_{n-1}$ is odd, using relation (2) it follows that x_n end with digit 7 for all integers $n \geq 3$.

(*Dorin Andrica*)

47. We have

$$(a_{n+1} - 2a_n)^2 = 3a_n^2 - 2, \quad n \geq 1.$$

Then

$$a_{n+1}^2 + a_n^2 - 4a_{n+1}a_n = -2$$

and

$$a_{n+2}^2 + a_{n+1}^2 - 4a_{n+2}a_{n+1} = -2, \quad n \geq 1.$$

Subtracting these relations yields

$$a_{n+2}^2 - a_n^2 - 4a_{n+1}(a_{n+2} - a_n) = 0$$

and

$$(a_{n+2} - a_n)(a_{n+2} + a_n - 4a_{n+1}) = 0, \quad n \geq 1.$$

Since the sequence $(a_n)_{n \geq 1}$ is increasing, it follows that

$$a_{n+2} = 4a_{n+1} - a_n, \quad n \geq 1.$$

Taking into account that $a_1 = 1$, $a_2 = 3$ and inducting on n we reach the conclusion.

(*Titu Andreescu*, Gazeta Matematică (GM-B), No. 11(1977), pp. 453, Problem 16947; Revista Matematică Timişoara (RMT), No. 1(1978), pp. 51, Problem 2840)

48. For $n = 2$ we have $a_2 = \dfrac{2}{1+2} = \dfrac{2}{3}$.

Suppose that $a_n = \dfrac{p_n}{q_n}$, where p_n, q_n are integers and $gcd(p_n, q_n) = 1$.
Then

$$a_{n+1} = \frac{2p_nq_n}{q_n^2 + 2p_n^2},$$

and it suffices to prove that $gcd(2p_nq_n, q_n^2 + 2p_n^2) = 1$.

Assume by way of contradiction that there are integers d and k_1, k_2 such that

$$2p_nq_n = k_1d \quad \text{and} \quad q_n^2 + 2p_n^2 = k_2d.$$

If $d = 2$, then $q_n^2 = 2k_2 - 2p_n^2$, so q_n is even. This is a contradiction since $q_1, q_2, \ldots, q_n$ are all odd.

If $d > 2$ then $q_n^3 = (k_2q_n - k_1p_n)d$ so $d|q_n$.

Since $q_n^2 + 2p_n^2 = k_2d$ it follows that $d|p_n$, which is false, because $gcd(p_n, q_n) = 1$. This proves our claim.

We prove that

$$q_n^2 - 2p_n^2 = 1, \quad n \geq 2. \tag{1}$$

For $n = 2$ we have $q_2^2 - 2p_2^2 = 3^2 - 2 \cdot 2^2 = 1$.

Suppose that $q_n^2 - 2p_n^2 = 1$. Because

$$\frac{p_{n+1}}{q_{n+1}} = \frac{2p_nq_n}{q_n^2 + 2p_n^2}$$

is irreducible, we obtain

$$q_{n+1} = q_n^2 + 2p_n^2 \quad \text{and} \quad p_{n+1} = 2p_nq_n.$$

Hence

$$q_{n+1}^2 - 2p_{n+1}^2 = (q_n^2 + 2p_n^2)^2 - 8p_n^2q_n^2 = (q_n^2 - 2p_n^2)^2 = 1,$$

as claimed.

Hence

$$b_n = \frac{1}{1 - 2a_{n-1}^2} = \frac{1}{1 - 2\dfrac{p_{n-1}^2}{q_{n-1}^2}} = \frac{q_{n-1}^2}{q_{n-1}^2 - 2p_{n-1}^2} = q_{n-1}^2$$

and so b_n is a perfect square for all $n \geq 2$.

(*Titu Andreescu*, Revista Matematică Timişoara (RMT), No. 2(1977), pp. 63, Problem 3083; Gazeta Matematică (GM-B), No. 1(1981), pp. 44, Problem C:88)

49. Inducting on n we obtain

$$x_n^2 - 2y_n^2 = 1, \quad n \geq 1.$$

Hence

$$z_n = 1 + 4x_n^2 y_n^2 = (x_n^2 - 2y_n^2)^2 + 4x_n^2 y_n^2 = (x_n^2 + 2y_n^2)^2 - 4x_n^2 y_n^2 =$$

$$= (x_n^2 + 2y_n^2 + 2x_n y_n)(x_n^2 + 2y_n^2 - 2x_n y_n), \text{ for all } n \geq 1.$$

Since both factors are greater than 1, it follows that all numbers z_n are not prime.
(*Titu Andreescu*, Revista Matematică Timişoara (RMT), No. 2(1976), pp. 54, Problem 2571)

50. We have

$$\left(x_{n+1} - \sqrt{p^2 + 1}x_n\right)^2 = p^2(x_n^2 + 1)$$

or

$$x_{n+1}^2 - 2\sqrt{p^2 + 1}x_{n+1}x_n + (p^2 + 1)x_n^2 = p^2(x_n^2 + 1).$$

Hence

$$x_n^2 - 2\sqrt{p^2 + 1}x_{n+1}x_n + x_{n+1}^2 - p^2 = 0,$$

and

$$x_n = \sqrt{p^2 + 1}x_{n+1} \pm p\sqrt{x_{n+1}^2 + 1}.$$

From hypothesis we have $x_{n+1} > x_n$, hence

$$x_n = \sqrt{p^2 + 1}x_{n+1} - p\sqrt{x_{n+1}^2 + 1}. \tag{1}$$

But

$$x_{n+2} = \sqrt{p^2 + 1}x_{n+1} + p\sqrt{x_{n+1}^2 + 1} \tag{2}$$

and so

$$x_{n+2} = 2\sqrt{p^2 + 1}x_{n+1} - x_n \tag{3}$$

by summing up the relations (1) and (2).

Because p is a positive integer, it follows that $\sqrt{p^2 + 1}$ is irrational. From (3) we deduce that among any three consecutive terms of the sequence there is at least an irrational term. Hence there are at least $\left[\dfrac{m}{3}\right]$ irrational terms among the first m terms of the sequence.

(*Titu Andreescu*, Revista Matematică Timişoara (RMT), No. 1-2(1980), pp. 68, Problem 4139; Gazeta Matematică (GM-B), No. 6(1980), pp. 281, Problem C:48)

51. Setting $n = 0$ and $n = 1$ yields $x_1 = x_1^2$ and $x_2 = x_2^2$, hence $x_1 = x_2 = 1$. From the given condition we obtain

$$x_{2n+1} = x_{n+1}^2 + x_n^2 \text{ and } x_{2n} = x_{n+1}^2 - x_{n-1}^2.$$

Subtracting these relations implies

$$x_{2n+1} - x_{2n} = x_n^2 + x_{n-1}^2 = x_{2n-1},$$

hence

$$x_{2n+1} = x_{2n} + x_{2n-1}, \quad n \geq 1. \tag{1}$$

We induct on n to prove that

$$x_{2n} = x_{2n-1} + x_{2n-2}, \quad n \geq 1. \tag{2}$$

Indeed, $x_2 = x_1 + x_0$ and assume that (2) is true up to n. Then

$$x_{2n+2} - x_{2n} = x_{n+2}^2 - x_n^2 - x_{n+1}^2 + x_{n-1}^2 \overset{(*)}{=} (x_{n+1} + x_n)^2 - x_n^2 - x_{n+1}^2 +$$

$$+(x_{n+1} - x_n)^2 = x_{n+1}^2 + x_n^2 = x_{2n+1},$$

as claimed (the equality $(*)$ holds because of (1) and the induction hypothesis).

From relations (1) and (2) it follows that $x_{n+2} = x_{n+1} + x_n$ for all $n \geq 0$. Because $x_0 = 0$ and $x_1 = 1$ the sequence $(x_n)_{n \geq 0}$ is the Fibonacci's sequence, hence

$$x_n = \frac{1}{\sqrt{5}} \left(\left(\frac{1 + \sqrt{5}}{2} \right)^n - \left(\frac{1 - \sqrt{5}}{2} \right)^n \right).$$

(*Titu Andreescu*, Romanian Winter Camp 1984; Revista Matematică Timişoara (RMT), No. 1(1985), pp. 73, Problem T.3)

52. From the hypothesis it follows that $a_4 = 12$, $a_5 = 25$, $a_6 = 48$. We have $\frac{a_1}{1}$, $\frac{a_2}{2} = 1$, $\frac{a_3}{3} = 2$, $\frac{a_4}{4} = 3$, $\frac{a_5}{5} = 5$, $\frac{a_6}{6} = 8$ so $\frac{a_n}{n} = F_n$ for all $n = 1, 2, 3, 4, 5, 6$, where $(F_n)_{n \geq 1}$ is the Fibonacci's sequence.

We prove by induction that $a_n = n F_n$ for all n. Indeed assuming that $a_k = k F_k$ for $k \leq n + 3$, we have

$$a_{n+4} = 2(n+3)F_{n+3} + (n+2)F_{n+2} - 2(n+1)F_{n+1} - nF_n =$$

$$= 2(n+3)F_{n+3} + (n+2)F_{n+2} - 2(n+1)F_{n+1} - n(F_{n+2} - F_{n+1}) =$$

$$= 2(n+3)F_{n+3} + 2F_{n+2} - (n+2)F_{n+1} =$$

$$= 2(n+3)F_{n+3} + 2F_{n+2} - (n+2)(F_{n+3} - F_{n+2}) =$$

$$= (n+4)(F_{n+3} + F_{n+2}) = (n+4)F_{n+4},$$

as desired.

(*Dorin Andrica*, Revista Matematică Timişoara (RMT), No. 1(1986), pp. 106, Problem C8:2)

53. Observe that setting $x_0 = 0$ the condition is safisfied for $n = 0$.

We prove that there is integer $k \leq m^3$ such that x_k divides m. Let r_t be the remainder of x_t when divided by m for $t = 0, 1, \ldots, m^3 + 2$. Consider the triples (r_0, r_1, r_2), $(r_1, r_2, r_3), \ldots, (r_{m^3}, r_{m^3+1}, r_{m^3+2})$. Since r_t can take m values, it follows by the Pigeonhole Principle that at least two triples are equal. Let p be the smallest number such that triple (r_p, r_{p+1}, r_{p+2}) is equal to another triple (r_q, r_{q+1}, r_{q+2}), $p < q \leq m^3$. We claim that $p = 0$.

Assume by way of contradiction that $p \geq 1$. Using the hypothesis we have

$$r_{p+2} \equiv r_{p-1} + r_p r_{p+1} \pmod{m}$$

and

$$r_{q+2} \equiv r_{q-1} + r_q r_{q+1} \pmod{m}.$$

Since $r_p = r_q$, $r_{p+1} = r_{q+1}$ and $r_{p+2} = r_{q+2}$, it follows that $r_{p-1} = r_{q-1}$ so $(r_{p-1}, r_p, r_{p+1}) = (r_{q-1}, r_q, r_{q+1})$, which is a contradiction with the minimality of p. Hence $p = 0$, so $r_q = r_0 = 0$, and therefore $x_q \equiv 0 \pmod{m}$.

(*Titu Andreescu* and *Dorel Miheţ*, Revista Matematică Timişoara (RMT), No. 1(1986), pp. 106, Problem C8:1)

54. Note that $a_2 = 1$, $a_3 = 4$, $a_4 = 9$, $a_5 = 25$, so $a_0 = F_0^2$, $a_1 = F_1^2$, $a_2 = F_2^2$, $a_3 = F_3^2$, $a_4 = F_4^2$, $a_5 = F_5^2$, where $(F_n)_{n \geq 0}$ is the Fibonacci sequence.

We induct on n to prove that $a_n = F_n^2$ for all $n \geq 0$. Assume that $a_k = F_k^2$ for all $k \leq n$. Hence

$$a_n = F_n^2, \quad a_{n-1} = F_{n-1}^2, \quad a_{n-2} = F_{n-2}^2. \tag{1}$$

From the given relation we obtain

$$a_{n+1} - 3a_n + a_{n-1} = 2(-1)^n$$

and

$$a_n - 3a_{n-1} + a_{n-2} = 2(-1)^{n-1}, \quad n \geq 2.$$

Summing up these equalities yields

$$a_{n+1} - 2a_n - 2a_{n-1} + a_{n-2} = 0, \quad n \geq 2. \tag{2}$$

Using the relations (1) and (2) we obtain

$$a_{n+1} = 2F_n^2 + 2F_{n-1}^2 - F_{n-2}^2 = (F_n + F_{n-1})^2 + (F_n - F_{n-1})^2 - F_{n-2}^2 =$$

$$= F_{n+1}^2 + F_{n-2}^2 - F_{n-2}^2 = F_{n+1}^2,$$

as desired.

(*Titu Andreescu*, Revista Matematică Timişoara (RMT), No. 2(1986), pp. 108, Problem C8:8)

55. The expressions $a^2 - 1$ and $2 + 2a$ ask for the substitution $a = \frac{1}{2}\left(b^2 + \frac{1}{b^2}\right)$.

The equality $\frac{1}{2}\left(b^2 + \frac{1}{b^2}\right) = 97$ implies $\left(b + \frac{1}{b}\right)^2 = 196$, hence $b + \frac{1}{b} = 14$. Setting

$b = c^2$ yields $\left(c + \dfrac{1}{c}\right)^2 = 16$, thus $c + \dfrac{1}{c} = 4$. Let $c = 2 + \sqrt{3}$. We will prove by induction that

$$a_n = \frac{1}{2}\left(c^{4F_n} + \frac{1}{c^{4F_n}}\right), \quad n \geq 1,$$

where F_n is the nth Fibonacci number.

Indeed, this is true for $n = 1$, $n = 2$ and, assuming that

$$a_k = \frac{1}{2}\left(c^{4F_k} + \frac{1}{c^{4F_k}}\right), \quad k \leq n$$

implies

$$a_{n+1} = \frac{1}{4}\left(c^{4F_n} + \frac{1}{c^{4F_n}}\right)\left(c^{4F_{n-1}} + \frac{1}{c^{4F_{n-1}}}\right) +$$

$$+ \frac{1}{4}\left(c^{4F_n} - \frac{1}{c^{4F_n}}\right)\left(c^{4F_{n-1}} - \frac{1}{c^{4F_{n-1}}}\right) = \frac{1}{2}\left(c^{4F_{n+1}} + \frac{1}{c^{4F_{n+1}}}\right).$$

Then

$$2 + 2a_n = 2 + c^{4F_n} + \frac{1}{c^{4F_n}} = \left(c^{2F_n} + \frac{1}{c^{2F_n}}\right)^2$$

and

$$2 + \sqrt{2 + 2a_n} = 2 + c^{2F_n} + \frac{1}{c^{2F_n}} = \left(c^{F_n} + \frac{1}{c^{F_n}}\right)^2.$$

Let us mention that $c^m + \dfrac{1}{c^m}$ is an integer for all positive integers m.

(*Titu Andreescu*, USA Mathematical Olympiad Shortlist, 1997)

56. We induct on m to prove that

$$\text{if } k^m \leq n < k^{m+1}, \text{ then } a_n = 1 + m. \tag{1}$$

For $m = 0$ the claim is true, since if $1 \leq n < k$, then $\left[\dfrac{n}{k}\right] = 0$ hence $a_n = 1 + a_0 = 1 + 0$.

Assume that (1) holds for m. Then if $k^{m+1} \leq n < k^{m+2}$, we have $k^m \leq \frac{n}{k} < k^{m+1}$, so

$$k^m \leq \left[\frac{n}{k}\right] < k^{m+1}.$$

Using the inductive hypothesis, we deduce that $a_{\left[\frac{n}{k}\right]} = 1 + m$ so

$$a_n = 1 + a_{\left[\frac{n}{k}\right]} = 1 + (m + 1)$$

as claimed.

Therefore for any positive integer n with $m \leq \log_k n < m + 1$, we have $a_n = 1 + m$ thus $a_n = 1 + [\log kn]$.

(*Titu Andreescu*, Revista Matematică Timişoara (RMT), No. 2(1982), pp. 66, Problem 4997)

57. We prove that $a_n - 2 = b_n^2$, where $b_0 = -1$, $b_1 = 1$ and $b_{n+1} = 3b_n - b_{n-1}$ for all $n \geq 1$. This is clear for $n = 0$ and $n = 1$.

Assume that for any $k \leq n$ we have $a_k - 2 = b_k^2$. Subtracting the relation $a_n = 7a_{n-1} - a_{n-2}$ from $a_{n+1} = 7a_n - a_{n-1}$ yields $a_{n+1} = 8a_n - 8a_{n-1} + a_{n-2}$ or

$$a_{n+1} - 2 = 8(a_n - 2) - 8(a_{n-1} - 2) + (a_{n-2} - 2)$$

Hence

$$a_{n+1} - 2 = 8b_n^2 - 8b_{n-1}^2 + b_{n-2}^2 = 8b_n^2 - 8b_{n-1}^2 + (3b_{n-1} - b_n)^2 =$$

$$= 9b_n^2 - 6b_n b_{n-1} + b_{n-1}^2 = (3b_n - b_{n-1})^2 = b_{n+1}^2$$

Alternative solution. The general term of the sequence is given by

$$a_n = \left(\frac{1+\sqrt{5}}{2}\right)^{4n-2} + \left(\frac{1-\sqrt{5}}{2}\right)^{4n-2}, \quad n \geq 0$$

Hence

$$a_n - 2 = \left[\left(\frac{1+\sqrt{5}}{2}\right)^{2n-1} + \left(\frac{1-\sqrt{5}}{2}\right)^{2n-1}\right]^2$$

and an inductive argument proves that

$$\left(\frac{1+\sqrt{5}}{2}\right)^{2n-1} + \left(\frac{1-\sqrt{5}}{2}\right)^{2n-1}$$

is an integer for all n.

(*Titu Andreescu*)

58. Note that all terms of the sequence are positive integers.

Assume by way of contradiction that there is a positive integer n_0 such that

$$x_{n_0}^2 = x_{n_0-1} x_{n_0+1}.$$

Then

$$\frac{x_{n_0+1}}{x_{n_0}} = \frac{x_{n_0}}{x_{n_0-1}} = t,$$

where t is rational.

Because $x_{n_0+1} = \alpha x_{n_0} + \beta x_{n_0-1}$, it follows that

$$\frac{x_{n_0+1}}{x_{n_0}} = \alpha + \beta \frac{x_{n_0}}{x_{n_0-1}}$$

or

$$t^2 - \alpha t - \beta = 0.$$

The last equation has no rational roots since the discriminant $\Delta = \alpha^2 + 4\beta$ is not a perfect square. This is a contradiction and hence the problem is solved.

Alternative solution. From the condition of the problem we obtain

$$\alpha x_n = x_{n+1} - \beta x_{n-1}, \quad n \geq 1. \tag{1}$$

Assume by way of contradiction that there is a positive integer n_0 such that

$$x_{n_0}^2 = x_{n_0-1}x_{n_0+1}. \tag{2}$$

From the relations (1) and (2) we deduce that

$$(\alpha^2 + 4\beta)x_{n_0}^2 = (x_{n_0+1} + \beta x_{n_0-1})^2$$

which is false, since $\alpha^2 + 4\beta$ is not a square. This completes the proof.

(*Dorin Andrica*)

59. Assume by way of contradiction that there is an irrational number a such that

$$A = \sqrt[n]{a + \sqrt{a^2 - 1}} + \sqrt[n]{a - \sqrt{a^2 - 1}}$$

is rational.

Define $\alpha = \sqrt[n]{a + \sqrt{a^2 - 1}}$ and observe that $\sqrt[n]{a - \sqrt{a^2 - 1}} = \dfrac{1}{\alpha}$.

Hence $A = \alpha + \dfrac{1}{\alpha}$ is rational.

We prove that $\alpha^n + \dfrac{1}{\alpha^n}$ is rational.

Indeed,

$$\alpha^2 + \frac{1}{\alpha^2} = \left(\alpha + \frac{1}{\alpha}\right)^2 - 2$$

is rational and

$$\alpha^3 + \frac{1}{\alpha^3} = \left(\alpha + \frac{1}{\alpha}\right)^3 - 3\left(\alpha + \frac{1}{\alpha}\right) \text{ is rational.}$$

Using the identity

$$\alpha^k + \frac{1}{\alpha^k} = \left(\alpha^{k-1} + \frac{1}{\alpha^{k-1}}\right)\left(\alpha + \frac{1}{\alpha}\right) - \left(\alpha^{k-2} + \frac{1}{\alpha^{k-2}}\right)$$

it follows by induction that $\alpha^k + \dfrac{1}{\alpha^k}$ is rational for all positive integers k, hence $\alpha^n + \dfrac{1}{\alpha^n}$ is rational.

Thus $\alpha + \sqrt{a^2 - 1} + a - \sqrt{a^2 - 1} = 2a$ is rational, which is false. The solution is complete.

(*Titu Andreescu*, Romanian IMO Selection Test 1977; Revista Matematică Timişoara (RMT), No. 1(1978), pp. 78, Problem 3344)

60. We induct on n. For $n = 1$, from $\pm 1 \pm 2 \pm 3 \pm 4 \pm 5$ we obtain all odd positive integers less than or equal to $(2+1)(4+1) = 15$:

$$+1 - 2 + 3 + 4 - 5 = 1$$

$$-1 + 2 + 3 + 4 - 5 = 3$$

$$-1 + 2 + 3 - 4 + 5 = 5$$

$$-1 + 2 - 3 + 4 + 5 = 7$$

$$-1 - 2 + 3 + 4 + 5 = 9$$

$$+1 - 2 + 3 + 4 + 5 = 11$$

$$-1 + 2 + 3 + 4 + 5 = 13$$

$$+1 + 2 + 3 + 4 + 5 = 15$$

Assume that from $\pm 1 \pm 2 \pm \cdots \pm (4n + 1)$ with suitable choices of signs $+$ and $-$ we obtain all odd positive integers less than or equal to $(2n + 1)(4n + 1)$.

Observe that $-(4n + 2) + (4n + 3) + (4n + 4) - (4n + 5) = 0$. Hence from $\pm 1 \pm 2 \pm \cdots \pm (4n + 5)$ for suitable choices of signs $+$ and $-$ we obtain all odd positive numbers less than or equal to $(2n + 1)(4n + 1)$.

It suffices to obtain all odd integers m such that

$$(2n + 1)(4n + 1) < m \leq (2n + 3)(4n + 5) \tag{1}$$

There are

$$\frac{(2n + 3)(4n + 5) - (2n + 1)(4n + 1)}{2} = 8n + 7$$

such odd integers m.

We have

$$(2n + 3)(4n + 5) = +1 + 2 + \cdots + (4n + 5)$$

$$(2n + 3)(4n + 5) - 2k = +1 + 2 + \cdots + (k - 1) - k +$$

$$+(k + 1) + \cdots + (4n + 4) + (4n + 5), \quad k = 1, 2, \ldots, 4n + 5$$

and

$$(2n + 1)(4n + 5) - 2l = +1 + 2 + \cdots + (l - 1) - l +$$

$$+(l + 1) + \cdots + (4n + 4) + (4n + 5), \quad l = 1, 2, \ldots, 4n + 1.$$

Hence all numbers m from (1) are obtained, as desired.

(*Dorin Andrica*, Gazeta Matematică (GM-B), No. 2(1986), pp. 63, Problem C570)

Chapter 3
GEOMETRY

PROBLEMS

1. Triangle ABC has side lengths equal to a, b, c. Find a necessary and sufficient condition for the angles of the triangle such that a^2, b^2, c^2 can be the side lengths of a triangle.

2. Prove that the triangle whose side lengths are equal to the length of the medians of a triangle ABC has area equal to $3/4$ of the area of triangle $[ABC]$.

3. In triangle ABC the median AM meets the internal bisector BN at P. Let Q be the point of intersection of lines CP and AB. Prove that triangle BNQ is isosceles.

4. In triangle ABC the midline parallel to AB meets the altitudes from A and B at points D and E. The midline parallel to AC intersects the altitudes from A and C at points F and G.
Prove that $DC\|BF\|GE$.

5. Let M be a point in the interior of triangle ABC. Lines AM, BM, CM intersect sides BC, CA, AB at points A', B', C', respectively. Denote by $S_1, S_2, S_3, S_4, S_5, S_6$ the areas of triangles $MA'B, MA'C, MB'C, MB'A, MC'A$ and $MC'B$, respectively.
Prove that if
$$\frac{S_1}{S_2} + \frac{S_3}{S_4} + \frac{S_5}{S_6} = 3,$$
then M is the centroid of the triangle ABC.

6. Let M be a point in the interior of triangle ABC and let M, P, Q be three colinear points on sides AB, BC and line CA.
Prove that if
$$\frac{S_{MAN}}{S_{MBN}} + \frac{S_{MBP}}{S_{MCP}} = 2\sqrt{\frac{S_{MAQ}}{S_{MCQ}}},$$
then MP is skew-parallel with AC.

7. Let a, b, c and S be the sides lengths and the area of a triangle ABC. Prove that if P is a point interior to triangle ABC such that
$$aPA + bPB + cPC = 4S$$

87

then P is the orthocenter of the triangle.

8. Let I_1, I_2 be the incenters of triangles $A_1 B_1 C_1$ and $A_2 B_2 C_2$. Prove that if I_1 and I_2 divide the internal bisectors $A_1 A_1'$, $A_2 A_2'$ in the same ratios they divide the internal bisectors $B_1 B_1'$, $B_2 B_2'$, then triangles $A_1 B_1 C_1$ and $A_2 B_2 C_2$ are similar.

9. On side BC of a triangle ABC consider points M and N such that $\widehat{BAM} \equiv \widehat{CAN}$.

Prove that

$$\frac{MB}{MC} + \frac{NB}{NC} \geq 2\frac{AB}{AC}$$

10. Let M be a point on the hypotenuse BC of a right triangle ABC and let points N, P be the feet of the perpendiculars from M to AB and AC.

Find the position of M such that the length NP is minimal.

11. Let ABC be an equilateral triangle and let P be a point in its interior. Let the lines AP, BP, CP meet the sides BC, CA, AB at the points A_1, B_1, C_1 respectively. Prove that

$$A_1 B_1 \cdot B_1 C_1 \cdot C_1 A_1 \geq A_1 B \cdot B_1 C \cdot C_1 A.$$

12. Let S be the set of all triangles ABC for which

$$5\left(\frac{1}{AP} + \frac{1}{BQ} + \frac{1}{CR}\right) - \frac{3}{\min\{P, BQ, CR\}} = \frac{6}{r},$$

where r is the imradius and P, Q, R are the points of tangency of the incircle with sides AB, BC, CA, respectively. Prove that all triangles in S are isosceles and similar to one another.

13. Let ABC be a triangle inscribed in a circle of radius R, and let P be a point in the interior of ABC. Prove that

$$\frac{PA}{BC^2} + \frac{PB}{CA^2} + \frac{PC}{AB^2} \geq \frac{1}{R}.$$

14. Let I be the incenter of an acute triangle ABC. Prove that

$$AI \cdot BC + BI \cdot CA + CI \cdot AB = S_{ABC}$$

if and only if triangle ABC is equilateral.

15. Let ABC be a triangle such that

$$(8AB - 7BC - 3CA)^2 = 6(AB^2 - BC^2 - CA^2).$$

Prove that $\widehat{A} = 60°$.

16. Let P be a point in the plane of triangle ABC such that the segments PA, PB and PC are the sides of an obtuse triangle. Assume that in this triangle the obtuse angle opposes the side congruent to PA. Prove that $\widehat{BAC}$ is acute.

17. Triangle ABC has the following property: there is an interior point P such that $\widehat{PAB} = 10°$, $\widehat{PBA} = 20°$, $\widehat{PCA} = 30°$, and $\widehat{PAC} = 40°$. Prove that the triangle ABC is isosceles.

18. Let ABC be a triangle such that $\max\{A, B\} = C + 30°$. Prove that ABC is right angled if and only if $\dfrac{R}{r} = \sqrt{3} + 1$.

19. Prove that in the interior of any triangle ABC there is a point P such that the circumradii of triangle PAB, PBC, PCA are equal.

20. The incircle of the triangle ABC touches the sides AB, BC, CA at the points C', A', B', respectively. Prove that the perpendiculars from the midpoints of $A'B'$, $B'C'$, $C'A'$ to AB, BC, CA, respectively, are concurrent.

21. Let $A_1 A_2 A_3$ be a non-isosceles triangle with the incentre I. Let C_i, $i = 1, 2, 3$, be the smaller circle through I tangent to $A_i A_{i+1}$ and $A_i A_{i+2}$ (the addition of indices being mod 3). Let B_i, $i = 1, 2, 3$, be the second point of intersection of C_{i+1} and C_{i+2}. Prove that the circumcenters of the triangles $A_1 B_1 I$, $A_2 B_2 I$, $A_3 B_3 I$ are collinear.

22. On sides AB and AC of a triangle ABC consider points B' and C' such that

$$\frac{AB'}{B'B} + \frac{AC'}{C'C} = k \quad \text{is constant.}$$

Find the locus of the intersection point of lines BC' and CB'.

23. Let ABC be an equilateral triangle of side length 1. Find the locus of points P such that

$$\max\{PA, PB, PC\} = \frac{2PA \cdot PB \cdot PC}{PA \cdot PB + PB \cdot PC + PC \cdot PA - 1}.$$

24. Prove that in any acute triangle

$$\sqrt{a^2 b^2 - 4S^2} + \sqrt{a^2 c^2 - 4S^2} = a^2.$$

25. Prove that a triangle in which

$$\sqrt{r_a} + \sqrt{r_b} + \sqrt{r_c} = \frac{\sqrt{r_a r_b r_c}}{r}$$

is equilateral.

26. Prove that a triangle is equilateral if and only if

$$\frac{1}{m_a^2} + \frac{1}{m_b^2} + \frac{1}{m_c^2} = \frac{1}{r_a^2} + \frac{1}{r_b^2} + \frac{1}{r_c^2}.$$

27. A triangle with side lengths a, b, c has circumradius equal to 1. Prove that

$$a + b + c \geq abc.$$

28. Prove that in any triangle

$$\sum \frac{a^2}{(p-b)(p-c)} \leq \frac{6R}{r}.$$

29. Prove that in any triangle

$$\frac{1}{h_a^2} + \frac{1}{h_b^2} + \frac{1}{h_c^2} \geq \frac{1}{3r^2}.$$

30. Prove that in any triangle

$$\sqrt{r_a r_b} + \sqrt{r_b r_c} + \sqrt{r_c r_a} \geq 9r.$$

31. Prove that in any triangle

$$m_a m_b m_c \geq r_a r_b r_c.$$

32. Prove that

$$2p^2 \geq 27Rr$$

for any triangle.

33. Let ABC be a triangle. Prove that $A \leq \dfrac{\pi}{3}$ if and only if

$$(p-b)(p-c) \leq \frac{bc}{4}.$$

34. Three equal circles of radii r are given such that each one passes through the centers of the other two.
Find the area of the common region.

35. Let $ABCD$ be a nonisosceles trapezoid with bases AB and CD. Prove that

$$\frac{AC^2 - BD^2}{AD^2 - BC^2} = \frac{AB + CD}{AB - CD}.$$

36. Let $ABCD$ be a trapezoid with bases AB and CD. Prove that if

$$(AB + CD)^2 = BD^2 + AC^2$$

then the diagonals of the trapezoid are perpendicular.

37. Prove that if in a trapezoid with perpendicular diagonals the altitude is equal to the midline, then the trapezoid is isosceles.

38. Let $ABCD$ be a trapezoid with bases AB and CD. Prove that

$$\frac{AB^2 - BC^2 + AC^2}{CD^2 - AD^2 + AC^2} = \frac{AB^2 - AD^2 + BD^2}{CD^2 - BC^2 + BD^2} = \frac{AB}{CD}.$$

39. Prove that a trapezoid whose difference of the diagonal lengths is equal to the difference of nonparallel side lengths is isosceles.

40. Let $ABCD$ be a cyclic quadrilateral. Prove that

$$|AB - CD| + |AD - BC| \geq 2|AC - BD|.$$

41. Prove that a right trapezoid whose altitude length is equal to the geometrical mean of the lengths of its bases has perpendicular diagonals.

42. Let E and F be the projections of the vertices A and B of a trapezoid $ABCD$ on line CD. Let M and N be the projections of E and F onto BD and AC, respectively and let P and Q be projections of E and F onto BC and AD, respectively.
Prove that the quadrilateral $MNPQ$ is cyclic.

43. Let $ABCD$ be a convex quadrilateral that is not a parallelogram and let M and N be the midpoints of the diagonals AC and BD. Prove that numbers

$$AB + CD, \quad BC + AD, \quad AC + BD, \quad 2MN$$

can be the side lengths of a cyclic quadrilateral.

44. Let $ABCD$ be a cyclic quadrilateral and let lines AB and CD meet at point E. Point F is the reflection of C across E. Prove that lines AF and BD are perpendicular if and only if lines AB and CD are perpendicular.

45. Find all cyclic quadrilaterals having the side lengths odd integers and the area a prime number.

46. A cyclic quadrilateral has the side lengths a, b, c, d, the diagonal lengths e, f and the semiperimeter p. Prove that

$$8e^2 f^2 - p^4 \leq 8(a^2 c^2 + b^2 d^2).$$

47. A cyclic quadrilateral has the side lengths a, b, c, d and the diagonal lengths e and f.

Prove that if $\max\{|a - c|, |b - d|\} \leq 1$, then

$$|e - f| \leq \sqrt{2}.$$

48. A cyclic quadrilateral has area S and semiperimeter p. Prove that if $S = \left(\dfrac{p}{2}\right)^2$, then the quadrilateral is a square.

49. Let $ABCD$ be a convex quadrilateral and let P be the intersection point of its diagonals.

Prove that

$$S_{PAB} + S_{PCD} = S_{PBC} + S_{PDA}$$

if and only if P is the midpoint of AC or BD.

50. Let M be a point on the circumcircle of the cyclic quadrilateral $ABCD$ and let points A', B', C', D' be the projections of M onto AB, BC, CD, DA, respectively. Prove that

(i) lines $A'B', C'D'$ and AC are concurrent

(ii) lines $B'C', D'A'$ and BD are concurrent.

51. A convex quadrilateral $ABCD$ with area 2002 contains a point P in its interior such that $PA = 24$, $PB = 32$, $PC = 28$, and $PD = 45$. Find the perimeter of $ABCD$.

52. Find the locus of points P in the plane of a square ABC such that

$$\max(PA, PC) = \frac{1}{\sqrt{2}}(PB + PD).$$

53. Let $\mathcal{P}$ be the set of all quadrialterals with the same diagonal lengths and let $\lambda_1(p)$ and $\lambda_2(p)$ be the lengths of the segments determined by the midpoints of two opposite sides of a quadrilateral $p \in \mathcal{P}$.

Prove that for all $p \in \mathcal{P}$ the sum $\lambda_1^2(p) + \lambda_2^2(p)$ is constant and find the value of this constant.

54. Let $ABCDEFGHIJKL$ be a regular dodecagon and let R be the circumradius.

Prove that

$$\frac{AB}{AF} + \frac{AF}{AB} = 4 \text{ and } AB^2 + AC^2 + AD^2 + AE^2 + AF^2 = 10R^2.$$

55. Prove that if inside a convex poligon there is a point such that the sum of the squares of its distances to the vertices of the poligon is twice the area of the poligon, then the poligon is a square.

56. Let $A_1A_2\ldots A_n$ be a cyclic polygon and let P be a point on its circumcircle. Let $P_1, P_2, \ldots, P_n$ be the projections of P onto the sides of the polygon. Prove that the product

$$\prod_{i=1}^{n} \frac{PA_i^2}{PP_i}$$

is constant.

57. Let $A_1A_2\ldots A_{2n}$ be a cyclic polygon and let M be a point on its circumcircle. Points $K_1, K_2, \ldots, K_{2n}$ are the projections of M onto sides $A_1A_2, A_2A_3, \ldots, A_{2n}A_1$ and points $H_1, H_2, \ldots, H_n$ are the projections of M onto diagonals $A_1A_{n+1}, A_2A_{n+2}, \ldots, A_nA_{2n}$. Prove that

$$MK_1 \cdot MK_3 \ldots MK_{2n-1} = MK_2 \cdot MK_4 \ldots MK_{2n} = MH_1 \cdot MH_2 \ldots MH_n.$$

58. Find the circumradius of a cyclic polygon with $2n$ sides if n sides have the length a and n sides have the length b.

59. Let P be a point in the interior of a tetrahedron $ABCD$ such that its projections A_1, B_1, C_1, D_1 onto the planes (BCD), (CDA), (DAB), (ABC), respectively, are all situated in the interior of the faces. If S is the total area and r the inradius of the tetrahedron, prove that

$$\frac{S_{BCD}}{PA_1} + \frac{S_{CDA}}{PB_1} + \frac{S_{DAB}}{PC_1} + \frac{S_{ABC}}{PD_1} \geq \frac{S}{r}$$

When does the equality hold?

60. Let $A_1A_2A_3A_4$ be a tetrahedron, G its centroid, and A_1', A_2', A_3', A_4' the points where the circumsphere of $A_1A_2A_3A_4$ intersects GA_1, GA_2, GA_3, GA_4 respectively. Prove that

$$GA_1 \cdot GA_2 \cdot GA_3 \cdot GA_4 \leq GA_1' \cdot GA_2' \cdot GA_3' \cdot GA_4'$$

and

$$\frac{1}{GA_1'} + \frac{1}{GA_2'} + \frac{1}{GA_3'} + \frac{1}{GA_4'} \leq \frac{1}{GA_1} + \frac{1}{GA_2} + \frac{1}{GA_3} + \frac{1}{GA_4}.$$

SOLUTIONS

1. The positive real numbers a^2, b^2, c^2 can be the side lengths of a triangle if and only if

$$a^2 + b^2 > c^2, \quad b^2 + c^2 > a^2, \quad c^2 + a^2 > b^2. \tag{1}$$

Because

$$\cos A = \frac{b^2 + c^2 - a^2}{2bc}, \quad \cos B = \frac{c^2 + a^2 - b^2}{2ca}, \quad \cos C = \frac{a^2 + b^2 - c^2}{2ab},$$

relation (1) is equivalent to $\cos A > 0$, $\cos B > 0$, $\cos C > 0$. Hence the necessary and sufficient condition is that triangle ABC is acute.

(*Dorin Andrica*, Revista Matematică Timişoara (RMT), No. 2(1978), pp. 48, Problem 3507)

2. Let A', B', C' be the midpoints of sides BC, CA, AB respectively. Construct point M such that $BCMC'$ is a parallelogram. Note that $AC'CM$ and $BB'MA'$ are also parallelograms hence $AM = CC'$ and $A'M = BB'$. Hence the triangle determined by the medians is $AA'M$.

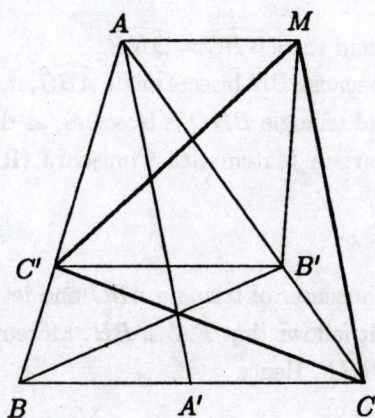

Let N be the intersection point of lines $B'C'$ and AA'. Because $AC'A'B'$ is a parallelogram, we have

$$C'N = B'N = \frac{1}{2}B'M,$$

95

so B' is the centroid of triangle $AA'M$. Hence

$$S_{AA'M} = 3S_{AA'B'} = \frac{3}{2}S_{AA'C} = \frac{3}{4}S_{ABC}.$$

Alternative solution: Consider the vectors $\bar{a} = \overline{BC}$, $\bar{b} = \overline{AC}$, $\bar{c} = \overline{AB}$, $\overline{m}_a = \overline{AA'}$, $\overline{m}_b = \overline{BB'}$ and observe that

$$\overline{m}_a = \frac{1}{2}(\bar{b} + \bar{c}), \quad \overline{m}_b = \frac{1}{2}(\bar{a} - \bar{c}) = \frac{1}{2}(\bar{b} - 2\bar{c}).$$

We obtain

$$\overline{m}_a \times \overline{m}_b = \frac{1}{4}(\bar{b} + \bar{c}) \times (\bar{b} - 2\bar{c}) = \frac{3}{4}(\bar{c} \times \bar{b}),$$

hence $|\overline{m}_a \times \overline{m}_b| = \frac{3}{4}|\bar{c} \times \bar{b}|$ and the conclusion follows.

(*Titu Andreescu*)

3. If BP meets AC at P, then by Ceva's theorem we obtain

$$\frac{QA}{QB} \cdot \frac{MB}{MC} \cdot \frac{NC}{NA} = 1.$$

Because $MB = MC$, we have

$$\frac{QA}{QB} = \frac{NA}{NC}.$$

Therefore $QN \| BC$ and then $\widehat{NBC} = \widehat{QNB}$.

On the other hand, because BN bisects angle $\widehat{ABC}$, it follows that $\widehat{NBC} = \widehat{QBN}$. Hence $\widehat{QNB} = \widehat{QBN}$ and triangle BNQ is isosceles, as desired.

(*Titu Andreescu*, Revista Matematică Timişoara (RMT), No. 1(1978), pp. 66, Problem 3286)

4. Let H be the orthocenter of triangle ABC and let A' be the midpoint of side BC. Because $FA' \| AC$, it follows that $FA' \perp BH$. Moreover $BA' \perp HF$, so A' is the orthocenter of triangle BHF. Hence

$$HA' \perp BF. \tag{1}$$

On the other hand, $A'D \| AB$, so $A'D \perp HC$. Since $HD \perp A'D$ it follows that D is the orthocenter of triangle $HA'C$ thus

$$DC \perp HA'. \tag{2}$$

Note that $GH \perp AB$ and $EH \perp AC$. Since $AB \| A'E$ and $AC \| GA'$, we have $GH \perp A'E$ and $EH \perp GA'$, so H is the orthocenter of triangle $A'EG$. Therefore

$$A'H \perp GE. \tag{3}$$

From relations (1), (2) and (3) we obtain

$$DC \| BF \| GE,$$

as desired.

(*Titu Andreescu*)

5. Using Ceva's theorem, we obtain

$$\frac{C'A}{C'B} \cdot \frac{A'B}{A'C} \cdot \frac{B'C}{B'A} = 1,$$

hence

$$\frac{S_1}{S_2} \cdot \frac{S_3}{S_4} \cdot \frac{S_5}{S_6} = 1.$$

The given condition now reads

$$\frac{S_1}{S_2} + \frac{S_3}{S_4} + \frac{S_5}{S_6} = 3\sqrt[3]{\frac{S_1}{S_2} \cdot \frac{S_3}{S_4} \cdot \frac{S_5}{S_6}}$$

so

$$\frac{S_1}{S_2} = \frac{S_3}{S_4} = \frac{S_5}{S_6} = 1.$$

This implies

$$\frac{C'A}{C'B} = \frac{A'B}{A'C} = \frac{B'C}{B'A} = 1.$$

It follows that A', B', C' are the midpoints of the triangle's sides and M is the centroid, as claimed.

(*Titu Andreescu*, Revista Matematică Timişoara (RMT), No. 1(1974), pp. 23, Problem 1904; Gazeta Matematică (GM-B), No. 2(1979), pp. 63, Problem O:16)

6. Using Menelaus' theorem yields

$$\frac{NA}{NB} \cdot \frac{AB}{BC} \cdot \frac{QC}{QA} = 1.$$

Hence

$$\frac{S_{MAN}}{S_{MBN}} \cdot \frac{S_{MBA}}{S_{MCA}} \cdot \frac{S_{MCQ}}{S_{MAQ}} = 1,$$

or

$$\frac{S_{MAN}}{S_{MBN}} \cdot \frac{S_{MBP}}{S_{MCP}} = \frac{S_{MQA}}{S_{MCQ}}.$$

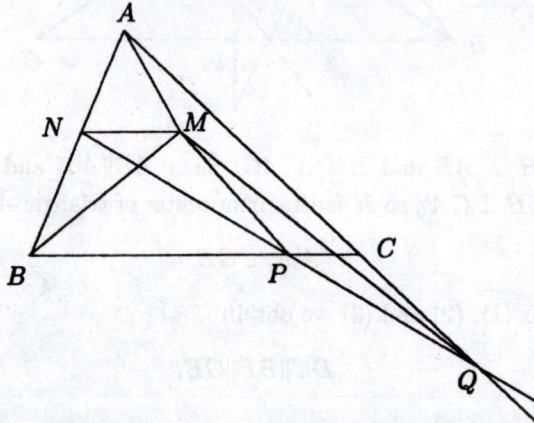

From the condition in the hypothesis it follows that

$$\frac{S_{MAN}}{S_{BMN}} + \frac{S_{MBP}}{S_{MCP}} = 2\sqrt{\frac{S_{MAN}}{S_{MBN}} \cdot \frac{S_{MBP}}{S_{MCP}}},$$

and so

$$\frac{S_{MAN}}{S_{MBN}} = \frac{S_{MBP}}{S_{MCP}}.$$

Thus

$$\frac{NA}{NB} = \frac{PB}{PC}$$

hence NP and AC are skew-parallel.

(*Titu Andreescu*, Revista Matematică Timişoara (RMT), No. 1(1978), pp. 66, Problem 3287; Gazeta Matematică (GM-B), No. 2(1979), pp. 56, Problem 17607)

7. Let A_1, B_1, C_1 be the feet of triangle's altitudes and let A', B', C' be the projections of P onto its sides.

If P is the orthocenter of the triangle, then the equality holds.

Assume by way of contradiction that P is not the orthocenter of the triangle and

$$aPA + bPN + cPC = 4S.$$

Then at least two of the inequalities

$$PA + PA \geq AA_1, \quad PB + PB' \geq BB_1, \quad PC + PC' \geq CC_1$$

are strict.

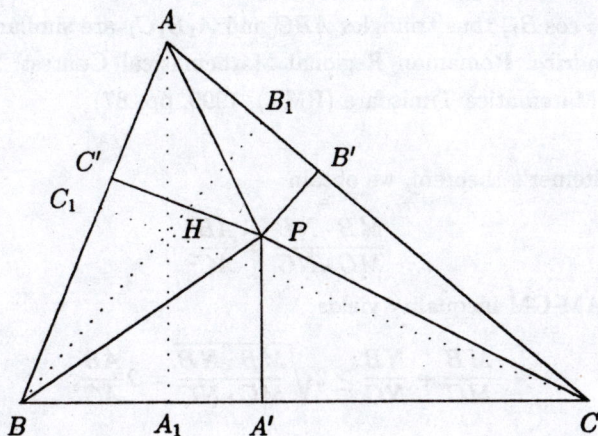

It follows that

$$aPA + bPB + cPC > a(AA_1 - PA') + b(BB_1 - PB') + c(CC_1 - PC')$$

or

$$4S > aAA_1 + bBB_1 + cCC_1 - (aPA' + bPB' + cPC').$$

Hence $4S > 6S - 2S = 4S$, which is false.

(*Titu Andreescu*, Revista Matematică Timişoara (RMT), No. 2(1978), pp. 74, Problem 3689; Gazeta Matematică (GM-B), No. 2(1980), pp. 64, Problem 18122)

8. Using the angle bisector theorem and Van Aubel's theorem, it follows that

$$\frac{IA}{IA'} = \frac{B'A}{B'C} + \frac{C'A}{C'B} = \frac{b+c}{a} = k_1$$

and

$$\frac{IB}{IB'} = \frac{A'B}{A'C} + \frac{C'B}{C'A} = \frac{c+a}{b} = k_2$$

Let

$$\frac{IC}{IC'} = \frac{a+b}{c} = k_3$$

and note that

$$k_1 + 1 = \frac{2p}{a}, \quad k_2 + 1 = \frac{2p}{b}, \quad k_3 + 1 = \frac{2p}{c},$$

where p is the semiperimeter. Hence

$$\frac{1}{k_1 + 1} + \frac{1}{k_2 + 1} + \frac{1}{k_3 + 1} = 1$$

so

$$k_3 = \frac{k_1 + k_2 + 2}{k_1 k_2 - 1}.$$

Furthermore, since

$$\cos A = \frac{1}{2}\left[\frac{k_2 + 1}{k_3 + 1} + \frac{k_3 + 1}{k_2 + 1} - \frac{(k_2 + 1)(k_3 + 1)}{(k_1 + 1)^2}\right],$$

we observe that $\cos A$ depends only on k_1 and k_3. Hence $\cos A = \cos A_1$ and, analogously, $\cos B = \cos B_1$, thus triangles ABC and $A_1B_1C_1$ are similar.

(*Dorin Andrica*, Romanian Regional Mathematical Contest "Grigore Moisil", 1999; Revista Matematică Timişoara (RMT), 1999, pp. 87).

9. Using Steiner's theorem, we obtain

$$\frac{MB \cdot NB}{MC \cdot NC} = \frac{AB^2}{AC^2}$$

Applying the AM-GM inequality yields

$$\frac{MB}{MC} + \frac{NB}{NC} \geq 2\sqrt{\frac{MB \cdot NB}{MC \cdot NC}} = 2\frac{AB}{AC},$$

as desired.

Note that the equality case occurs only if AM and AN coincide with the internal bisector of angle A.

(*Titu Andreescu*)

10. The quadrilateral $APMN$ is a rectangle, therefore $NP = AM$. Hence NP is minimal if $AM \perp BC$, so M is the foot of the altitude from A.

(*Titu Andreescu*)

11. Applying the law of cosines to triangle A_1B_1C we obtain

$$A_1B_1^2 = A_1C^2 + B_1C^2 - A_1C \cdot B_1C,$$

and using the inequality $x^2 + y^2 - xy \geq xy$, which holds for all real numbers x, y, we get

$$A_1B_1^2 \geq A_1C \cdot B_1C.$$

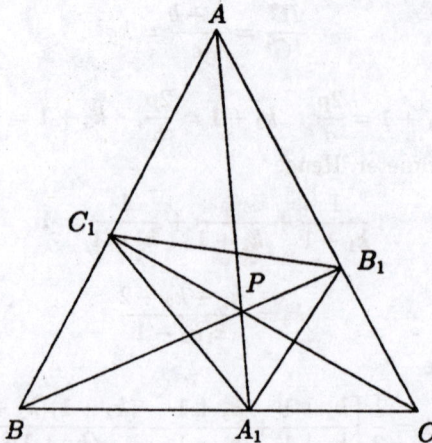

Similarly, we obtain $B_1C_1^2 \geq B_1A \cdot C_1A$ and $C_1A_1^2 \geq C_1B \cdot A_1B$. Multiplying the three inequalities together, we obtain

$$(A_1B_1 \cdot B_1C_1 \cdot C_1A_1)^2 \geq A_1B \cdot A_1C \cdot B_1A \cdot B_1C \cdot C_1A \cdot C_1B.$$

Now the lines AA_1, BB_1, CC_1 concur, so

$$A_1B \cdot B_1C \cdot C_1A = A_1C \cdot B_1A \cdot C_1B,$$

and after substituting and taking square roots, we have

$$A_1B_1 \cdot B_1C_1 \cdot C_1A_1 \geq A_1B \cdot B_1C \cdot C_1A,$$

the desired inequality. Equality holds if and only if $CA_1 = CB_1$, $AB_1 = AC_1$ and $BC_1 = BA_1$, which in turn holds if and only if P is the center of triangle ABC.
(*Titu Andreescu*, IMO 1996 Shortlist)

12. We start with the following lemma.
Lemma. *Let A, B, C be the angle of a triangle ABC. Then*

$$\tan \frac{A}{2} + \tan \frac{B}{2} + \tan \frac{B}{2} \tan \frac{C}{2} + \tan \frac{C}{2} \tan \frac{A}{2} = 1.$$

Proof. We present two arguments.
First approach. Since

$$\tan(\alpha + \beta)[1 - \tan\alpha \tan\beta] = \tan\alpha + \tan\beta,$$

$\tan(90° - \alpha) = \cot\alpha = 1/\tan\alpha$, and $A/2 + B/2 + C/2 = 90°$, the desired identity follows from

$$\tan \frac{A}{2} \tan \frac{B}{2} + \tan \frac{B}{2} \tan \frac{C}{2} = \tan \frac{B}{2} \left(\tan \frac{A}{2} + \tan \frac{C}{2} \right) =$$

$$= \tan \frac{B}{2} \tan \left(\frac{A}{2} + \frac{C}{2} \right) \left[1 - \tan \frac{A}{2} \tan \frac{C}{2} \right] =$$

$$= \tan \frac{B}{2} \tan \left(90° - \frac{B}{2} \right) \left[1 - \tan \frac{A}{2} \tan \frac{C}{2} \right] =$$

$$= 1 - \tan \frac{A}{2} \tan \frac{C}{2}.$$

Second approach. Let a, b, c, r, s denote the side lengths, inradius and semiperimeter of triangle ABC, respectively. Then $S_{ABC} = rs$, $AP = s - a$, and $\tan(A/2) = r/(s - a)$. Hence

$$\tan \frac{A}{2} = \frac{S_{ABC}}{s(s - a)}.$$

Likewise,

$$\tan \frac{B}{2} = \frac{S_{ABC}}{s(s - b)} \quad \text{and} \quad \tan \frac{C}{2} = \frac{S_{ABC}}{s(s - c)}.$$

Hence

$$\tan\frac{A}{2}\tan\frac{B}{2} + \tan\frac{B}{2}\tan\frac{C}{2} + \tan\frac{C}{2}\tan\frac{A}{2} =$$

$$= \frac{S_{ABC}^2}{s^2}\left(\frac{(s-c)+(s-a)+(s-b)}{(s-a)(s-b)(s-c)}\right) =$$

$$= \frac{S_{ABC}^2}{s(s-a)(s-b)(s-c)} = 1,$$

by Heron's formula. □

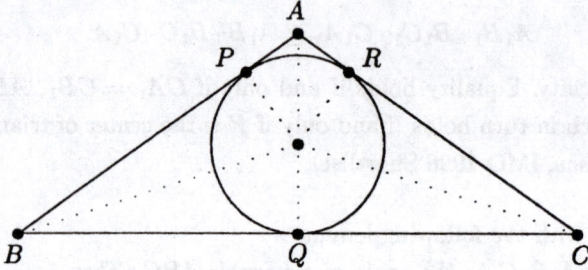

Without loss of generality assume that $AP = \min\{AP, BQ, CR\}$. Let $x = \tan(\widehat{A/2})$, $y = \tan(\widehat{B/2})$, and $z = \tan(\widehat{C/2})$. Then $AP = r/x$, $BQ = r/y$, and $CR = r/z$. The condition given in the problem statement becomes

$$2x + 5y + 5z = 6, \tag{1}$$

and the equation in the lemma is

$$xy + yz + zx = 1. \tag{2}$$

Eliminating x from (1) and (2) yields

$$5y^2 + 5z^2 + 8yz - 6y - 6z + 2 = 0.$$

Completing squares, we obtain

$$(3y - 1)^2 + (3z - 1)^2 = 4(y - z)^2.$$

Setting $3y - 1 = u$, $3z - 1 = v$ (i.e., $y = (u+1)/3$, $z = (v+1)/3$) gives

$$5u^2 + 8uv + 5v^2 = 0.$$

Because the discriminant of this quadratic equation is $8^2 - 4 \times 25 < 0$, the only real solution to the equation is $u = v = 0$. Hence there is only one possible set of values for the tangents of half-angles of ABC (namely $x = 4/3$, $y = z = 1/3$). Thus all triangles in S are isosceles and similar to one another.

Indeed, we have $x = r/AP = 4/3$ and $y = z = r/BQ = r/CQ = 1/3 = 4/12$, so we can set $r = 4$, $AP = AR = 3$, and $BP = BQ = CQ = CR = 12$. This leads to $AB = AC = 15$ and $BC = 24$. By scaling, all triangles in S are similar to the triangle with side lengths 5, 5, 8.

We can also use half-angle formulas to calculate

$$\sin B = \sin C = \frac{2 \tan \dfrac{C}{2}}{1 + \tan^2 \dfrac{C}{2}} = \frac{3}{5}.$$

From this it follows that $AQ : QB : BA = 3 : 4 : 5$ and $BC : AC : BC = 5 : 5 : 8$.

Alternative solution. By introducing the variables $p = y + z$ and $q = yz - 1$, relations (1) and (2) become $2x + 5p = 6$ and $xp + q = 0$, respectively. Eliminating x yields

$$p(6 - 5p) + 2q = 0. \tag{3}$$

Note that y and z are the roots of the equation

$$t^2 - pt + (q + 1) = 0. \tag{4}$$

Expressing q in terms of p in (3), and substituting in (4), we obtain the following quadratic equation in t:

$$t^2 - pt + \frac{5p^2 - 6p + 2}{2} = 0.$$

This equation has discriminant $-(3p - 2)^2 \leq 0$. Hence the equation has real solutions only if $p = 2/3$, and $y = z = 1/3$.

Note. We can also let $x = AP$, $y = BQ$, $z = CR$ and use the fact that

$$r(x + y + z) = S_{ABC} = \sqrt{xyz(x + y + z)}$$

to obtain a quadratic equation in three variables. Without loss of generality, we may set $x = 1$. Then the solution proceeds as above.

(*Titu Andreescu*, USA Mathematical Olympiad, 2000)

13. Let a, b, c, A, B, C be the side lengths and angles of triangle ABC. Let X, Y, Z be the feet of the perpendiculars from P to lines BC, CA, AB, respectively. Recall the inequality (the key ingredient in the proof of the Erdös-Mordell inequality):

$$PA \sin A \geq PY \sin C + PZ \sin B. \tag{1}$$

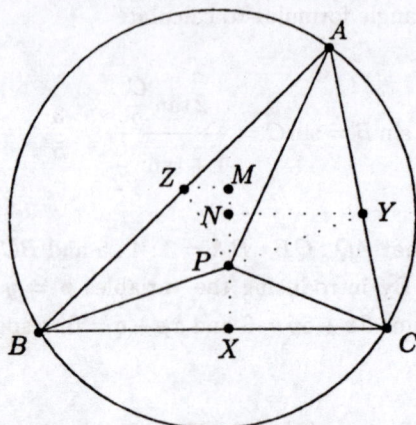

This says that the length of YZ is greater than equal to its projection onto BC, the latter being equal to the sum of the lengths of the projections of PY and PZ onto BC. In fact, since $\widehat{AYP} = \widehat{AZP} = 90°$, $AZPY$ is cyclic with AP as a diameter of its circumcircle. By the Extended Law of Sines, $YZ = PA \sin A$. Let M and N be the feet of perpendiculars from Z and Y to the line PX. Since $\widehat{BZP} = \widehat{BXP} = 90°$, $PZBX$ is cyclic. Hence $\widehat{MPZ} = \widehat{B}$ and $ZM = PZ \sin B$. Similarly, $YN = PY \sin C$. Thus (1) is equivalent to $YZ \geq YN + MZ$. Multiplying by $2R$ and using the Extended Law of Sines, (1) becomes

$$aPA \geq cPY + bPZ.$$

Likewise, we have $bPB \geq aPZ + cPX$ and $cPC \geq bPX + aPY$. Using these inequalities, we obtain

$$\frac{PA}{a^2} + \frac{PB}{b^2} + \frac{PC}{c^2} \geq PX\left(\frac{b}{c^3} + \frac{c}{b^3}\right) + PY\left(\frac{c}{a^3} + \frac{a}{c^3}\right) + PZ\left(\frac{a}{b^3} + \frac{b}{a^3}\right) \geq$$

$$\geq \frac{2PX}{bc} + \frac{2PY}{ca} + \frac{2PZ}{ab} \quad \text{(AM-GM inequality)}$$

$$= \frac{4S_{ABC}}{abc} = \frac{1}{R}.$$

Equality in the first step requires that YZ be parallel to BC and so on. This occurs if and only if P is the circumcenter of ABC. Equality in the second step requires that $a = b = c$. Thus equality holds if and only if ABC is equilateral and P is its center.

(*Titu Andreescu*, USA IMO Team Selection Test, 2000)

14. It is known that if H is the orthocenter of a triangle ABC then

$$AH \cdot BC + BH \cdot CA + CH \cdot AB = 4S_{ABC}.$$

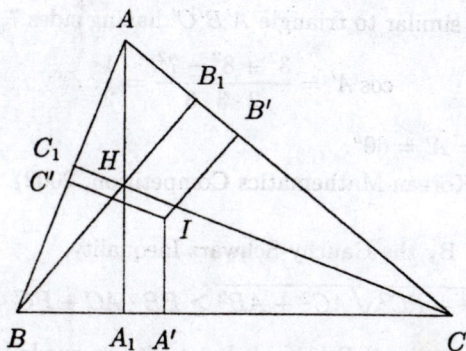

We prove that $I \equiv H$.

Assume by way of contradiction that points I and H are distinct. Let A_1, B_1, C_1 be the feet of the altitudes from A, B, C and let A', B', C' be the projection of I onto the sides BC, CA, AB, respectively. Hence at least two of the inequalities

$$IA + IA' \geq AA_1, \quad IB + IB' \geq BB_1, \quad IC + IC' \geq CC_1$$

are strict. It follows that

$$a \cdot IA + b \cdot IB + c \cdot IC > a(AA_1 - IA') + b(BB_1 - IB') + c(CC_1 - IC'),$$

or

$$4S_{ABC} > 6S_{ABC} - 2S_{ABC},$$

which is false.

Therefore $I = H$ and ABC is an equilateral triangle, as desired.

(*Titu Andreescu*, Revista Matematică Timişoara (RMT), No. 2(1981), pp. 67, Problem 4616)

15. Using standard notations, we have

$$64c^2 + 49a^2 + 9b^2 - 112ac - 48bc + 42ab = 6c^2 - 6a^2 - 6b^2.$$

This is equivalent to

$$15b^2 + 2b(21a - 24c) + 55a^2 - 112ac + 58c^2 = 0.$$

Viewing this as a quadratic equation in b, the condition $\Delta \geq 0$ is satisfied. That is

$$441a^2 - 1008ac + 576c^2 - 825a^2 + 1680ac - 870c^2 \geq 0.$$

The last relation is equivalent to

$$-6(64a^2 - 112ac + 49c^2) \geq 0,$$

or $(8a - 7c)^2 \leq 0$. It follows that $8a = 7c$. Substituting back into the given condition yields $3a = 7b$. We obtain

$$\frac{a}{7} = \frac{b}{3} = \frac{c}{8},$$

hence triangle ABC is similar to triangle $A'B'C'$ having sides 7, 3, 8. In this triangle

$$\cos A' = \frac{3^2 + 8^2 - 7^2}{2 \cdot 3 \cdot 8} = \frac{1}{2}.$$

It follows that $\widehat{A} = \widehat{A'} = 60°$.

(*Titu Andreescu*, Korean Mathematics Competition, 2002)

16. *First solution.* By the Cauchy-Schwarz Inequality,

$$\sqrt{PB^2 + PC^2}\sqrt{AC^2 + AB^2} \geq PB \cdot AC + PC \cdot AB.$$

Applying the (Generalized) Ptolemy's Inequality to quadrilateral $ABPC$ yields

$$PB \cdot AC + PC \cdot AB \geq PA \cdot BC.$$

Because PA is the longest side of an obtuse triangle with side lengths PA, PB, PC, we have $PA > \sqrt{PB^2 + PC^2}$, and hence

$$PA \cdot BC \geq \sqrt{PB^2 + PC^2} \cdot BC.$$

Combining these three inequalities yields

$$\sqrt{AB^2 + AC^2} \geq BC,$$

implying that angle BAC is acute.

Note. With some careful argument, it can be proved that quadrilateral $ABPC$ is indeed convex. We leave it as an exercise for the reader.

Second solution. Let D and Q be the feet of the perpendiculars from B and P to line AC, respectively. Then $DQ \leq BP$. Furthermore, the given conditions imply that $AP^2 > BP^2 + PC^2$, which can be written as $AP^2 - PC^2 > BP^2$. Hence,

$$AQ^2 \geq AQ^2 - QC^2 = (AP^2 - PQ^2) - (CP^2 - PQ^2) =$$
$$= AP^2 - PC^2 > BP^2 \geq DQ^2.$$

Let l be the ray AC minus the point A. Note that, since $PA > PC$, Q lies on ray l. If D did not lie on l, then AQ would be less than or equal to DQ, a contradiction. Thus, D lies on l, and angle BAC is acute.

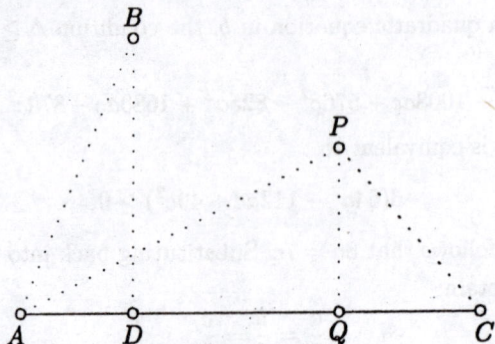

Third solution. Set up a coordinate system on the plane with $A = (0,0)$, $B = (a,0)$, $C = (b,c)$, and $P = (x,y)$. Without loss of generality, we may assume that $a > 0$ and that $c > 0$. Proving that angle BAC is acute is equivalent to proving that $b > 0$. Since $PA^2 > PB^2 + PC^2$,

$$x^2 + y^2 > (x-a)^2 + y^2 + (x-b)^2 + (y-c)^2.$$

Hence

$$0 > (x-a)^2 - 2bx + b^2 + (y-c)^2 \geq -2bx.$$

Since $PA > PB$, we have $x > \dfrac{a}{2} > 0$. It follows that $b > 0$, as desired.

Fourth solution. We first prove the following Lemma.

Lemma. *For any four points W, X, Y, Z in the plane,*

$$WY^2 + XZ^2 \leq WX^2 + XY^2 + YZ^2 + ZW^2.$$

Proof. Pick an arbitrary origin O and let w, x, y, z denote the vectors from O to W, X, Y, Z, respectively. Then

$$WX^2 + XY^2 + YZ^2 + ZW^2 - WY^2 - XZ^2 =$$

$$= |w-x|^2 + |x-y|^2 + |y-z|^2 + |z-w|^2 - |w-y|^2 - |x-z|^2 =$$

$$= w\cdot w + x\cdot x + y\cdot y + z\cdot z - 2(w\cdot x + x\cdot y + y\cdot z + z\cdot w - w\cdot y - x\cdot z) =$$

$$= |w+y-x-z|^2,$$

which is always nonnegative. Equality holds if and only if $w+y = x+z$, which is true if and only if $WXYZ$ is a (possibly degenerate) parallelogram. $\square$

Applying the Lemma to points A, B, C, P gives

$$0 \leq AB^2 + BP^2 + PC^2 + CA^2 - AP^2 - BC^2 =$$

$$= (PB^2 + PC^2 - PA^2) + (AB^2 + AC^2 - BC^2) <$$

$$< 0 + (AB^2 + AC^2 - BC^2) = AB^2 + AC^2 - BC^2.$$

Therefore angle BAC is acute.

Fifth solution. In this solution, $\sin^{-1}$ takes on values between $0°$ and $90°$. Note that $\widehat{PAB} < 90°$, since $PB < PA$. Applying the Law of Sines to triangle PAB yields

$$\sin\widehat{PAB} = \frac{PB}{PA}\sin\widehat{ABP} \leq \frac{PB}{PA}.$$

It follows that

$$\widehat{PAB} \leq \sin^{-1}\frac{PB}{PA}.$$

Since $PA^2 > PB^2 + PC^2$, we have similarly

$$\widehat{PAC} \leq \sin^{-1}\frac{PC}{PA} < \sin^{-1}\frac{\sqrt{PA^2-PB^2}}{PA}.$$

Thus
$$\widehat{BAC} \le \widehat{BAP} + \widehat{PAC} < \sin^{-1}\frac{PB}{PA} + \sin^{-1}\frac{\sqrt{PA^2 - PB^2}}{PA}.$$

If $\theta = \sin^{-1}\dfrac{PB}{PA}$, then

$$\sin(90° - \theta) = \cos\theta = \sqrt{1 - \sin^2\theta} = \frac{\sqrt{PA^2 - PB^2}}{PA}.$$

Hence
$$\widehat{BAC} < \sin^{-1}\frac{PB}{PA} + \sin^{-1}\frac{\sqrt{PA^2 - PB^2}}{PA} = 90°,$$

and angle BAC is acute.

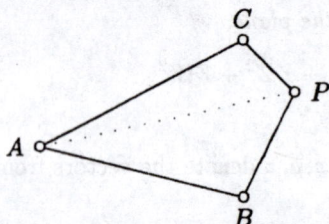

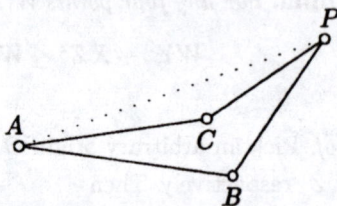

As we mentioned at the end of the first solution, the conditions in the problem imply that quadrilateral $ABPC$ is indeed convex. Thus, the diagram on the right-hand side is not possible, but this solution does not depend on this fact.

Sixth solution.

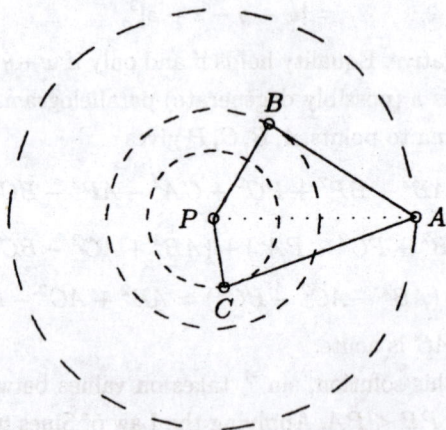

Note that $PA^2 > PB^2 + PC^2$. Regard P as fixed and A, B, C as free to rotate on circles of radii PA, PB, PC about P, respectively. As A, B, C vary, $\widehat{BAC}$ will be maximized when B and C are on opposite sides of line PA and $\widehat{ABP}$ and $\widehat{ACP}$ are right angles, i.e., lines AB and AC are tangent to the circles passing through B and C.

Without loss of generality, we assume that $PA > PB \ge PC$. In this case, $ABPC$ is cyclic and $AB^2 = PA^2 - PB^2 > PC^2$, and similarly $AC^2 > PB^2$. Hence on the circumcircle of $ABPC$, arcs AB and AC are bigger than arcs PC and PB, respectively. Thus, $\widehat{BPC} > \widehat{BAC}$. Because these two angles are supplementary, angle BAC is acute.

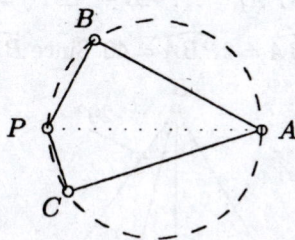

(*Titu Andreescu*, USA Mathematical Olympiad, 2001)

17. All angles will be in degrees. Let $x = \widehat{PCB}$. Then $\widehat{PBC} = 80 - x$. By the Law of Sines (or the trigonometric form of Ceva's Theorem),

$$1 = \frac{PA}{PB}\frac{PB}{PC}\frac{PC}{PA} = \frac{\sin\widehat{PBA}\sin\widehat{PCB}\sin\widehat{PAC}}{\sin\widehat{PAB}\sin\widehat{PBC}\sin\widehat{PCA}} =$$

$$= \frac{\sin 20 \sin x \sin 40}{\sin 10 \sin(80-x)\sin 30} = \frac{4\sin x \sin 40 \cos 10}{\sin(80-x)}.$$

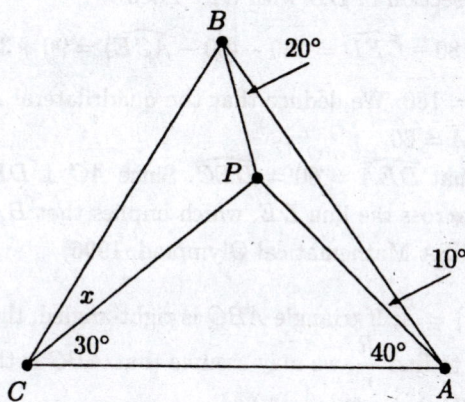

The identity $2\sin a \cos b = \sin(a - b) + \sin(a + b)$ (a consequence of the addition formula) now yields

$$1 = \frac{2\sin x(\sin 30 + \sin 50)}{\sin(80-x)} = \frac{\sin x(1 + 2\cos 40)}{\sin(80-x)},$$

so

$$2\sin x \cos 40 = \sin(80 - x) - \sin x = 2\sin(40 - x)\cos 40.$$

This gives $x = 40 - x$ and thus $x = 20$. It follows that $\widehat{ACB} = 50 = \widehat{BAC}$, so triangle ABC is isosceles.

Alternative solution. Let D be the reflection of A across the line BP. Then triangle APD is isosceles with vertex angle

$$\widehat{APD} = 2(180 - \widehat{BPA}) = 2(\widehat{PAB} + \widehat{ABP}) = 2(10 + 20) = 60,$$

and so is equilateral. Also, $\widehat{DBA} = 2\widehat{PBA} = 40$. Since $\widehat{BAC} = 50$, we have $DB \perp AC$.

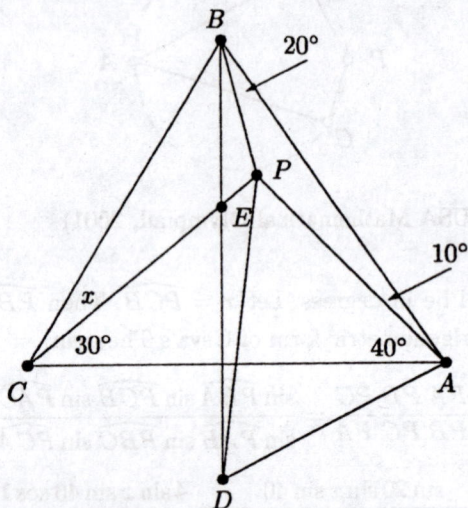

Let E be the intersection of DB with CP. Then

$$\widehat{PED} = 180 - \widehat{CED} = 180 - (90 - \widehat{ACE}) = 90 + 30 = 120$$

and so $\widehat{PED} + \widehat{DAP} = 180$. We deduce that the quadrilateral $APED$ is cyclic, and therefore $\widehat{DEA} = \widehat{DPA} = 60$.

Finally, we note that $\widehat{DEA} = 60 = \widehat{DEC}$. Since $AC \perp DE$, we deduce that A and C are symmetric across the line DE, which implies that $BA = BC$, as desired.

(*Titu Andreescu*, USA Mathematical Olympiad, 1996)

18. Let $\max\{A, B\} = A$. If triangle ABC is right-angled, then $A = 90°$, $B = 30°$ and $C = 60°$. In order to find $\dfrac{R}{r}$, we may assume that ABC is the triangle with sides $a = 2$, $b = 1$, $c = \sqrt{3}$. We have $R = 1$ and

$$r = \frac{S_{ABC}}{s} = \frac{\dfrac{\sqrt{3}}{2}}{\dfrac{2 + 1 + \sqrt{3}}{2}} = \frac{\sqrt{3}}{3 + \sqrt{3}},$$

so $\dfrac{R}{r} = \dfrac{3 + \sqrt{3}}{\sqrt{3}} = \sqrt{3} + 1.$

Conversely, assume that $\dfrac{R}{r} = \sqrt{3} + 1$. From the identity

$$r = 4R \sin \frac{A}{2} \sin \frac{B}{2} \sin \frac{C}{2}.$$

it follows that

$$r = 4(\sqrt{3}+1)r \sin \frac{A}{2} \sin \frac{B}{2} \sin \frac{C}{2}$$

or

$$\frac{1}{2(\sqrt{3}+1)} = 2\left(\sin \frac{A}{2} \sin \frac{C}{2}\right) \sin \frac{B}{2}.$$

Then

$$\frac{\sqrt{3}-1}{4} = \left(\cos \frac{A-C}{2} - \cos \frac{A+C}{2}\right) \sin \frac{B}{2}$$

and, since $A - C = 30°$, we obtain

$$\frac{\sqrt{3}-1}{4} = \left(\frac{\sqrt{6}+\sqrt{2}}{4} - \sin \frac{B}{2}\right) \sin \frac{B}{2}.$$

Letting $\sin \frac{B}{2} = x$ yields

$$x^2 - \frac{\sqrt{6}+\sqrt{2}}{4}x + \frac{\sqrt{3}-1}{4} = 0,$$

whose solutions are $x = \frac{\sqrt{6}-\sqrt{2}}{4}$ and $x = \frac{\sqrt{2}}{2}$. It follows that $\frac{B}{2} = 15°$ or $\frac{B}{2} = 45°$. The second solution is not acceptable, because $A \geq B$. Hence $B = 30°$, $A = 90°$ and $C = 60°$. Thus triangle ABC is right angled.

(*Titu Andreescu*, Korean Mathematics Competition, 2002)

19. Construct in the exterior of triangle ABC three circles equal to the circumcircle ABC that pass through two vertices of the triangle. By the five-coin theorem the circles will have a common point P, as desired (see Dorin Andrica, Csaba Varga, Daniel Văcăreţu, "Selected Topics and Problems in Geometry", PLUS, Bucharest, 2002, pp. 51-56).

Alternative solution. Let H be the orthocenter of triangle ABC. The reflections of H across the sides of the triangle are points of the circumcircle of triangle ABC. Therefore the circumcircles of HAB, HBC, HCA are equal to the circumcircle of ABC and for $P = H$ the claim holds.

(*Dorin Andrica*, Revista Matematică Timişoara (RMT), No. 2(1978), pp. 74)

20. Denote the midpoints of $A'B', B'C', C'A'$ by C_0, A_0, B_0, respectively, and the three perpendiculars in question by l_C, l_A, l_B. Consider the centroid of triangle $A'B'C'$.

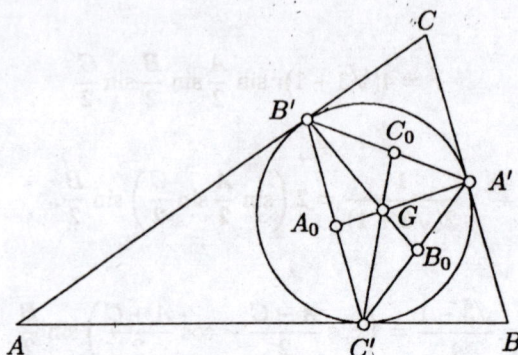

Since $A_0G : GA' = B_0G : GB' = C_0G : GC' = 1 : 2$, the dilatation h with center G and coefficient -2 takes A_0, B_0, C_0 to A', B', C', respectively. Since dilatations carry straight lines into parallel lines, h transforms l_C into the line through C' perpendicular to AB. But C' is the point of tangency of the incircle and AB, so this line passes through the incenter of triangle ABC. The same applies to the images of l_A and l_B under h. Since the images of l_A, l_B, l_C under h are concurrent, so are l_A, l_B, l_C themselves.

(*Titu Andreescu*, Romanian IMO Selection Test, 1986)

21. Because triangle $A_1A_2A_3$ is not isosceles, it is not difficult to see that the circumcenter of the triangles A_1B_1I, A_2B_2I, A_3B_3I are defined. We start with a simple lemma.

Lemma. *Let ABC be a triangle with the incenter I. Let T be the circumcenter of the triangle BIC. Then T lies on the internal bisector of the angle A.*

Proof. Let us draw the external bisectors of the angles B and C as shown in the figure below.

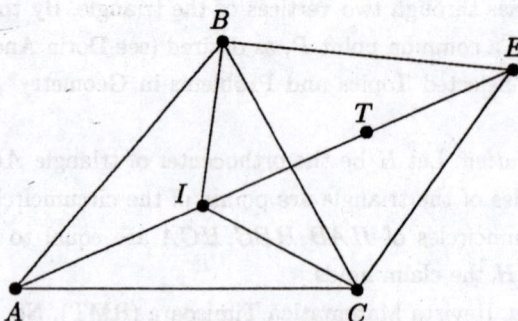

They intersect at the excenter E, which lies on the internal bisector of the angle A. Since $BE \perp BI$ and $CE \perp CI$, the quadrilateral $BECI$ is cyclic with the center of the circumscribed circle on IE. This center will be also the circumcenter of BIC. The lemma is proved.

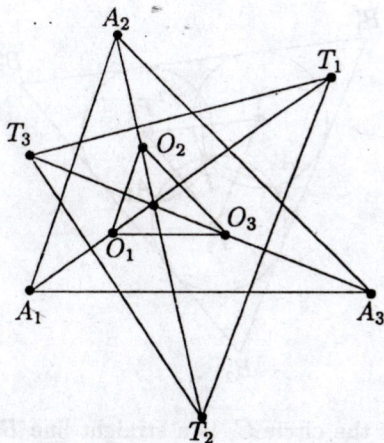

Let us prove the main statement. For $i = 1, 2, 3$ we denote by Q_i the center of the circle C_i and by T_i the circumcenter of the triangle $A_{i+1}IA_{i+2}$. Clearly, O_i lies on the internal bisector of the angle A_i. By the lemma, T_i also lies on the same bisector. Thus the triangles $O_1O_2O_3$ and $T_1T_2T_3$ are perspective from the point I. By Desargues' theorem these triangles are perspective from a line. This is to say that if we denote $Q_i, i = 1, 2, 3$, to be the point of intersection of the lines $O_{i+1}O_{i+2}$ and $T_{i+1}T_{i+2}$, then the points Q_1, Q_2, Q_3 are collinear. But since $T_{i+1}T_{i+2}$ is the perpendicular bisector of A_iI and $O_{i+1}O_{i+2}$ is the perpendicular bisector of B_iI, these points are exactly the circumcenter of the triangles A_1B_1I, A_2B_2I, A_3B_3I, respectively.

Remark. A student not familiar with Desargues' theorem may proceed from the point as follows. Applying Menelaus' theorem to the triangles IO_1O_2, IO_2O_3, IO_3O_1 and to the triples of points (T_1, T_2, Q_3), (T_2, T_3, Q_1), (T_3, T_1, Q_2), respectively, one can, observing usual agreement about the signs, write:

$$\frac{O_1T_1}{IT_1} \cdot \frac{IT_2}{O_2T_2} \cdot \frac{O_2Q_3}{O_1Q_3} = 1,$$

$$\frac{IT_3}{O_3T_3} \cdot \frac{O_2T_2}{IT_2} \cdot \frac{Q_3Q_1}{O_2Q_1} = 1,$$

$$\frac{IT_1}{O_1T_1} \cdot \frac{O_3T_3}{IT_3} \cdot \frac{O_1Q_2}{O_3Q_2} = 1.$$

Multiplying them all one gets

$$\frac{O_2Q_3}{O_1Q_3} \cdot \frac{O_3Q_1}{O_2Q_1} \cdot \frac{O_1Q_2}{O_3Q_2} = 1,$$

which means that the points Q_1, Q_2, Q_3 are collinear.

Alternative solution. This proof will be based on inversion. We take the incenter I to be the center of the inversion and the power of the inversion is arbitrary. Using primes to denote images of points under the inversion we have the following "dual" figure shown below.

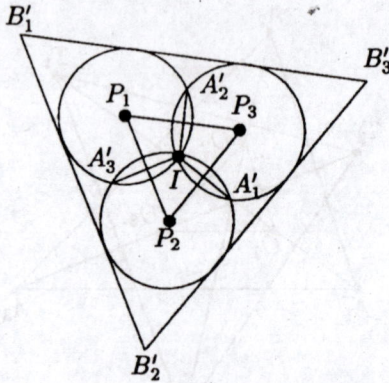

Indeed, the image of the circle C_i is a straight line $B'_{i+1}B'_{i+2}$, with these lines forming the triangle $B'_1B'_2B'_3$. The line A_iA_{i+1} will be transformed into the circle Γ_{i+2}, with the side A_iA_{i+1} becoming the arc $A'_iA'_{i+1}$ which does not contain I. Note that all these circles have equal radii since the distances from I to the sides of $A_1A_2A_3$ were equal.

Let us note that if Σ_1, Σ_2, Σ_3 are three circles passing through the common point I and no two of them touch, then their centres are collinear if and only if there is another common point $J \neq I$ through which all these three circles pass.

We will use this observation for Σ_i being the circumcircle of A_iB_iI. Since the inversion takes Σ_i to the line $A'_iB'_i$, the desired result is to show that the lines $A'_1B'_1$, $A'_2B'_2$, $A'_3B'_3$ are concurrent. For this, it suffices to show that the triangles $A'_1A'_2A'_3$ and $B'_1B'_2B'_3$ are homothetic, which is the same to say that their corresponding sides are parallel. Since the radii of the circles Γ_1, Γ_2, Γ_3 are equal, the triangle $P_1P_2P_3$ formed by their centre has its sides parallel to the corresponding sides of the triangle $B'_1B'_2B'_3$. The homothety of ratio $1/2$ centred at I takes the triangle $A'_1A'_2A'_3$ into the triangle whose vertices are the midpoints of the triangle $P_1P_2P_3$. Therefore the corresponding sides of the triangles $A'_1A'_2A'_3$ and $P_1P_2P_3$ are also parallel and the result follows.

(*Titu Andreescu*, IMO 1997 Shortlist)

22. Let I be the intersection point of lines CB' and $C'B$ and let A' be the intersection point of lines AI and BC.

We have

$$\frac{AB'}{B'B} + \frac{AC'}{C'C} = \frac{AI}{IA'},$$

from Van Aubel's theorem, therefore $\dfrac{AI}{IA'}$ is constant. Hence the locus of point I is a line segment parallel to BC.

(*Titu Andreescu*)

23. Without loss of generality assume that

$$PC = \max\{PA, PB, PC\}.$$

The condition in the hypothesis is

$$PB \cdot PC + PA \cdot PC = PA \cdot PB + 1$$

or

$$\frac{PC}{1} = \frac{PA \cdot PB + 1 \cdot 1}{PA \cdot 1 + PC \cdot 1}.$$

From the converse of the second theorem of Ptolemy it follows that $PACB$ is a cyclic quadrilateral. Note that P cannot be A, B or C otherwise the denominator of the right-hand side equals 0. Hence the locus of point P is the circumcircle of triangle ABC without the vertices A, B, C.

(*Titu Andreescu*, Revista Matematică Timişoara (RMT), No. 1(1985), Problem C7:3)

24. We have

$$\sqrt{a^2b^2 - 4S^2} + \sqrt{a^2c^2 - 4S^2} = \sqrt{a^2b^2 - a^2b^2 \sin^2 C} +$$

$$+ \sqrt{a^2c^2 - a^2c^2 \sin^2 B} = ab\cos C + ac\cos B =$$

$$= ab\frac{a^2 + b^2 - c^2}{2ab} + ac\frac{a^2 + c^2 - b^2}{2ac} = a^2,$$

as desired.

(*Titu Andreescu*, Revista Matematică Timişoara (RMT), No. 8(1971), pp. 25, Problem 1006)

25. The relation is equivalent to

$$\frac{\sqrt{r_a} + \sqrt{r_b} + \sqrt{r_c}}{\sqrt{r_a r_b r_c}} = \frac{1}{r},$$

or

$$\frac{1}{\sqrt{r_a}\sqrt{r_b}} + \frac{1}{\sqrt{r_c}\sqrt{r_a}} + \frac{1}{\sqrt{r_a}\sqrt{r_b}} = \frac{1}{r}.$$

On the other hand,

$$\frac{1}{r_a} + \frac{1}{r_b} + \frac{1}{r_c} = \frac{1}{r},$$

so

$$\frac{1}{\sqrt{r_a}\sqrt{r_b}} + \frac{1}{\sqrt{r_b}\sqrt{r_c}} + \frac{1}{\sqrt{r_c}\sqrt{r_a}} = \frac{1}{r_a} + \frac{1}{r_b} + \frac{1}{r_c}.$$

Then

$$\left(\frac{1}{\sqrt{r_a}} - \frac{1}{\sqrt{r_b}}\right)^2 + \left(\frac{1}{\sqrt{r_b}} - \frac{1}{\sqrt{r_c}}\right)^2 + \left(\frac{1}{\sqrt{r_c}} - \frac{1}{\sqrt{r_a}}\right)^2 = 0,$$

so $r_a = r_b = r_c$. It follows that the triangle is equilateral, as desired.

(*Titu Andreescu*, Revista Matematică Timişoara (RMT), No. 1(1974), pp. 21, Problem 1903)

26. If the triangle is equilateral the conclusion is true.

To prove the converse, we assume by way of contradiction that the triangle is not equilateral and say that $b \neq c$. Then

$$m_a^2 = \frac{b^2 + c^2}{2} - \frac{a^2}{4} > \frac{(b+c)^2 - a^2}{4} = p(p-a)$$

and likewise $m_b^2 \geq p(p-b)$, $m_c^2 \geq p(p-c)$.

It follows that

$$\frac{1}{m_a^2} + \frac{1}{m_b^2} + \frac{1}{m_c^2} < \frac{1}{p}\left(\frac{1}{p-a} + \frac{1}{p-b} + \frac{1}{p-c}\right) =$$

$$= \frac{-p^2 + ab + bc + ca}{S^2}.$$

On the other hand

$$\frac{1}{r_a^2} + \frac{1}{r_b^2} + \frac{1}{r_c^2} = \frac{1}{S^2}[(p-a)^2 + (p-b)^2 + (p-c)^2] = \frac{-p^2 + a^2 + b^2 + c^2}{S^2}.$$

Since $b \neq c$ then $ab + bc + ca < a^2 + b^2 + c^2$ hence

$$\frac{1}{m_a^2} + \frac{1}{m_b^2} + \frac{1}{m_c^2} < \frac{1}{r_a^2} + \frac{1}{r_b^2} + \frac{1}{r_c^2},$$

which is a contradiction.

(*Titu Andreescu*, Revista Matematică Timişoara (RMT), No. 2(1977), pp. 66, Problem 3063)

27. We know that

$$\sin\frac{A}{2}\sin\frac{B}{2}\sin\frac{C}{2} \leq \frac{1}{8},$$

so

$$\cos\frac{A}{2}\cos\frac{B}{2}\cos\frac{C}{2} \geq \sin A \sin B \sin C. \qquad (1)$$

On the other hand,

$$\sin A + \sin B + \sin C = 4\cos\frac{A}{2}\cos\frac{B}{2}\cos\frac{C}{2},$$

so inequality (1) gives

$$\sin A + \sin B + \sin C \geq 4\sin A \sin B \sin C. \qquad (2)$$

Since the circumradius is 1, we have

$$a = 2\sin A, \quad b = 2\sin B, \quad c = 2\sin C,$$

and relation (2) yields

$$a + b + c \geq abc,$$

as claimed.

Alternative solution: Let z_1, z_2, z_3 be the afixes of points A, B, C such that $|z_1| = |z_2| = |z_3| = 1$. We have

$$a = BC = |z_2 - z_3|, \quad b = AC = |z_3 - z_1|, \quad c = AB = |z_1 - z_2|.$$

Using the identity

$$z_1^2(z_2 - z_3) + z_2^2(z_3 - z_1) + z_3^2(z_1 - z_2) = (z_1 - z_2)(z_2 - z_3)(z_3 - z_1)$$

and triangle inequality it follows

$$abc = |z_1 - z_2||z_2 - z_3||z_3 - z_1| \leq |z_1|^2|z_2 - z_3| + |z_2|^2|z_3 - z_1| + |z_3|^2|z_1 - z_2| =$$

$$= |z_2 - z_3| + |z_3 - z_1| + |z_1 - z_2| = a + b + c.$$

(*Titu Andreescu*, Revista Matematică Timişoara (RMT), No. 2(1978), pp. 49, Problem 3513; Gazeta Matematică (GM-B), No. 11(1981), Problem O258; No. 2(1988), pp. 78, Problem 21353)

28. For any positive real numbers x, y, z we have

$$8xyz \leq (x + y)(y + z)(z + x)$$

Setting

$$x = -a + b + c, \quad y = a - b + c, \quad z = a + b - c,$$

gives

$$(-a + b + c)(a - b + c)(a + b - c) \leq abc,$$

so

$$-\sum a^3 + \sum a^2(b + c) - 2abc \leq abc.$$

It follows that

$$\sum a^2(-a + b + c) \leq 3abc,$$

then

$$\sum a^2(p - a) \leq \frac{3}{2}abc.$$

Hence

$$\sum \frac{a^2}{(p - b)(p - c)} \leq \frac{3}{2} \frac{abc}{(p - a)(p - b)(p - c)} = \frac{3}{2} \cdot \frac{pabc}{S^2} =$$

$$= 6\frac{abc}{4S} \cdot \frac{p}{S} = \frac{6R}{r},$$

as desired.

(*Titu Andreescu*, Revista Matematică Timişoara (RMT), No. 2(1974), pp. 51, Problem 2028)

29. Using the inequality

$$3(a^2 + b^2 + c^2) \geq (a + b + c)^2,$$

we obtain

$$\frac{a^2 + b^2 + c^2}{4S^2} \geq \frac{p^2}{3S^2}.$$

Hence

$$\frac{1}{h_a^2} + \frac{1}{h_b^2} + \frac{1}{h_c^2} \geq \frac{1}{3r^2},$$

as desired.

(*Titu Andreescu*, Revista Matematică Timişoara (RMT), No. 2(1977), pp. 66, Problem 3062)

30. From the inequality

$$\frac{1}{r_a} + \frac{1}{r_b} + \frac{1}{r_c} \geq \frac{1}{\sqrt{r_b r_c}} + \frac{1}{\sqrt{r_c r_a}} + \frac{1}{\sqrt{r_a r_b}},$$

we obtain

$$\frac{1}{r} \geq \frac{1}{\sqrt{r_b r_c}} + \frac{1}{\sqrt{r_c r_a}} + \frac{1}{\sqrt{r_a r_b}}.$$

Then

$$\frac{1}{r} \sum \sqrt{r_b r_c} \geq \left(\sum \sqrt{r_b r_c} \right) \left(\sum \frac{1}{\sqrt{r_b r_c}} \right) \geq 9,$$

hence

$$\sqrt{r_a r_b} + \sqrt{r_b r_c} + \sqrt{r_c r_a} \geq 9r,$$

as claimed.

(*Titu Andreescu*, Revista Matematică Timişoara (RMT), No. 2(1978), pp. 64, Problem 3277)

31. We have

$$m_a = \sqrt{\frac{b^2 + c^2}{2} - \frac{a^2}{4}} \geq \sqrt{\frac{(b+c)^2 - a^2}{4}} = \sqrt{p(p-a)}$$

and likewise

$$m_b \geq \sqrt{p(p-b)}, \quad m_c \geq \sqrt{p(p-c)}.$$

It follows that

$$m_a m_b m_c \geq p\sqrt{p(p-a)(p-b)(p-c)} = pS = r_a r_b r_c,$$

as desired.

(*Titu Andreescu*, Revista Matematică Timişoara (RMT), No. 1(1978), pp. 64, Problem 3276)

32. By the AM-GM inequality,

$$(a + b + c)^3 \geq 27abc,$$

so $8p^3 \geq 27abc$. Hence

$$2p^2 \geq 27\frac{abc}{4S} \cdot \frac{S}{p} = 27Rr,$$

as desired.

(*Titu Andreescu*, Revista Matematică Timişoara (RMT), No. 1(1973), pp. 43, Problem 1585)

33. We have

$$\frac{A}{2} \le \frac{\pi}{6} \Leftrightarrow \sin\frac{A}{2} \le \frac{1}{2}.$$

It follows that

$$\sqrt{\frac{(p-b)(p-c)}{bc}} \le \frac{1}{2},$$

hence

$$(p-b)(p-c) \le \frac{bc}{4},$$

as desired.

(*Titu Andreescu*, Revista Matematică Timişoara (RMT), No. 1(1984), pp. 67, Problem 5221)

34. Let O_1, O_2, O_3 be the centers of the three circles and S the area of the common region.

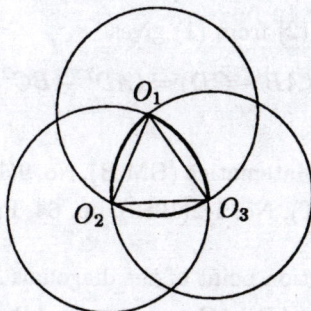

The three sectors with centers O_1, O_2, O_3 which subtend the arcs O_2O_3, O_1O_3, O_2O_1, respectively, cover the surface of area S and twice more the surface of triangle $O_1O_2O_3$ (which is $\frac{r^2\sqrt{3}}{4}$). On the other hand, the area of these three circular sectors equals the area of a semicircle, which is $\frac{1}{2}\pi r^2$. Hence

$$\frac{1}{2}\pi r^2 = S + 2 \cdot \frac{r^2\sqrt{3}}{4},$$

therefore

$$S = \frac{1}{2}r^2(\pi - \sqrt{3}).$$

(*Dorin Andrica*, Revista Matematică Timişoara (RMT), No. 2(1978), pp. 50, Problem 3522)

35. The parallel BD through C meets AB at point E. By Stewart's formula, we obtain

$$AC^2 \cdot BE + CE^2 \cdot AB - CB^2 \cdot AE = AB \cdot BE \cdot AE$$

Because $CE = BD$ and $BE = CD$, we deduce

$$AC^2 \cdot CD + BD^2 \cdot AB - BC^2 \cdot (AB + CD) = AB \cdot CD \cdot (AB + CD) \qquad (1)$$

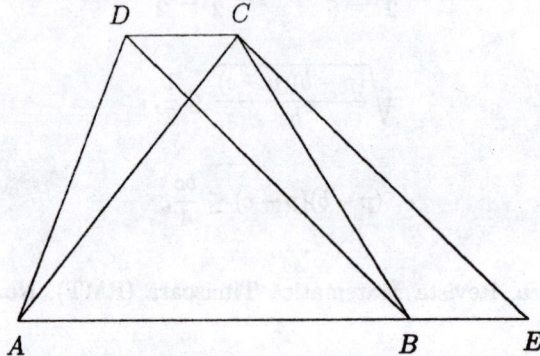

Drawing the parallel to AC through D and using similar computations yields

$$BD^2 \cdot CD + AC^2 \cdot AB - AD^2 \cdot (AB + CD) = AB \cdot CD \cdot (AB + CD) \qquad (2)$$

Subtracting the relation (2) from (1) gives

$$(AC^2 - BD^2)(AB - CD) = (AD^2 - BC^2)(AB + CD),$$

as desired.

(*Dorin Andrica*, Gazeta Matematică (GM-B), No. 9(1977), Problem 6852; Revista Matematică Timişoara (RMT), No. 1-2(1980), pp. 64, Problem 4119)

36. Let I be the intersection point of the diagonals AC and BD. Since

$$IA = \frac{AB \cdot AC}{AB + CD} \quad \text{and} \quad IB = \frac{AB \cdot BD}{AB + CD}$$

the condition in the statement becomes

$$IA^2 + IB^2 = AB^2.$$

Hence $\widehat{AIB} = 90°$, as desired.

(*Dorin Andrica*, Revista Matematică Timişoara (RMT), No. 2(1978), pp. 59, Problem 3524)

37. Let $ABCD$ be the trapezoid. Point I is the intersection of diagonals and M, N are the midpoints of AB and DC. In a right triangle the length of the median corresponding to the hypothenuse is half of lenght of the the hypothenuse. Hence

$$IM = \frac{AB}{2} \quad \text{and} \quad IN = \frac{CD}{2}.$$

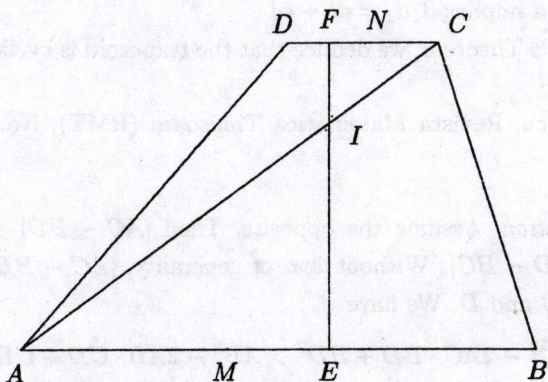

Then

$$IM + IN = \frac{AB + CD}{2} = EF,$$

which is the length of the midline and hence the length of the altitude. It follows that IM and IN are also altitudes in triangles IAB and ICD therefore IAB and ICD are isosceles. Thus $ABCD$ is isosceles, as claimed.

(*Titu Andreescu*, Revista Matematică Timişoara (RMT), No. 1(1978), pp. 48, Problem 2817)

38. From the Law of Cosines we deduce that

$$2AB \cdot AC \cos \widehat{BAC} = AB^2 - BC^2 + AC^2 \tag{1}$$

$$2DC \cdot AC \cos \widehat{DCA} = CD^2 - AD^2 + AC^2 \tag{2}$$

$$2AB \cdot DB \cos \widehat{DBA} = AB^2 - AD^2 + DB^2 \tag{3}$$

$$2DC \cdot DB \cos \widehat{CDB} = CD^2 - BC^2 + DB^2 \tag{4}$$

Note that

$$\widehat{BAC} = \widehat{DCA}, \quad \widehat{DBA} = \widehat{CDB},$$

so dividing relations (1) and (2), (3) and (4) yields

$$\frac{AB^2 - BC^2 + AC^2}{CD^2 - AD^2 + AC^2} = \frac{AB^2 - AD^2 + DB^2}{CD^2 - BC^2 + DB^2} = \frac{AB}{DC},$$

as desired.

(*Dorin Andrica*)

39. Let a, b the lengths of the bases, c, d be the lengths of the nonparallel sides and d_1, d_2 be the lengths of the diagonals. From Euler's theorem for quadrilaterals, it follows that

$$d_1^2 + d_2^2 + (a - b)^2 = a^2 + b^2 + c^2 + d^2.$$

Hence

$$(d_1 - d_2)^2 + 2d_1 d_2 = (c - d)^2 + 2(ab + cd),$$

and $d_1 - d_2 = c - d$ implies $d_1 d_2 = ab + cd$.

From Ptolemy's Theorem, we deduce that the trapezoid is cyclic and so isosceles, as claimed.

(*Titu Andreescu*, Revista Matematică Timişoara (RMT), No. 1(1978), pp. 48, Problem 2817)

40. *First solution.* Assume the opposite. Then $|AC - BD| > |AB - CD|$ or $|AC - BD| > |AD - BC|$. Without loss of generality, $|AC - BD| > |AB - CD|$, otherwise switch B and D. We have

$$AC^2 - 2AC \cdot BD + BD^2 > AB^2 - 2AB \cdot CD + CD^2 \tag{1}$$

and, from Euler's relation,

$$AB^2 + BC^2 + CD^2 + AD^2 = AC^2 + BD^2 + 4MN^2, \tag{2}$$

where M and N are the midpoints of AC and BD, respectively.

From (1) and (2),

$$AD^2 + BC^2 - 2AC \cdot BD > 4MN^2 - 2AB \cdot CD. \tag{3}$$

Let P be the midpoint of AB. Then $NP = AD/2$, $MP = BC/2$ and since $MN \geq |NP - MP|$, it follows that

$$4MN^2 \geq (AD - BC)^2. \tag{4}$$

From (3) and (4), $-2AC \cdot BD > -2AB \cdot CD - 2AD \cdot BC$, in contradiction with Ptolemy's Theorem. We are done.

Note. The cyclicity is essential. The inequality fails if $ABCD$ is a parallelogram.

Second solution. Let E be the intersection of AC and BD. Then the triangles ABE and DCE are similar, so if we let $x = AE$, $y = BE$, $z = AB$, then there exists k such that $kx = DE$, $ky = CE$, $kz = CD$. Now

$$|AB - CD| = |k - 1|z$$

and

$$|AC - BD| = |(kx + y) - (ky + z)| = |k - 1| \cdot |x - y|.$$

Since $|x - y| \leq z$ by the triangle inequality, we conclude that $|AB - CD| \geq |AC - BD|$, and similarly $|BC - DA| \geq |AC - BD|$. These two inequalities imply the desired result.

Third solution. Let $2\alpha, 2\beta, 2\gamma, 2\delta$ be the measures of the arcs subtended by AB, BC, CD, DA, respectively, and take the radius of the circumcircle of $ABCD$ to be 1. Assume without loss of generality that $\beta \leq \delta$. Then $\alpha + \beta + \gamma + \delta = \pi$, and (by the Extended Law of Sines)

$$|AB - CD| = 2|\sin \alpha - \sin \gamma| = \left| \sin \frac{\alpha - \gamma}{2} \cos \frac{\alpha + \gamma}{2} \right|$$

and

$$|AC - BD| = 2|\sin(\alpha + \beta) - \sin(\beta + \gamma)| = \left|\sin\frac{\alpha - \gamma}{2}\cos\left(\frac{\alpha + \gamma}{2} + \beta\right)\right|.$$

Since $0 \leq (\alpha + \gamma)/2 \leq (\alpha + \gamma)/2 + \beta \leq \pi/2$ (by the assumption $\beta \leq \delta$) and the cosine function is nonnegative and decreasing on $[0, \pi/2]$, we conclude that $|AB - CD| \geq |AC - BD|$, and similarly $|AD - BC| \geq |AC - BD|$.

(*Titu Andreescu*, USA Mathematical Olympiad, 1999)

41. Let E be the intersection point of the diagonals. Consider $AD < BC$ the basis of the trapezoid and AB the altitude. Since

$$AB^2 = AD \cdot BC,$$

then

$$\frac{AB}{AD} = \frac{BC}{AB},$$

so the right triangles ABC and ABD are similar.

On the other hand we have

$$\widehat{BCA} + \widehat{CAB} = 90°$$

hence

$$\widehat{ABD} + \widehat{CAB} = 90°$$

It follows that $\widehat{AEB} = 90°$ so the diagonals are perpendicular, as claimed.

(*Titu Andreescu*, Revista Matematică Timişoara (RMT), No. 2(1972), pp. 28, Problem 1164)

42. Let I be the intersection point of the diagonals AF and BE of the rectangle $ABFE$. Notice that NI is the median of the right triangle ANF with hypothenuse AF, so

$$IN = \frac{AF}{2} = IA$$

Likewise,

$$IM = \frac{BE}{2} = IE, \quad IQ = \frac{AF}{2} = IF, \quad IP = \frac{BE}{2} = IB.$$

Since $IA = IE = IF = IB$, it follows that $IM = IN = IP = IQ$. Hence $MNPQ$ is cyclic, as desired.

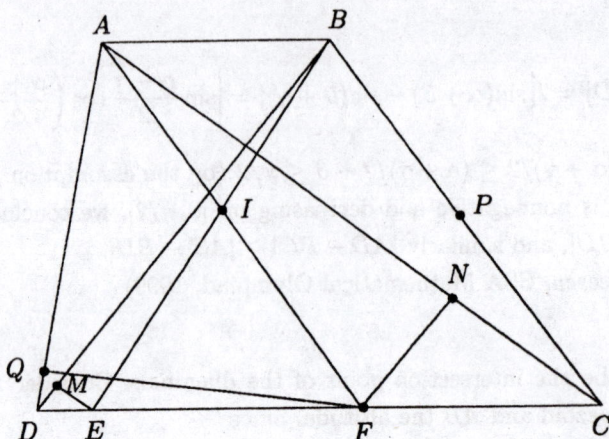

(*Titu Andreescu*)

43. By Sturm's theorem, we know that if $0 < a_1 \leq a_2 \leq a_3 \leq a_4 < a_1 + a_2 + a_3$, then there is a cyclic quadrilateral having side lengths a_1, a_2, a_3, a_4.

Denote by a, b, c, d, e, f, m the lengths of the segments AB, BC, CD, DA, AC, BD, MN, respectively. Without loss of generality assume that $b + d \geq a + c$.

Let P be the midpoint of the side BC. The segments MP and NP are midlines in triangles CAB and BDC, so

$$MP = \frac{1}{2}a \text{ and } NP = \frac{1}{2}c.$$

Then

$$2m = 2MN < 2MP + 2NP = a + c$$

so

$$2m < a + c < b + d.$$

On the other hand, if O is the intersection point of the diagonals, we have

$$b + d = BC + DA < BO + OC + DO + OA = AC + BD = e + f,$$

hence $2m < a + c < b + d < e + f$.

It suffices to prove that $e + f < 2m + a + c + b + d$. Note that

$$e < c + d, \quad f < b + c, \quad e < a + b, \quad f < a + d.$$

Summing up these inequalities yields

$$e + f < a + b + c + d < a + b + c + d + 2m$$

and the proof is complete.

(*Titu Andreescu*, Revista Matematică Timişoara (RMT), No. 1(1978), pp. 66, Problem 3288; Gazeta Matematică (GM-B), No. 10(1981), pp. 402, Problem C148)

44. Let I be the intersection point of lines BD and AF. The parallel to BD through C meets line AF at point T. First we consider $AF \perp BD$ and prove that $AB \perp CD$.

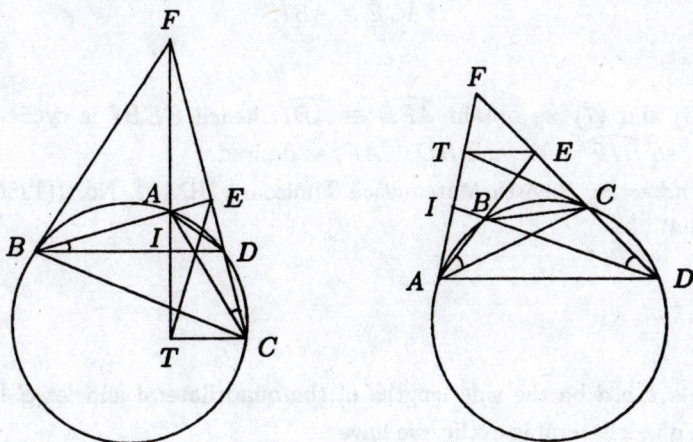

i) Assume that D lies on the segment CE. Then $\widehat{ATC} = 90°$. Since $\widehat{BAC} \equiv \widehat{BDC}$, we obtain

$$\widehat{FAE} \equiv \widehat{BDE}. \tag{1}$$

On the other hand $CT \| BD$ so

$$\widehat{BDE} \equiv \widehat{ECT}. \tag{2}$$

Relations (1) and (2) imply $\widehat{FAE} \equiv \widehat{ECT}$, therefore $EATC$ is cyclic. It follows that $\widehat{BEC} = 90°$, hence $AB \perp CD$, as desired.

ii) Assume that C lies on the segment DE. In the right triangle CTF, TE is the median, so

$$\widehat{ETC} \equiv \widehat{ECT}. \tag{3}$$

Because $CT \| BD$, we have

$$\widehat{ECT} \equiv \widehat{CDB}. \tag{4}$$

Also,

$$\widehat{CDB} \equiv \widehat{BAC} \tag{5}$$

so from (3), (4), (5), we obtain $\widehat{ETC} \equiv \widehat{BAC}$. Hence $ATEC$ is cyclic, then $\widehat{AEC} = \widehat{ATC} = 90°$, and $AB \perp CD$, as desired.

Conversely, consider that $AB \perp CD$.

i) If D is on the segment CE, then $\widehat{AFE} \equiv \widehat{ACE}$. On the other hand $\widehat{ACE} \equiv \widehat{ACD} \equiv \widehat{ABD}$, so $\widehat{AFE} \equiv \widehat{ABD}$, and $FBIE$ is cyclic. It follows that $\widehat{BIF} = \widehat{BEF} = 90°$, hence $BD \perp AF$, as desired.

ii) If C is on the segment DE, then

$$\widehat{AFE} \equiv \widehat{ACE}. \tag{6}$$

Moreover, $\widehat{ACD} \equiv \widehat{ABD}$, so

$$\widehat{ACE} \equiv \widehat{ABI}. \tag{7}$$

From (6) and (7) we obtain $\widehat{AFE} \equiv \widehat{ABI}$, hence $FEBI$ is cyclic. Note that $\widehat{BEF} = 90°$, so $\widehat{BIF} = 90°$ and $BD \perp AF$, as desired.

(*Titu Andreescu*, Revista Matematică Timişoara (RMT), No. 1(1986), pp. 106, Problem C6:4)

45. Let a, b, c, d be the side lengths of the quadrilateral and let S be its area. Because the quadrilateral is cyclic, we have

$$S^2 = (p-a)(p-b)(p-c)(p-d). \tag{1}$$

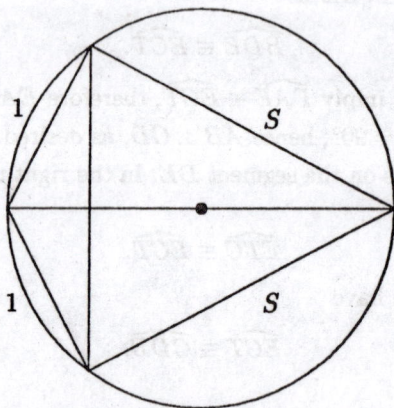

Numbers a, b, c, d are odd, hence

$$p = \frac{a+b+c+d}{2}$$

is an integer.

If p is odd, then $p-a$, $p-b$, $p-c$, $p-d$ are even and so s^2 is divisible by 16, which is false. Hence p is even.

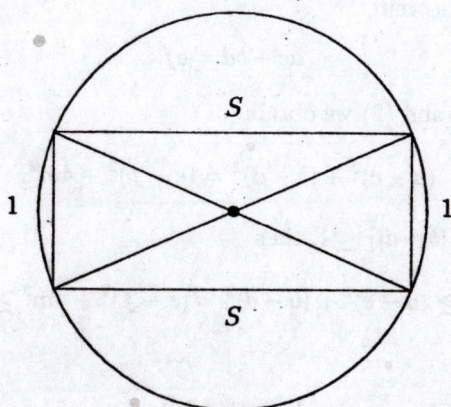

Without loss of generality assume that $a \leq b \leq c \leq d$. Since S is a prime number, from relation (1) we obtain

$$p - d = p - c = 1 \text{ and } p - a = p - b = S.$$

Summing up these equalities yields $4p - 2p = 2 + 2S$ so $p = S + 1$. Hence $a = b = 1$ and $c = d = S$.

The required quadrilaterals are either rectangles or kites.

(*Titu Andreescu*, Revista Matematică Timişoara (RMT), No. 2(1977), pp. 66, Problem 3067)

46. From the AM-GM inequality it follows that

$$abcd \leq \left(\frac{a+b+c+d}{4} \right)^4 = \frac{1}{4}p^4.$$

Hence

$$16abcd \leq p^4,$$

or

$$8(ac + bd)^2 - p^4 \leq 8(a^2c^2 + b^2d^2).$$

The desired inequality is now obtained from Ptolemy's Theorem:

$$ac + bd = ef.$$

(*Titu Andreescu*, Revista Matematică Timişoara (RMT), No. 3(1973), pp. 36, Problem 1811; Gazeta Matematică (GM-B), No. 8(1980), pp. 364, Problem 18370)

47. Let m be the length of the segment determined by the midpoints of the diagonals.

From Euler's Theorem for quadrilaterals we have

$$a^2 + b^2 + c^2 + d^2 = e^2 + f^2 + 4m^2 \qquad (1)$$

and from Ptolemy's Theorem,

$$ac + bd = ef. \tag{2}$$

From relations (1) and (2) we obtain

$$(a - c)^2 + (b - d)^2 = (e - f)^2 + 4m^2.$$

Since $\max\{|a - c|, |b - d|\} \leq 1$, then

$$2 = 1 + 1 \geq (a - c)^2 + (b - d)^2 = (e - f)^2 + 4m^2 \geq (e - f)^2.$$

Hence

$$|e - f| \leq \sqrt{2},$$

as desired.

(*Titu Andreescu*, Revista Matematică Timişoara (RMT), No. 2(1978), pp. 51, Problem 3527)

48. The quadrilateral is cyclic so

$$S = \sqrt{(p - a)(p - b)(p - c)(p - d)}$$

Since $S = \left(\dfrac{p}{2}\right)^2$, we have

$$\sqrt[4]{(p - a)(p - b)(p - c)(p - d)} = \frac{p}{2} =$$

$$= \frac{(p - a) + (p - b) + (p - c) + (p - d)}{4}.$$

Note that this is the equality case in the AM-GM inequality, hence $p - a = p - b = p - c = p - d$. It follows that $a = b = c = d$, so the quadrilateral is a square.

(*Titu Andreescu*, Revista Matematică Timişoara (RMT), No. 1(1977), pp. 24, Problem 2136)

49. Observe that $S_{PAB} \cdot S_{PCD} = S_{PBC} \cdot S_{PDA}$, since both are equal to $\frac{1}{4}PA \cdot PB \cdot PC \cdot PD \cdot \sin P$. The numbers S_{PAB}, S_{PCD} and S_{PBC}, S_{PDA} have the same sum and the same product, thus $S_{PAB} = S_{PBC}$ and $S_{PCD} = S_{PDA}$ or $S_{PAB} = S_{PDA}$ and $S_{PBC} = S_{PCD}$, i.e. P is the midpoint of AC or BD, as desired.

(*Titu Andreescu*, Korean Mathematics Competitions, 2001)

50. (i) Let M' and M'' be the projections of point M onto diagonals AC and BD.

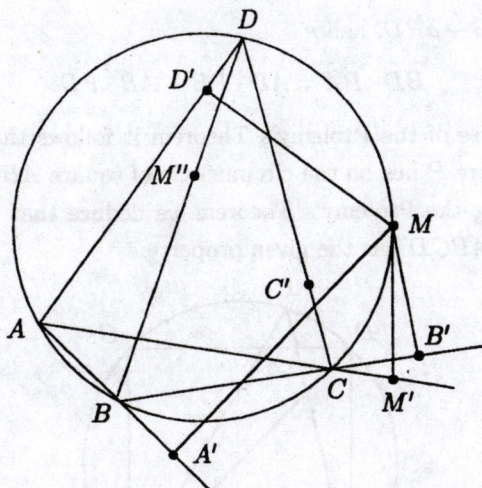

We recall the Simpson's theorem: the projections of a point of the circumcircle of a triangle onto the sides of the triangle are collinear. Applying this result to triangles ABC and DAC yields that A', M', B' are collinear and C', M', D' are collinear.

Hence the lines $A'B'$, $C'D'$ and AC meet at M', as claimed.

(ii) From Simpson's Theorem for triangles ABD and BDC we deduce that M'' is on the lines $B'C'$ and $D'A'$. Since M'' is a point of AC, the conclusion follows.

(*Dorin Andrica*, Revista Matematică Timişoara (RMT), No. 1(1979), pp. 54, Problem 3855; Romanian Regional Mathematical Contest "Grigore Moisil", 1995)

51. We have
$$S_{ABCD} \leq \frac{1}{2} AC \cdot BD,$$
with equality if and only if $AC \perp BD$. Since
$$2002 = S_{ABCD} \leq \frac{1}{2} AC \cdot BD \leq$$
$$\leq \frac{1}{2}(AP + PC) \cdot (BP + PD) = \frac{52 \cdot 77}{2} = 2002,$$
it follows that the diagonals AC and BD are perpendicular and intersect at P. Thus, $AB = \sqrt{24^2 + 32^2} = 40$, $BC = \sqrt{28^2 + 32^2} = 4\sqrt{113}$, $CD = \sqrt{28^2 + 45^2} = 53$, and $DA = \sqrt{45^2 + 24^2} = 51$. The perimeter of $ABCD$ is therefore
$$144 + 4\sqrt{113} = 4(36 + \sqrt{113}).$$

(*Titu Andreescu*, American Mathematics Contest 12 (AMC 12 - Contest B), 2002, Problem 24)

52. Let a be the side length of the square $ABCD$. Assume without loss of generality that $\max(PA, PC) = PA$. We have
$$\sqrt{2}PA = PB + PD.$$

Then $a\sqrt{2}PA = aPB + aPD$, hence

$$BD \cdot PA = AD \cdot PB + AB \cdot PD.$$

From the converse of the Ptolemy's Theorem it follows that $PDAB$ is a cyclic quadrilateral, therefore P lies on the circumcircle of square $ABCD$.

Conversely, using the Ptolemy's Theorem we deduce that any point of the circumcircle of square $ABCD$ has the given property.

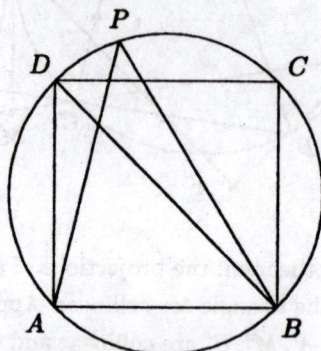

It follows that the locus of point P is the circumcircle of square $ABCD$.

Alternative solution. Let $P(x, y)$ be a point with the given property and assume $y > 0$. Point A, B, C, D are considered like in the diagram.

Note that $PC > PA$, so

$$\sqrt{2}PC = PB + PD$$

Squaring both sides yields

$$2x^2 + 2(y + b)^2 = (x - b)^2 + (x + b)^2 + 2y^2 + 2\sqrt{(x - b)^2 + y^2} + 2\sqrt{(x + b)^2 + y^2},$$

then

$$2by = \sqrt{(x - b)^2 + y^2} + \sqrt{(x + b)^2 + y^2},$$

hence

$$(x^2 + y^2 + b^2 - 2bx)(x^2 + y^2 + b^2 + 2bx) = 4b^2y^2.$$

It follows that

$$(x^2 + y^2 + b^2)^2 - 4b^2x^2 = 4b^2y^2,$$

so

$$(x^2 + y^2 - b^2)^2 = 0.$$

Thus

$$x^2 + y^2 = b^2$$

and so point P lies on the semicircle of diameter BD that contains A. Likewise, for $y \leq 0$ we deduce that P·lies on the semicircle of diameter BD that contains C and finally we obtain the circumcircle of square $ABCD$.

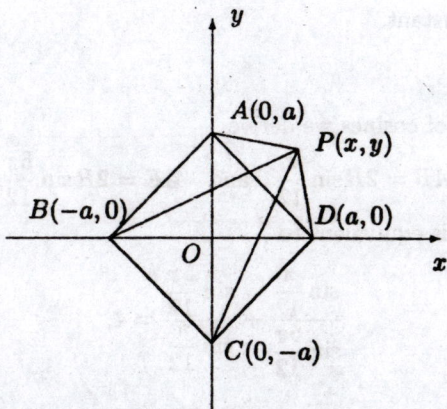

(*Titu Andreescu*, Romanian IMO Selection Test, 1981; **Revista Matematică** Timişoara (RMT), No. 2(1981), pp. 87, Problem 4751)

53. Let $ABCD$ be a quadrilateral from the set $\mathcal{P}$ and let M, N, P, Q be the midpoints of sides AB, CD, BC, AD, respectively.

The Euler's relation for the parallelogram $MNPQ$ is

$$MP^2 + PN^2 + NQ^2 + QM^2 = MN^2 + PQ^2,$$

or

$$2(MQ^2 + MP^2) = MN^2 + PQ^2.$$

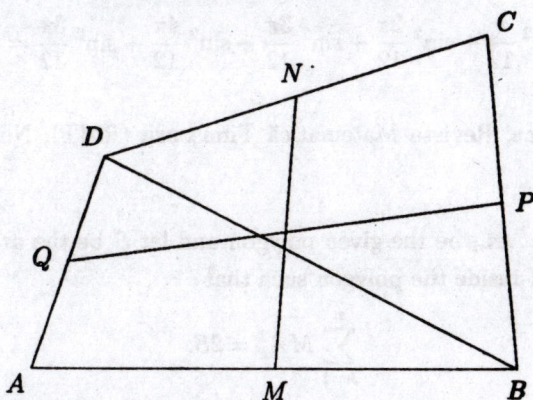

On the other hand, we have

$$MQ = \frac{DB}{2}, \quad MP = \frac{AC}{2}$$

so

$$\frac{AC^2 + BD^2}{2} = MN^2 + PQ^2.$$

Hence

$$\lambda_1^2(p) + \lambda_2^2(p) = \frac{AC^2 + BD^2}{2},$$

which is, clearly, a constant.

(*Dorin Andrica*)

54. From the law of cosines we derive

$$AB = 2R\sin\frac{\pi}{12} \quad \text{and} \quad AF = 2R\sin\frac{5\pi}{12}.$$

The first equality is equivalent to

$$\frac{\sin\dfrac{\pi}{12}}{\sin\dfrac{5\pi}{12}} + \frac{\sin\dfrac{5\pi}{12}}{\sin\dfrac{\pi}{12}} = 4,$$

or

$$1 = 4\sin\frac{5\pi}{12}\sin\frac{\pi}{12}.$$

Furthermore,

$$1 = 4\cos\frac{\pi}{12}\sin\frac{\pi}{12} \text{ or } 1 = 2\sin\frac{\pi}{6}$$

which is clear.

For the second equality, we have

$$AC^2 = 4R^2\sin^2\frac{2\pi}{12}, \quad AD^2 = 4R^2\sin^2\frac{3\pi}{12},$$

$$AE^2 = 4R^2\sin^2\frac{4\pi}{12}, \quad AF^2 = 4R^2\sin^2\frac{5\pi}{12}.$$

It reduces to

$$\sin^2\frac{\pi}{12} + \sin^2\frac{2\pi}{12} + \sin^2\frac{3\pi}{12} + \sin^2\frac{4\pi}{12} + \sin^2\frac{5\pi}{12} = \frac{5}{2},$$

which is also clear.

(*Titu Andreescu*, Revista Matematică Timişoara (RMT), No. 6(1971), pp. 27, Problem 821)

55. Let $A_1 A_2 \ldots A_n$ be the given polygon and let S be the area of $A_1 A_2 \ldots A_n$. There is a point M inside the polygon such that

$$\sum_{k=1}^{n} MA_k^2 = 2S.$$

We write

$$S = \sum_{k=1}^{n} S_{A_k M A_{k+1}}, \quad A_{n+1} = A_1.$$

Hence

$$S = \sum_{k=1}^{n} \frac{MA_k MA_{k+1}\sin A_k\widehat{M}A_{k+1}}{2} \le \frac{1}{2}\sum_{k=1}^{n} MA_k MA_{k+1} \le$$

$$\le \frac{1}{4}\sum_{k=1}^{n}(MA_k^2 + MA_{k+1}^2) = \frac{1}{2}\sum_{k=1}^{n} MA_k^2 = S.$$

In order to have equality everywhere we must have

$$\sin A_k \widehat{MA_{k+1}} = 1 \quad \text{and} \quad MA_k = MA_{k+1}, \quad k = 1, 2, \ldots, n.$$

It follows that M is the circumcenter of a cyclic polygon and all sides subtent arcs of $90°$. That is the polygon is a square, as desired.

(*Titu Andreescu*, Revista Matematică Timişoara (RMT), No. 2(1978), pp. 50, Problem 3528)

56. In a triangle ABC with the altitude AA' and the circumradius R the following equality holds:

$$AB \cdot AC = 2R \cdot AA'. \tag{1}$$

Let R be the circumradius of the polygon $A_1 A_2 \ldots A_n$ and let $P_1, P_2, \ldots, P_n$ be the projections of a point P on the circumcircle onto the sides $A_1 A_2, A_2 A_3, \ldots, A_n A_1$, respectively.

Applying (1) for triangles $PA_i A_{i+1}$, where $A_{n+1} = A_1$, yields

$$PA_i \cdot PA_{i+1} = 2R \cdot PP_i, \quad i = 1, 2, \ldots, n.$$

Hence

$$\prod_{i=1}^{n} \frac{PA_i^2}{PP_i} = 2^n R^n$$

which is a constant, as claimed.

(*Dorin Andrica*, Revista Matematică Timişoara (RMT), No. 1-2(1980), pp. 65, Problem 4123)

57. Applying relation (1) from the previous problem to triangles $MA_1 A_2$, $MA_3 A_4, MA_5 A_6, \ldots, MA_{2n-1} A_{2n}$, we obtain

$$MA_1 \cdot MA_2 = 2R \cdot MK_1, \quad MA_3 \cdot MA_4 = 2R \cdot MK_3, \ldots,$$

$$MA_{2n-1} \cdot MA_{2n} = 2R \cdot MK_{2n-1}.$$

Multiplying these equalities yields

$$MK_1 \cdot MK_3 \ldots MK_{2n-1} = \frac{MA_1 \cdot MA_2 \ldots MA_{2n}}{2^n R^n}. \tag{2}$$

For the triangles

$$MA_2 A_3, \ MA_4 A_5, \ldots, MA_{2n-2} A_{2n-1}, \ MA_{2n} A_1$$

relation (1) yields

$$MA_2 \cdot MA_3 = 2R \cdot MK_2, \quad MA_4 \cdot MA_5 = 2R \cdot MK_4, \ldots,$$

$$MA_{2n-2} \cdot MA_{2n-1} = 2R \cdot MA_{2n-2}, \quad MA_{2n} \cdot MA_1 = 2R \cdot MK_{2n}.$$

Multiplying these equalities gives

$$MK_2 \cdot MK_4 \ldots MK_{2n} = \frac{MA_1 \cdot MA_2 \ldots MA_{2n}}{2^n R^n}. \tag{3}$$

Similarly, we obtain

$$MH_1 \cdot MH_2 \ldots MH_n = \frac{MA_1 \cdot MA_2 \cdot MA_{2n}}{2^n R^n} \tag{4}$$

by applying relation (1) to triangles $MA_1A_{n+1}, MA_2A_{n+2}, \ldots, MA_nA_{2n}$.

From equalities (2), (3) and (4) we draw the conclusion.

(*Dorin Andrica*, Revista Matematică Timișoara (RMT), No. 2(1981), pp. 68, Problem 4622)

58. Let x and y be the measures of the arcs subtended by the sides a and b, respectively. We have

$$nx + ny = 2\pi,$$

or

$$x + y = \frac{2\pi}{n}.$$

Let R be the circumradius of the polygon. Then

$$\sin\frac{x}{2} = \frac{a}{2R} \quad \text{and} \quad \sin\frac{y}{2} = \frac{b}{2R}.$$

Now $y = \frac{2\pi}{n} - x$ so

$$\sin\frac{y}{2} = \sin\left(\frac{\pi}{n} - \frac{x}{2}\right) = \sin\frac{\pi}{n}\cos\frac{x}{2} - \cos\frac{\pi}{n}\sin\frac{x}{2} = \frac{b}{2R},$$

hence

$$\sin\frac{\pi}{n}\cos\frac{x}{2} = \frac{b}{2R} + \cos\frac{\pi}{n}\sin\frac{x}{2}.$$

Squaring boths sides yields

$$\sin^2\frac{\pi}{n}\cos^2\frac{x}{2} = \frac{b^2}{4R^2} + 2\frac{b}{2R}\cos\frac{\pi}{n}\sin\frac{x}{2} + \cos^2\frac{\pi}{n}\sin^2\frac{x}{2}$$

or

$$\sin^2\frac{\pi}{n}\left(1 - \sin^2\frac{x}{2}\right) = \frac{b^2}{4R^2} + 2\frac{b}{2R}\cos\frac{\pi}{n}\sin\frac{x}{2} + \cos^2\frac{\pi}{n}\sin^2\frac{x}{2}.$$

Since $\sin\frac{x}{2} = \frac{a}{2R}$, we obtain

$$\sin^2\frac{\pi}{n}(4R^2 - a^2) = b^2 + 2ab\cos\frac{\pi}{n} + a^2\cos^2\frac{\pi}{n}.$$

Therefore

$$R = \frac{1}{2\sin\dfrac{\pi}{n}}\sqrt{a^2 + 2ab\cos\frac{\pi}{n} + b^2}.$$

(*Dorin Andrica*)

59. We have from the Cauchy-Schwarz Inequality that

$$\left(\sum_{i=1}^{n} \frac{a_i}{b_i} \right) \left(\sum_{i=1}^{n} a_i \cdot b_i \right) \geq \left(\sum_{i=1}^{n} a_i \right)^2$$

for any positive numbers a_i, b_i, $i = 1, 2, \ldots, n$.

Setting $n = 4$,

$$a_1 = S_{BCD}, \quad a_2 = S_{CDA},$$

$$a_3 = S_{DAB}, \quad a_4 = S_{ABC},$$

$$b_1 = PA_1, \quad b_2 = PB_1,$$

$$b_3 = PC_1, \quad b_4 = PD_1,$$

yields

$$3V \sum \frac{S_{BCD}}{PA} \geq S^2,$$

where V is the volume of the tetrahedron. Then

$$\sum \frac{S_{BCD}}{PA} \geq \frac{S^2}{3V} = \frac{S^2}{rS} = \frac{S}{r},$$

as desired.

The equality occurs if and only if

$$\sqrt{\frac{a_i}{b_i}} = \alpha \sqrt{a_i b_i}$$

for $i = 1, 2, 3, 4$ hence $b_i = \alpha^{-1}$, $i = 1, 2, 3, 4$. Then

$$PA_1 = PB_1 = PC_1 = PD_1,$$

so P is the incenter of tetrahedron $ABCD$.

Remark. The inequality holds for convex polyhedra circumscribed about a sphere.

(*Titu Andreescu*, Romanian IMO Selection Test, 1982; Revista Matematică Timişoara (RMT), No. 1(1982), pp. 82, Problem 4910)

60. All summations here range from $i = 1$ to $i = 4$. Let O be the circumcenter and R be the circumradius of $A_1A_2A_3A_4$. By the Power-of-a-point Theorem, $GA_i \cdot GA_i' = R^2 - OG^2$, for $1 \leq i \leq 4$. Hence the desired inequalities are equivalent to

$$(R^2 - OG^2)^2 \geq GA_1 \cdot GA_2 \cdot GA_3 \cdot GA_4 \tag{1}$$

and

$$(R^2 - OG^2) \sum \frac{1}{GA_i} \geq \sum GA_i.$$

Now (1) follows immediately from

$$4(R^2 - OG^2) = \sum GA_i^2 \tag{3}$$

by the Arithmetic-Geometric-Mean Inequality. To prove (3), let P denote the vector from O to the point P. Then

$$\sum A_i^2 = \sum G^2 + \sum (G - A_i)^2 + 2G \sum (G - A_i). \qquad (4)$$

This is equivalent to (3), since the last term of (4) vanishes. By Cauchy-Schwarz Inequality,

$$4 \sum GA_i^2 \geq \left(\sum GA_i \right)^2 \quad \text{and} \quad \sum GA_i \sum \frac{1}{GA_i} \geq 16,$$

so

$$\frac{1}{4} \sum GA_i^2 \sum \frac{1}{GA_i} \geq \frac{1}{16} \left(\sum (GA_i)^2 \right)^2 \sum \frac{1}{GA_i} \geq \sum GA_i.$$

Hence (2) also follows from (3).

(*Titu Andreescu*, IMO 1995 Shortlist)

Chapter 4
TRIGONOMETRY

PROBLEMS

1. Prove that

$$\operatorname{ctg}^2 \frac{\pi}{7} + \operatorname{ctg}^2 \frac{2\pi}{7} + \operatorname{ctg}^2 \frac{3\pi}{7} = 5.$$

2. Prove that

$$\cos^3 \frac{x}{3} + \cos^3 \frac{x + 2\pi}{3} + \cos^3 \frac{x + 4\pi}{3} = \frac{3}{4} \cos x$$

for all $x \in \mathbb{R}$.

3. Evaluate the sum

$$S_n = \sum_{k=1}^{n-1} \sin kx \cos(n - k)x.$$

4. Evaluate the sums

$$S_1 = \sin x \cos 2y + \sin 2x \cos 3y + \cdots + \sin(n - 1)x \cos ny,$$

$$S_2 = \cos x \sin 2y + \cos 2x \sin 3y + \cdots + \cos(n - 1)x \sin ny.$$

5. Evaluate the products
1) $P_1 = (1 - \operatorname{tg}1°)(1 - \operatorname{tg}2°)\ldots(1 - \operatorname{tg}89°)$;
2) $P_2 = (1 + \operatorname{tg}1°)(1 + \operatorname{tg}2°)\ldots(1 + \operatorname{tg}44°)$.

6. Prove that

$$(4\cos^2 9° - 3)(4\cos^2 27° - 3) = \tan 9°.$$

7. Let x be a real number such that $\sec x - \tan x = 2$. Evaluate $\sec x + \tan x$.

8. Evaluate the product

$$P_n = \prod_{k=1}^{n} \frac{1 + \operatorname{tg}^2 2^k x}{(1 - \operatorname{tg}^2 2^k x)^2},$$

where $|x| < \dfrac{\pi}{2^{n+2}}$.

9. Let a, b, c, d, x be real numbers such that $x \neq k\pi$, $k \in \mathbf{Z}$ and

$$\frac{\sin x}{a} = \frac{\sin 2x}{b} = \frac{\sin 3x}{c} = \frac{\sin 4x}{d}.$$

Prove that $2a^3(2b^2 - d^2) = b^4(3a - c)$.

10. Let $a, b, c, d \in [0, \pi]$ such that

$$2\cos a + 6\cos b + 7\cos c + 9\cos d = 0$$

and

$$2\sin a - 6\sin b + 7\sin c - 9\sin d = 0.$$

Prove that $3\cos(a + d) = 7\cos(b + c)$.

11. Prove that if

$$\arccos a + \arccos b + \arccos c = \pi,$$

then

$$ab\sqrt{1 - c^2} + bc\sqrt{1 - a^2} + ca\sqrt{1 - b^2} = \sqrt{(1 - a^2)(1 - b^2)(1 - c^2)}$$

12. Let a, b, c be positive real numbers such that

$$ab + bc + ca = 1.$$

Prove that

$$\text{arctg}\frac{1}{a} + \text{arctg}\frac{1}{b} + \text{arctg}\frac{1}{c} = \pi.$$

13. Let x and y be real numbers from the interval $\left(0, \frac{\pi}{2}\right)$ such that

$$\cos^2(x - y) = \sin 2x \sin 2y$$

Prove that $x + y = \frac{\pi}{2}$.

14. Consider the numbers $\alpha, \beta, \gamma \in \left(0, \frac{\pi}{4}\right)$ such that

$$\frac{1}{2}(1 - \text{tg}\alpha)(1 - \text{tg}\beta)(1 - \text{tg}\gamma) = 1 - (\text{tg}\alpha + \text{tg}\beta + \text{tg}\gamma).$$

Prove that $\alpha + \beta + \gamma = \frac{\pi}{4}$.

15. Let $a, b \in \left(0, \frac{\pi}{2}\right)$. Prove that

$$\left(\frac{\sin^2 a}{\sin b}\right)^2 + \left(\frac{\cos^2 a}{\cos b}\right)^2 = 1$$

if and only if $a = b$.

16. Prove that
$$\frac{\sin^3 a}{\sin b} + \frac{\cos^3 a}{\cos b} \geq \sec(a - b)$$
for all $0 < a, b < \dfrac{\pi}{2}$.

17. Let α, β be real numbers with $\beta \geq 1$. Prove that
$$(1 + 2\sin^2 \alpha)^\beta + (1 + 2\cos^2 \alpha)^\beta \geq 2^{\beta+1}$$
for all $\alpha \in \mathbb{R}$.

18. Let x be a real number, $x \in [-1, 1]$. Prove that
$$\frac{1}{2^{n-1}} \leq x^{2n} + (1 - x^2)^n \leq 1$$
for all positive integers n.

19. Prove that
$$\sec^{2n} x + \operatorname{cosec}^{2n} x \geq 2^{n+1}$$
for all integers $n \geq 0$ and for all $x \in \left(0, \dfrac{\pi}{2}\right)$.

20. Prove that
$$(1 + \sin x)(1 + \cos x) \leq \frac{3}{2} + \sqrt{2}$$
for all real numbers x.

21. Find the maximal value of the expression
$$E = \sin x_1 \cos x_2 + \sin x_2 \cos x_3 + \cdots + \sin x_n \cos x_1,$$
when $x_1, x_2, \ldots, x_n$ are real numbers.

22. Find the extreme values of the function $f : \mathbb{R} \to \mathbb{R}$,
$$f(x) = a \cos 2x + b \cos x + c,$$
where a, b, c are real numbers and $a, b > 0$.

23. Let $a_0, a_1, \ldots, a_n$ be numbers from the interval $(0, \pi/2)$ such that
$$\tan\left(a_0 - \frac{\pi}{4}\right) + \tan\left(a_1 - \frac{\pi}{4}\right) + \cdots + \tan\left(a_n - \frac{\pi}{4}\right) \geq n - 1.$$
Prove that
$$\tan a_0 \tan a_1 \ldots \tan a_n \geq n^{n+1}.$$

24. Find the period of the function
$$f(x) = \cos px + \cos qx, \quad x \in \mathbb{R}$$
if p, q are positive integers.

25. Let $a_0 = \sqrt{2} + \sqrt{3} + \sqrt{6}$ and let $a_{n+1} = \dfrac{a_n^2 - 5}{2(a_n + 2)}$ for $n \geq 0$. **Prove that**

$$a_n = \cot\left(\frac{2^{n-3}\pi}{3}\right) - 2$$

for all n.

26. Let n be an odd positive integer. Solve the equation

$$\cos nx = 2^{n-1}\cos x.$$

27. Solve the equation

$$A\sin^2 x + B\sin 2x + C = 0,$$

where A, B, C are real parameters.

28. Solve the equation

$$\sin x \cos y + \sin y \cos z + \sin z \cos x = \frac{3}{2}.$$

29. Prove that the equation

$$\sin x \sin 2x \sin 3x \sin 4x = \frac{3}{4}$$

has no real solutions.

30. Solve the system of equations

$$\begin{cases} 2\sin x + 3\cos y = 3 \\ 3\sin y + 2\cos x = 4. \end{cases}$$

31. Solve the system of equations

$$\begin{cases} x\sin y + \sqrt{1 - x^2}\cos y = \dfrac{\sqrt{2}}{2} \\ x + y = \dfrac{\pi}{4}. \end{cases}$$

32. Solve the system of equations

$$\begin{cases} x + y + z = \dfrac{3\pi}{4} \\ \operatorname{tg} x + \operatorname{tg} y + \operatorname{tg} z = 5 \\ \operatorname{tg} x \cdot \operatorname{tg} y \cdot \operatorname{tg} z = 1. \end{cases}$$

33. Prove that in any triangle

$$a\cos A + b\cos B + c\cos C = \frac{abc}{2R^2}$$

34. Prove that in any triangle

$$\sum \cos^3 \frac{A}{2} \sin \frac{B}{2} \sin \frac{C}{2} = \cos \frac{A}{2} \cos \frac{B}{2} \cos \frac{C}{2} \sum \sin^2 \frac{A}{2}.$$

35. Let n be a positive integer. Prove that in any triangle

$$\sum \sin nA \sin nB \sin nC = (-1)^{n+1} + \cos nA \cos nB \cos nC$$

and

$$\sum \cos nA \cos nB \sin nC = \sin nA \sin nB \sin nC.$$

36. Consider a triangle ABC such that

$$\sin A \sin B + \sin B \sin C + \sin C \sin A = \lambda$$

and

$$(1 + \sin A)(1 + \sin B)(1 + \sin C) = 2(\lambda + 1)$$

Prove that triangle ABC has a right angle.

37. Let $\lambda > 1$ be a real number and let ABC be a triangle such that

$$a^\lambda \cos B + b^\lambda \cos A = c^\lambda$$

and

$$a^{2\lambda-1} \cos B + b^{2\lambda-1} \cos A = c^{2\lambda-1}.$$

Prove that the triangle is isosceles.

38. Prove that the triangle ABC is equilateral if and only if

$$\operatorname{tg} \frac{A}{2} + \operatorname{tg} \frac{B}{2} + \operatorname{tg} \frac{C}{2} = \frac{1}{4S}(a^2 + b^2 + c^2).$$

39. Let ABC be a triangle such that

$$\sin^2 B + \sin^2 C = 1 + 2 \sin B \sin C \cos A.$$

Prove that triangle ABC has a right angle.

40. Let ABC be a triangle such that

$$\left(\cot \frac{A}{2}\right)^2 + \left(2\cot \frac{B}{2}\right)^2 + \left(3\cot \frac{C}{2}\right)^2 = \left(\frac{6s}{7r}\right)^2,$$

where s and r denote its semiperimeter and its inradius, respectively. Prove that triangle ABC is similar to a triangle T whose side lengths are all positive integers with no common divisor and determine these integers.

41. Prove that in any triangle

$$\sum \sin \frac{A}{2} \cos \frac{B}{2} \cos \frac{C}{2} \leq \frac{9}{8}.$$

42. Prove that in any triangle

$$\frac{a^2}{bc} + \frac{b^2}{ca} + \frac{c^2}{ab} \geq 4 \left(\sin^2 \frac{A}{2} + \sin^2 \frac{B}{2} + \sin^2 \frac{C}{2} \right).$$

43. Prove that in any triangle

$$\frac{\cos A}{a^3} + \frac{\cos B}{b^3} + \frac{\cos C}{c^3} \geq \frac{81}{16p^3}.$$

44. Prove that in any triangle

$$\frac{\sec^2 \frac{A}{2}}{bc} + \frac{\sec^2 \frac{B}{2}}{ca} + \frac{\sec^2 \frac{C}{2}}{ab} \geq \frac{9}{p^2}.$$

45. Prove that in any triangle

$$\frac{p}{r} \geq 3\sqrt{3}.$$

46. Let ABC be a triangle. Prove that

$$\sin \frac{3A}{2} + \sin \frac{3B}{2} + \sin \frac{3C}{2} \leq \cos \frac{A-B}{2} + \cos \frac{B-C}{2} + \cos \frac{C-A}{2}.$$

47. Find the number of ordered pairs (a, b) such that $(a+bi)^{2002} = a - bi$, $a, b \in \mathbb{R}$.

48. Find

$$\min_{z \in \mathbb{C}\setminus\mathbb{R}} \frac{\mathrm{Im}z^5}{\mathrm{Im}^5 z}$$

and the values of z for which the minimum is reached.

49. Let $z_1, z_2, \ldots, z_{2n}$ be complex numbers such that $|z_1| = |z_2| = \cdots = |z_{2n}|$ and $\arg z_1 \leq \arg z_2 \leq \cdots \leq \arg z_{2n} \leq \pi$. Prove that

$$|z_1 + z_{2n}| \leq |z_2 + z_{2n-1}| \leq \cdots \leq |z_n + z_{n+1}|.$$

50. For all positive integers k define

$$A_k = \{z \in \mathbb{C} \mid z^k = 1\}.$$

Prove that for any integers m and n with $0 < m < n$ we have

$$A_1 \cup A_2 \cup \cdots \cup A_m \subset A_{n-m+1} \cup A_{n-m+2} \cup \cdots \cup A_n.$$

51. Let z_1, z_2, z_3 be complex numbers, not all real, such that $|z_1| = |z_2| = |z_3| = 1$ and $2(z_1 + z_2 + z_3) - 3z_1z_2z_3 \in \mathbb{R}$.

Prove that

$$\max(\arg z_1, \arg z_2, \arg z_3) \geq \frac{\pi}{6}.$$

52. Let n be an even positive integer such that $\frac{n}{2}$ is odd and $\varepsilon_0, \varepsilon_1, \ldots, \varepsilon_{n-1}$ the complex roots of unity of order n. Prove that

$$\prod_{k=0}^{n-1} (a + b\varepsilon_k^2) = (a^{\frac{n}{2}} + b^{\frac{n}{2}})^2$$

for any complex numbers a and b.

53. Let n be an odd positive integer and $\varepsilon_0, \varepsilon_1, \ldots, \varepsilon_{n-1}$ the complex roots of unity of order n. Prove that

$$\prod_{k=0}^{n-1} (a + b\varepsilon_k^2) = a^n + b^n$$

for all complex numbers a and b.

54. Let z_1, z_2, z_3 be distinct complex numbers such that $|z_1| = |z_2| = |z_3| = r$. Prove that

$$\frac{1}{|z_1 - z_2||z_1 - z_3|} + \frac{1}{|z_2 - z_1||z_2 - z_3|} + \frac{1}{|z_3 - z_1||z_3 - z_2|} \geq \frac{1}{r^2}.$$

55. Let z_1, z_2, z_3 be distinct complex numbers such that $|z_1| = |z_2| = |z_3| = r$ and $z_2 \neq z_3$.

Prove that

$$\min_{a \in \mathbb{R}} |az_2 + (1-a)z_3 - z_1| = \frac{|z_1 - z_2||z_1 - z_3|}{2r}.$$

56. If z is a complex number satisfying $|z^3 + z^{-3}| \leq 2$, the inequality show that $|z + z^{-1}| \leq 2$.

57. The pair (z_1, z_2) of nonzero complex numbers has the following property: there is a real number $a \in [-2, 2]$ such that $z_1^2 - az_1z_2 + z_2^2 = 0$. Prove that all pairs (z_1^n, z_2^n), $n = 2, 3, \ldots$, have the same property.

58. Let $A_1 A_2 \ldots A_n$ be a regular polygon with the circumradius equal to 1. Find the maximum value of $\max \prod_{j=1}^{n} PA_j$ when P describes the circumcircle.

59. Let n be an odd positive integer and let $\alpha_1, \alpha_2, \ldots, \alpha_n$ be numbers from the interval $[0, \pi]$.

Prove that

$$\sum_{1 \le i < j \le n} \cos(\alpha_i - \alpha_j) \ge \frac{1-n}{2}.$$

60. Let n be a positive integer. Find the real numbers a_0 and a_{kl}, $k, l = \overline{1, n}$, $k > l$, such that

$$\frac{\sin^2 nx}{\sin^2 x} = a_0 + \sum_{1 \le l < k \le n} a_{kl} \cos 2(k - l)x$$

for all real numbers $x \neq m\pi$, $m \in \mathbb{Z}$.

SOLUTIONS

1. We prove that

$$\sum_{k=1}^{n} \cot^2 \frac{k\pi}{2n+1} = \frac{n(2n-1)}{3}, \tag{1}$$

for all integers $n > 0$.

Consider the equation

$$\sin(2n+1)x = 0,$$

with roots

$$\frac{\pi}{2n+1}, \frac{2\pi}{2n+1}, \dots, \frac{n\pi}{2n+1}.$$

Expressing $\sin(2n+1)x$ in terms of $\sin x$ and $\cos x$, we obtain

$$\sin(2n+1)x = \binom{2n+1}{1} \cos^{2n} x \sin x - \binom{2n+1}{3} \cos^{2n-2} x \sin^3 x + \cdots =$$

$$= \sin^{2n+1} x \left(\binom{2n+1}{1} \cot^{2n} x - \binom{2n+1}{3} \cot^{2n-2} x + \dots \right)$$

Set $x = \frac{k\pi}{2n+1}$, $k = 1, 2, \dots, n$. Since $\sin^{2n+1} x \neq 0$, we have

$$\binom{2n+1}{1} \cot^{2n} x - \binom{2n+1}{3} \cot^{2n-2} x + \cdots = 0.$$

Substituting $y = \cot^2 x$ yields

$$\binom{2n+1}{1} y^n - \binom{2n+1}{3} y^{n-1} + \cdots = 0,$$

with roots $\cot^2 \frac{\pi}{2n+1}, \cot^2 \frac{2\pi}{2n+1}, \dots, \cot^2 \frac{n\pi}{2n+1}$. Using the relation between coefficients and roots, we obtain

$$\sum_{k=1}^{n} \cot^2 \frac{k\pi}{2n+1} = \frac{\binom{2n+1}{3}}{\binom{2n+1}{1}} = \frac{n(2n-1)}{3}.$$

Setting $n = 3$, the desired conclusion follows.

(*Dorin Andrica*, Revista Matematică Timişoara (RMT), No. 1-2(1979), pp. 51, Problem 3831)

2. Applying the identity

$$\cos t = 4 \cos^3 \frac{t}{3} - 3 \cos \frac{t}{3}, \quad t \in \mathbb{R}$$

for $t = x, t = x + 2\pi$, $t = x + 4\pi$ and summing up the three relations, we obtain

$$3 \cos x = 4 \left(\cos^3 \frac{x}{3} + \cos^3 \frac{x + 2\pi}{3} + \cos^3 \frac{x + 4\pi}{3} \right) -$$

$$-3 \left(\cos \frac{x}{3} + \cos \frac{x + 2\pi}{3} + \cos \frac{x + 4\pi}{3} \right).$$

On the other hand,

$$\cos \frac{x}{3} + \cos \frac{x + 2\pi}{3} + \cos \frac{x + 4\pi}{3} = 2 \cos \frac{4\pi}{6} \cos \frac{2x + 4\pi}{6} + \cos \frac{x + 2\pi}{3} =$$

$$= \left(2 \cos \frac{2\pi}{3} + 1 \right) \cos \frac{x + 2\pi}{3} = 0$$

and the desired identity follows.

(*Dorin Andrica*, Revista Matematică Timişoara (RMT), No. 2(1975), pp. 44, Problem 2124)

3. We have

$$2S_n = S_n + S_n =$$

$$= \sin x \cos(n-1)x + \sin 2x \cos(n-2)x + \cdots + \sin(n-1)x \cos x +$$

$$+ \sin(n-1)x \cos x + \sin(n-2)x \cos 2x + \cdots + \cos(n-1)x \sin x =$$

$$= \sin nx + \sin nx + \cdots + \sin nx = (n-1) \sin nx,$$

so

$$S_n = \frac{n-1}{2} \sin nx.$$

(*Dorin Andrica*, Gazeta Matematică (GM-B), No. 8(1977), pp. 324, Problem 16803; Revista Matematică Timişoara (RMT), No. 2(1978), pp. 30, Problem 3055)

4. Note that

$$S_1 + S_2 = \sin(x + 2y) + \sin(2x + 3y) + \cdots + \sin[(n-1)x + ny]$$

and

$$S_2 - S_1 = \sin(2y - x) + \sin(3y - 2x) + \cdots + \sin[ny - (n-1)x].$$

Setting

$$x + y = h_1 \quad \text{and} \quad y - x = h_2$$

yields

$$S_1 + S_2 = \sin(y + h_1) + \sin(y + 2h_1) + \cdots + \sin(y + (n-1)h_1) =$$

$$= \frac{\sin \frac{nh_1}{2} \sin \left[y + (n-1)\frac{h_1}{2} \right]}{\sin \frac{h_1}{2}},$$

$$S_2 - S_1 = \sin(y + h_2) + \sin(y + 2h_2) + \cdots + \sin(y + (n-1)h_2) =$$

$$= \frac{\sin \frac{nh_2}{2} \sin \left[y + (n-1)\frac{h_2}{2} \right]}{\sin \frac{h_2}{2}}.$$

Hence

$$S_1 = \frac{1}{2} \frac{\sin \frac{nh_1}{2} \sin \left[y + (n-1)\frac{h_1}{2} \right]}{\sin \frac{h_1}{2}} - \frac{1}{2} \frac{\sin \frac{nh_2}{2} \sin \left[y + (n-1)\frac{h_2}{2} \right]}{\sin \frac{h_2}{2}}$$

and

$$S_2 = \frac{1}{2} \frac{\sin \frac{nh_1}{2} \sin \left[y + (n-1)\frac{h_1}{2} \right]}{\sin \frac{h_1}{2}} + \frac{1}{2} \frac{\sin \frac{nh_2}{2} \sin \left[y + (n-1)\frac{h_2}{2} \right]}{\sin \frac{h_2}{2}}.$$

(*Dorin Andrica*, Revista Matematică Timişoara (RMT), No. 2(1977), pp. 65, Problem 3056)

5. We have $P_1 = 0$ because of the factor $1 - \tan 45° = 0$.

On the other hand we have

$$P_2 = \frac{(\cos 1° + \sin 1°) \ldots (\cos 44° + \sin 44°)}{\cos 1° \ldots \cos 44°} =$$

$$= \frac{\left(\frac{\sqrt{2}}{2} \cos 1° + \frac{\sqrt{2}}{2} \sin 1° \right) \ldots \left(\frac{\sqrt{2}}{2} \cos 44° + \frac{\sqrt{2}}{2} \sin 44° \right)}{\left(\frac{\sqrt{2}}{2} \right)^{44} \cos 1° \ldots \cos 44°} =$$

$$= \frac{\sin 46° \ldots \sin 89°}{\cos 1° \ldots \cos 44°} \left(\sqrt{2} \right)^{44} = 2^{22}.$$

(*Titu Andreescu*)

6. We have $\cos 3x = 4\cos^3 x - 3\cos x$, so $4\cos^2 x - 3 = \frac{\cos 3x}{\cos x}$ for all $x \neq (2k+1) \cdot 90°$, $k \in \mathbb{Z}$. Thus

$$(4\cos^2 9° - 3)(4\cos^2 27° - 3) = \frac{\cos 27°}{\cos 9°} \cdot \frac{\cos 81°}{\cos 27°} = \frac{\cos 81°}{\cos 9°} = \frac{\sin 9°}{\cos 9°} = \tan 9°,$$

as desired.

(*Titu Andreescu*)

7. From the identity $1 + \tan^2 x = \sec^2 x$ it follows that

$$1 = \sec^2 x - \tan^2 x = (\sec x - \tan x)(\sec x + \tan x) = 2(\sec x + \tan x),$$

so $\sec x + \tan x = 0.5$.

(*Titu Andreescu*, American High School Mathematics Examination, 1999, Problem 15)

8. Since

$$\frac{1 + \tan^2 2^k x}{(1 - \tan^2 2^k x)^2} = \frac{\cos^2 2^k x}{\cos^2 2^{k+1} x}$$

for all $|x| < \dfrac{\pi}{2^{n+2}}$, it follows that

$$P_n = \prod_{k=1}^{n} \frac{\cos^2 2^k x}{\cos^2 2^{k+1} x} = \frac{\cos^2 2x}{\cos^2 2^{n+1} x}.$$

(*Dorin Andrica*)

9. Let

$$\frac{\sin x}{a} = \frac{\sin 2x}{b} = \frac{\sin 3x}{c} = \frac{\sin 4x}{d} = \lambda.$$

Then

$$\sin^2 4x = 2\sin^2 2x(1 - \sin^2 2x).$$

Because $\sin^2 4x = 2\sin^2 2x(1 - \sin^2 2x)$, we obtain

$$d^2 = 2b^2(1 - \lambda^2 b^2). \tag{1}$$

On the other hand, $\sin 3x = \lambda c$, $\sin x = \lambda a$, and since

$$\sin 3x = \sin x(3 - 4\sin^2 x),$$

we have

$$c = a(3 - 4\lambda^2 a^2). \tag{2}$$

Eliminating λ from the relations (1) and (2) yields

$$2a^3(2b^3 - d^2) = b^4(3a - c),$$

as desired.

(*Dorin Andrica*)

10. Rewrite the two equalities as

$$2\sin a - 9\sin d = 6\sin b - 7\sin c$$

$$2\cos a + 9\cos d = -6\cos b - 7\cos c.$$

By squaring the two relations and adding them up we obtain

$$85 + 18\cos(a + d) = 85 + 42\cos(b + c),$$

and the conclusion follows.

(*Titu Andreescu*, Korean Mathematics Competition, 2002)

11. From the hypothesis it follows that

$$\sin(\arccos a + \arccos b + \arccos c) = 0.$$

Using the identity

$$\sum \cos\alpha \cos\beta \sin\gamma = \sin(\alpha + \beta + \gamma) + \sin\alpha \sin\beta \sin\gamma$$

and the formulas

$$\sin(\arccos x) = \sqrt{1 - x^2} \text{ and } \sin(\arcsin x) = x, \quad x \in [-1, 1],$$

we obtains

$$ab\sqrt{1 - c^2} + bc\sqrt{1 - a^2} + ca\sqrt{1 - b^2} = \sqrt{(1 - a^2)(1 - b^2)(1 - c^2)},$$

as desired.

(*Titu Andreescu*, Revista Matematică Timişoara (RMT), No. 2(1977), pp. 64, Problem 3054)

12. The identity

$$\text{arctg}\, x + \text{arctg}\, y + \text{arctg}\, z = \text{arctg}\frac{x + y + z - xyz}{1 - (xy + yz + zx)} + k\pi$$

implies

$$\text{arctg}\frac{1}{a} + \text{arctg}\frac{1}{b} + \text{arctg}\frac{1}{c} = \text{arctg}\frac{ab + bc + ca - 1}{abc - (a + b + c)} + k\pi.$$

Because $ab + bc + ca = 1$, we obtain

$$\text{arctg}\frac{1}{a} + \text{arctg}\frac{1}{b} + \text{arctg}\frac{1}{c} = k\pi,$$

where k is integer.

Note that $0 < \text{arctg}\, x < \dfrac{\pi}{2}$ for all real $x > 0$, hence

$$0 < \text{arctg}\frac{1}{a} + \text{arctg}\frac{1}{b} + \text{arctg}\frac{1}{c} < \frac{3\pi}{2}.$$

Therefore $k = 1$ and

$$\text{arctg}\frac{1}{a} + \text{arctg}\frac{1}{b} + \text{arctg}\frac{1}{c} = \pi,$$

as claimed.

(*Titu Andreescu*, Revista Matematică Timişoara (RMT), No. 1(1977), pp. 42, Problem 2827)

13. The given relation is equivalent to

$$(\cos x \cos y + \sin x \sin y)^2 = 4\sin x \sin y \cos x \cos y,$$

or

$$(\cos x \cos y - \sin x \sin y)^2 = \bar{0}$$

Hence
$$\cos^2(x+y) = 0,$$
and since $x, y \in \left(0, \dfrac{\pi}{2}\right)$, we obtain $x + y = \dfrac{\pi}{2}$, as desired.

(*Titu Andreescu*, Revista Matematică Timişoara (RMT), No. 1(1977), pp. 42, Problem 2826)

14. Expanding yields
$$\frac{1}{2}(1 - \tan\alpha - \tan\beta - \tan\gamma + \tan\alpha\tan\beta + \tan\beta\tan\gamma +$$
$$+ \tan\gamma\tan\alpha - \tan\alpha\tan\beta\tan\gamma) =$$
$$= 1 - (\tan\alpha + \tan\beta + \tan\gamma),$$

or
$$\tan\alpha + \tan\beta + \tan\gamma - \tan\alpha\tan\beta\tan\gamma =$$
$$= 1 - \tan\alpha\tan\beta - \tan\beta\tan\gamma - \tan\gamma\tan\alpha. \qquad (1)$$

Since $\alpha, \beta, \gamma \in \left(0, \dfrac{\pi}{4}\right)$, we have $0 < \alpha + \beta + \gamma < \pi$, hence
$$\tan\alpha + \tan\beta + \tan\gamma \neq \tan\alpha\tan\beta\tan\gamma.$$

From relation (1) we derive
$$\frac{1 - \tan\alpha\tan\beta - \tan\beta\tan\gamma - \tan\gamma\tan\alpha}{\tan\alpha + \tan\beta + \tan\gamma - \tan\alpha\tan\beta\tan\gamma} = 1,$$

therefore
$$\cot(\alpha + \beta + \gamma) = 1.$$

Hence $\alpha + \beta + \gamma = \dfrac{\pi}{4}$, as desired.

(*Titu Andreescu*, Revista Matematică Timişoara (RMT), No. 1(1973), pp. 42, Problem 1582)

15. The relation in the statement is equivalent to
$$(\sin^2 b + \cos^2 b)\left(\frac{\sin^4 a}{\sin^2 b} + \frac{\cos^4 a}{\cos^2 b}\right) = 1,$$

or
$$\sin^4 a + \cos^4 a + \frac{\cos^2 b}{\sin^2 b}\sin^4 a + \frac{\sin^2 b}{\cos^2 b}\cos^4 a = 1.$$

It follows that
$$1 - 2\sin^2 a\cos^2 a + \frac{\cos^2 b}{\sin^2 b}\sin^4 a + \frac{\sin^2 b}{\cos^2 b}\cos^4 a = 1,$$

hence
$$\left(\frac{\cos b}{\sin b}\sin^2 a - \frac{\sin b}{\cos b}\cos^2 a\right)^2 = 0.$$

Furthermore,
$$\frac{\cos b}{\sin b}\sin^2 a = \frac{\sin b}{\cos b}\cos^2 a,$$

or $\tan^2 a = \tan^2 b$.

Because $a, b \in \left(0, \dfrac{\pi}{2}\right)$, we obtain $a = b$.

The converse is clear and we are done.

Alternative solution. From the given relation we deduce that there is a number $c \in \left(0, \dfrac{\pi}{2}\right)$ such that

$$\frac{\sin^2 a}{\sin b} = \sin c \quad \text{and} \quad \frac{\cos^2 a}{\cos b} = \cos c$$

Hence

$$\sin^2 a = \sin b \sin c \quad \text{and} \quad \cos^2 a = \cos b \cos c.$$

It follows that

$$1 = \cos(b - c) \quad \text{and} \quad \cos 2a = \cos(b + c)$$

Since $a, b, c \in \left(0, \dfrac{\pi}{2}\right)$, we have $b - c = 0$ and $2a = b + c$, hence $a = b$, as desired.

(*Titu Andreescu*, Revista Matematică Timişoara (RMT), No. 1(1977), pp. 41, Problem 2825; Gazeta Matematică (GM-B), No. 11(1977), pp. 452, Problem 16934)

16. Multiplying the inequality by $\sin a \sin b + \cos a \cos b = \cos(a - b)$, we obtain the equivalent form

$$\left(\frac{\sin^3 a}{\sin b} + \frac{\cos^3 a}{\cos b}\right)(\sin a \sin b + \cos a \cos b) \geq 1.$$

But this follows from Cauchy-Schwarz Inequality, because, according to this inequality, the left-hand side is greater than or equal to $(\sin^2 a + \cos^2 a)^2 = 1$.

(*Titu Andreescu*)

17. Using the inequality

$$\frac{x_1^n + x_2^m}{2} \geq \left(\frac{x_1 + x_2}{2}\right)^m$$

for $m \geq 1$ we obtain

$$(1 + 2\sin^2 \alpha)^\beta + (1 + 2\cos^2 \alpha)^\beta \geq 2\left(\frac{2 + 2\sin^2 \alpha + 2\cos^2 \alpha}{2}\right)^\beta = 2^{\beta+1},$$

as desired.

(*Titu Andreescu*, Revista Matematică Timişoara (RMT), No. 1(1974), pp. 30, Problem 1942)

18. Because $x \in [-1, 1]$, there is a real number y such that $x = \sin y$. It suffices to prove that

$$1 \geq \sin^{2n} y + \cos^{2n} y \geq \frac{1}{2^{n-1}}$$

For the left-hand side note that $|\sin y| \le 1$ and $|\cos y| \le 1$, hence

$$\sin^{2n} y + \cos^{2n} y \le \sin^{2n-2} y + \cos^{2n-2} y \le \cdots \le \sin^2 y + \cos^2 y = 1,$$

as desired.

For the right-hand side we use the inequality

$$\frac{x_1^n + x_2^n}{2} \ge \left(\frac{x_1 + x_2}{2}\right)^n.$$

Hence

$$\frac{\sin^{2n} y + \cos^{2n} y}{2} \ge \left(\frac{\sin^2 y + \cos^2 y}{2}\right)^n = \frac{1}{2^n}$$

as claimed.

Alternative Solution. By setting $u = x^2$ and $v = 1 - x^2$ the inequality becomes $\frac{1}{2^{n-1}} \le u^n + v^n \le 1$. Because $u, v \in [0,1]$ and $u + v = 1$, we have $u^n \le u$, $v^n \le v$, implying $u^n + v^n \le u + v = 1$. Also, by the power mean inequality,

$$u^n + v^n \ge 2\left(\frac{u+v}{2}\right)^n = 2\left(\frac{1}{2}\right)^n = \frac{1}{2^{n-1}}.$$

(*Dorin Andrica*)

19. We have

$$\sec^2 x = \tan^2 x + 1 \ge 2\tan x \text{ and } \operatorname{cosec}^2 x = \cot^2 x + 1 \ge 2\cot x$$

by the AM-GM inequality. It follows that

$$\sec^{2n} x + \operatorname{cosec}^{2n} x \ge 2^n (\tan^n x + \cot^n x).$$

Since $\tan^n x + \cot^n x \ge 2$, we obtain

$$\sec^{2n} x + \operatorname{cosec}^{2n} x \ge 2^{n+1},$$

as desired.

Alternative Solution. Using the AM-GM inequality we obtain

$$\sec^{2n} x + \operatorname{cosec}^{2n} x \ge 2\sqrt{\sec^{2n} x \operatorname{cosec}^{2n} x} = 2\frac{1}{\sin^n x \cos^n x} =$$

$$= 2^{n+1} \frac{1}{\sin^n 2x} \ge 2^{n+1}.$$

(*Dorin Andrica*, Gazeta Matematică (GM-B), No. 3(1975), pp. 104, Problem 14900)

20. We have

$$(1+\sin x)(1+\cos x) \le \frac{(1+\sin x)^2 + (1+\cos x)^2}{2} =$$

$$= \frac{2 + 2(\sin x + \cos x) + (\sin^2 x + \cos^2 x)}{2} =$$

$$= \frac{3}{2} + (\sin x + \cos x) = \frac{3}{2} + \sqrt{2}\sin\left(x + \frac{\pi}{4}\right) \leq \frac{3}{2} + \sqrt{2},$$

as desired.

Note that equality holds for $x = \frac{\pi}{4} + 2k\pi$, where k is integer.

Alternative Solution. Expanding the left-hand side, we see that

$$1 + (\sin x + \cos x) + \frac{1}{2}\sin 2x = 1 + \sqrt{2}\sin\left(x + \frac{\pi}{4}\right) + \frac{1}{2}\sin 2x \leq$$

$$\leq 1 + \sqrt{2} + \frac{1}{2} = \frac{3}{2} + \sqrt{2}.$$

(*Titu Andreescu*, Revista Matematică Timişoara (RMT), No. 2(1978), pp. 47, Problem 3500)

21. We have $E = \sin x_1 \cos x_2 + \sin x_2 \cos x_3 + \cdots + \sin x_n \cos x_1 \leq$

$$\leq \frac{\sin^2 x_1 + \cos^2 x_2}{2} + \frac{\sin^2 x_2 + \cos^2 x_3}{2} + \cdots + \frac{\sin^2 x_n + \cos^2 x_1}{2} = \frac{n}{2}$$

Therefore the maximal value of E is $\frac{n}{2}$ and it is reached, for example, when $x_1 = x_2 = \cdots = x_n = \frac{\pi}{4}$.

(*Dorin Andrica*, Revista Matematică Timişoara (RMT), No. 2(1977), pp. 65, Problem 3058)

22. Because $a, b > 0$, it follows that the maximal value of f is $a + b + c$.

Setting $y = \cos x$ yields

$$f(x) = a(2y^2 - 1) + by + c = 2ay^2 + by + c - a.$$

If $-\frac{b}{4a} \in [-1, 0)$, then the minimal value of f is

$$-\frac{\Delta}{8a} = \frac{-b^2 + 8a(c - a)}{8a}.$$

If $-\frac{b}{4a} \in (-\infty, -1)$, then the minimal value of f is

$$f(-1) = 2a - b + c - a = a - b + c.$$

(*Dorin Andrica*, Revista Matematică Timişoara (RMT), No. 1(1981), pp. 52, Problem 4315)

23. *First Solution.* Let $b_k = \tan(a_k - \pi/4)$, $k = 0, 1, \ldots, n$. It follows from the hypothesis that for each k, $-1 < b_k < 1$ and

$$1 + b_k \geq \sum_{0 \leq l \neq k \leq n} (1 - b_l). \tag{1}$$

Applying the Arithmetic-Geometric-Mean Inequality to the positive numbers $1 - b_l$, $l = 0, 1, \ldots, k-1, k+1, \ldots, n$, we obtain

$$\sum_{0 \leq l \neq k \leq n} (1 - b_l) \geq n \left(\prod_{0 \leq l \neq k \leq n} (1 - b_l) \right)^{1/n}. \tag{2}$$

From (1) and (2) it follows that

$$\prod_{k=0}^{n} (1 + b_k) \geq n^{n+1} \left(\prod_{l=0}^{n} (1 - b_l)^n \right)^{1/n},$$

and hence that

$$\prod_{k=0}^{n} \frac{1 + b_k}{1 - b_k} \geq n^{n+1}.$$

Because

$$\frac{1 + b_k}{1 - b_k} = \frac{1 + \tan \left(a_k - \dfrac{\pi}{4} \right)}{1 - \tan \left(a_k - \dfrac{\pi}{4} \right)} = \tan \left(\left(a_k - \frac{\pi}{4} \right) + \frac{\pi}{4} \right) = \tan a_k,$$

the conclusion follows.

Second Solution. We first prove a short lemma:

Let w, x, y, z be real numbers with $x + y = w + z$ and $|x - y| < |w - z|$. Then $wz < xy$.

Proof. Let $x + y = w + z = 2L$. Then there are non-negative numbers r, s with $r < s$ and

$$wz = (L - s)(L + s) < (L - r)(L + r) = xy.$$

We now use this lemma to solve the problem. For $0 \leq k \leq n$, let $b_k = \tan(a_k - \pi/4)$ and let

$$t_k = \tan a_k = \frac{1 + b_k}{1 - b_k}.$$

Then $-1 < b_k < 1$ and

$$t_j t_k = \left(\frac{1 + b_j}{1 - b_j} \right) \left(\frac{1 + b_k}{1 - b_k} \right) = 1 + \frac{2}{\dfrac{1 + b_j b_k}{b_j + b_k} - 1}. \tag{1}$$

First note that because $-1 < b_k < 1$ and $b_0 + b_1 + \cdots + b_n \geq n - 1$, it follows that $b_j + b_k > 0$ for all $0 \leq j, k \leq n$ with $j \neq k$. Next note that if $b_j + b_k > 0$ and $b_j \neq b_k$, then it follows from the lemma applied to (1) that the value of $t_j t_k$ can be made smaller by replacing b_j and b_k by two numbers closer together and with the same sum. In particular, if $b_j < 0$, then replacing b_j and b_k by their average reduces the problem to the case where $b_i > 0$ for all i.

We may now successively replace the b_i's by their arithmetic mean. As long as the b_i are not equal, one is greater than the mean and another one is less than the mean. We can replace one of this pair by the arithmetic mean of all the b_i's, and the other by a positive number chosen so that the sum of the pair does not change. Each such change decreases the product of the t_i's. It follows that for a given sum of the b_i's, the minimum product is attained when all of the b_i's are equal. In this case we have $b_i \geq \dfrac{n-1}{n+1}$, for each i, so

$$t_0 t_1 \ldots t_n \geq \left(\frac{1 + \dfrac{n-1}{n+1}}{1 - \dfrac{n-1}{n+1}} \right)^{n+1} = \left(\frac{2n}{2} \right)^{n+1} = n^{n+1}.$$

This completes the proof.

Third Solution. We present a solution based on calculus. We set

$$a = b_0 + b_1 + \cdots + b_n,$$

where $-1 < b_i < 1$, and assume that $a \geq n - 1$. We then show that the product

$$\prod_{k=0}^{n} \frac{1 + b_k}{1 - b_k}$$

attains its minimum when all of the b_k's are equal, that is, their common value is $a/(n+1)$. The desired inequality will follow immediately.

We proceed by induction. The case $n = 1$ was established in the discussion of (1) in the previous solution. For $n \geq 2$, set

$$\sum_{k=0}^{n-1} b_k = a' = a - b_n > n - 2.$$

The last inequality follows from $a \geq n - 1$ and $b_n < 1$. Set $b = b_n$ and $c = a'/n$, so $b + nc = a$. By the induction hypothesis,

$$\left(\prod_{k=0}^{n-1} \frac{1 + b_k}{1 - b_k} \right) \frac{1 + b_n}{1 - b_n} \geq \left(\frac{1 + c}{1 - c} \right)^n \frac{1 + b}{1 - b}.$$

Thus we need to prove that

$$\left(\frac{1 + c}{1 - c} \right)^n \left(\frac{1 + b}{1 - b} \right) \geq \left(\frac{n + 1 + a}{n + 1 - a} \right)^{n+1}, \tag{1}$$

where the right-hand side is obtained by substituting $a/(n+1)$ for each b_k, $k = 0, 1, \ldots, n$, in the product. Next, recall that a is fixed, and that $b + nc = a$. Thus we can eliminate b from (1) to obtain the equivalent inequality

$$\left(\frac{1 + c}{1 - c} \right)^n \left(\frac{1 + a - nc}{1 - a + nc} \right) \geq \left(\frac{n + 1 + a}{n + 1 - a} \right)^{n+1}. \tag{2}$$

Now bring all terms in (2) to the left-hand side of the inequality, clear denominators, and replace c by x. Let the expression on the left define a function f with

$$f(x) = (1 + x)^n (1 + a - nx)(n + 1 - a)^{n+1} - (1 - x)^n (1 - a + nx)(n + 1 + a)^{n+1}.$$

To establish (2) it is sufficient to show that for $0 \le x < 1$, $f(x)$ attains its minimum value at $x = a/(n+1)$. Towards this end we differentiate to obtain

$$f'(x) = n(a - (n+1)x)((1+x)^{n-1}(n+1-a)^{n+1} - (1-x)^{n-1}(n+1+a)^{n+1}) =$$

$$= n(a - (n+1)x)g(x),$$

where $g(x) = (1+x)^{n-1}(n+1-a)^{n+1} - (1-x)^{n-1}(n+1+a)^{n+1}$. It is clear that $f'\left(\dfrac{a}{n+1}\right) = 0$, so we check the second derivative. We find

$$f''\left(\frac{a}{n+1}\right) = -n(n+1)g\left(\frac{a}{n+1}\right) > 0,$$

so f has a local minimum at $x = a/(n+1)$. But $f'(x)$ could have another zero, t, obtained by solving the equation $g(x) = 0$. Because

$$g'(x) = (n-1)(1+x)^{n-2}(n+1-a)^{n+1} + (n-1)(1-x)^{n-2}(n+1+a)^{n+1}$$

is obviously positive for all $x \in [0,1)$, there is at most one solution to the equation $g(x) = 0$ in this interval. It is easy to check that $g(a/(n+1)) < 0$ and $g(1) > 0$. Thus there is a real number t, $a/(n+1) < t < 1$, with $g(t) = 0$. For this t we have

$$f''(t) = n(a - (n+1)t)g'(t) < 0.$$

Thus, t is a local maximum for f, and no other extrema exist on the interval $(0, 1)$.

The only thing left is to check that $f(1) \ge f(a/(n+1))$. Note that the case $x = 1$ is also an extreme case with $b_0 = b_1 = \cdots = b_{n-1} = 1$. This case does not arise in our problem, but we must check to be sure that on the interval $0 \le x < 1$, $f(x)$ has a minimum at $x = a/(n+1)$. We have

$$f(1) = 2^n(1 + a - n)(n+1-a)^{n+1} \ge 0,$$

since $n - 1 \le a \le n + 1$, and $f(a/(n+1)) = 0$ (by design). Thus $f(x)$ indeed attains a unique minimum at $x = a/(n+1)$.

(*Titu Andreescu*, USA Mathematical Olympiad, 1998, Problem 3)

24. Let d be the greatest common divisor of p and q. We prove that $T = \dfrac{2\pi}{d}$ is the lowest positive period of the function f.

It is clear that

$$f(x + T_1) = f(x)$$

for all real x, therefore T is a period of function f.

Suppose there are $T_1 > 0$ and an integer $\lambda > 0$ such that $T = \lambda T_1$ and $f(x+T_1) = f(x)$ for all real x. Then $f(T_1) = f(0) = 2$, so

$$\cos pT_1 + \cos qT_1 = 2,$$

therefore

$$\cos pT_1 = \cos qT_1 = 1.$$

It follows that

$$T_1 = \frac{2k_1\pi}{p} = \frac{2k_2\pi}{q}$$

for some integers $k_1, k_2 > 0$.

Since $T = \lambda T_1$ and $T_1 = \dfrac{2\pi}{\lambda d}$,

$$\frac{k_1}{p} = \frac{k_2}{q} = \frac{1}{\lambda d} \text{ and so } p = k_1(\lambda d), \ q = k_2(\lambda d).$$

On the other hand, $d = gcd(p, q)$, so $\lambda = 1$, hence $T = T_1$ as desired.

(*Dorin Andrica*, Revista Matematică Timişoara (RMT), No. 2(1978), pp. 75, Problem 3695)

25. We have

$$\cot\frac{\pi}{24} = \frac{\cos\dfrac{\pi}{24}}{\sin\dfrac{\pi}{24}} = \frac{2\cos^2\dfrac{\pi}{24}}{2\sin\dfrac{\pi}{24}\cos\dfrac{\pi}{24}} = \frac{1+\cos\dfrac{\pi}{12}}{\sin\dfrac{\pi}{12}} =$$

$$= \frac{1+\cos\left(\dfrac{\pi}{3}-\dfrac{\pi}{4}\right)}{\sin\left(\dfrac{\pi}{3}-\dfrac{\pi}{4}\right)} = \frac{1+\dfrac{\sqrt{2}}{4}+\dfrac{\sqrt{6}}{4}}{\dfrac{\sqrt{6}}{4}-\dfrac{\sqrt{2}}{4}} = \frac{4+\sqrt{6}+\sqrt{2}}{\sqrt{6}-\sqrt{2}} =$$

$$= \frac{4(\sqrt{6}+\sqrt{2})+(\sqrt{6}+\sqrt{2})^2}{6-2} = \frac{4(\sqrt{6}+\sqrt{2})+8+4\sqrt{3}}{4} =$$

$$= 2+\sqrt{2}+\sqrt{3}+\sqrt{6} = a_0 + 2.$$

Hence $a_n = \cot\left(\dfrac{2^{n-3}\pi}{3}\right) - 2$ is true for $n = 0$.

It suffices to prove that $b_n = \cot\left(\dfrac{2^{n-3}\pi}{3}\right)$, where $b_n = a_n + 2$, $n \geq 1$. The recursive relation becomes

$$b_{n+1} - 2 = \frac{(b_n - 2)^2 - 5}{2b_n},$$

or $b_{n+1} = \dfrac{b_n^2 - 1}{2b_n}$. Assuming, inductively, that $b_k = \cot c_k$, where $c_k = \dfrac{2^{k-3}\pi}{3}$, yields

$$b_{k+1} = \frac{\cot^2 c_k - 1}{2\cot c_k} = \cot(2c_k) = \cot c_{k+1},$$

and we are done.

(*Titu Andreescu*, Korean Mathematics Competition, 2002)

26. If $n = 1$, then all real numbers x are solutions to the equation.

Let $n > 1$ and note that

$$\cos nx = \binom{n}{0} \cos^n x - \binom{n}{2} \cos^{n-2} x \sin^2 x + \cdots +$$

$$+ (-1)^{\frac{n-1}{2}} \binom{n}{n-1} \cos x \sin^{n-1} x.$$

We have two cases:

a) $x \neq (2k+1) \dfrac{\pi}{2}$ for any integer k. Then

$$|\cos nx| = |\cos x| \left| \binom{n}{0} \cos^{n-1} x - \binom{n}{2} \cos^{n-3} x \sin^2 x + \cdots + \right.$$

$$\left. + (-1)^{\frac{n-1}{2}} \binom{n}{n-1} \sin^{n-1} x \right| \leq$$

$$\leq |\cos x| \left(\binom{n}{0} |\cos^{n-1} x| + \binom{n}{2} |\cos^{n-3} x \sin^2 x| + \cdots + \binom{n}{n-1} |\sin^{n-1} x| \right) <$$

$$< |\cos x| \left(\binom{n}{0} + \binom{n}{2} + \cdots + \binom{n}{n-1} \right) = 2^{n-1} |\cos x|,$$

hence there are no solutions in this case.

b) $x = (2k+1) \dfrac{\pi}{2}$ for some integer k. Then

$$\cos x = 0 \quad \text{and} \quad \cos nx = 0,$$

since n is odd, so $\left\{ (2k+1) \dfrac{\pi}{2} | k \text{ integer} \right\}$ is the set of solutions.

Alternative Solution. With the substitution $x = \dfrac{\pi}{2} - y$ the equation becomes

$$\cos \left(n \frac{\pi}{2} - ny \right) = 2^{n-1} \sin y. \qquad (1)$$

Because n is odd, (1) is equivalent to

$$\pm \sin ny = 2^{n-1} \sin y.$$

Taking modules gives

$$|\sin ny| = 2^{n-1} |\sin y|. \qquad (2)$$

But $|\sin ny| \leq n |\sin y|$ for all y in $\mathbb{R}$, hence

$$n |\sin y| \geq 2^{n-1} |\sin y|.$$

If $y \neq k\pi$, $k \in \mathbb{Z}$, then $n \geq 2^{n-1}$, which implies $n \in \{1, 3\}$. The case $n = 1$ is clear and for $n = 3$ the original equation reduces to $\cos 3x = 4 \cos x$, that is $4 \cos^3 x - 3 \cos x = 4 \cos x$. Taking into account that $\cos x \neq 0$, this yields $\cos^2 x = \dfrac{7}{3}$, which is not possible.

It follows that $y = k\pi$, which gives the solutions $x = (2k+1) \dfrac{\pi}{2}$, $k \in \mathbb{Z}$.

(*Titu Andreescu*, Gazeta Matematică (GM-B), No. 7(1978), pp. 304, Problem 17297; Revista Matematică Timişoara (RMT), No. 1-2(1980), pp. 63, Problem 4107)

27. The equation is equivalent to

$$(A + C)\sin^2 x + 2B \sin x \cos x + C \cos^2 x = 0$$

We have the following cases:

i) $A + C = 0$ and $C \neq 0$. Then

$$\cos x = 0 \quad \text{or} \quad \cot x = -\frac{2B}{C},$$

hence

$$x \in \left\{ \frac{(2k+1)\pi}{2} \mid k \in \mathbb{Z} \right\} \cup \left\{ \operatorname{arccotg}\left(-\frac{2B}{C}\right) + k\pi \mid k \in \mathbb{Z} \right\}.$$

ii) $A + C \neq 0$ and $C = 0$. Then

$$\sin x = 0 \quad \text{or} \quad \tan x = -\frac{2B}{A+C},$$

hence

$$x \in \{k\pi \mid k \in \mathbb{Z}\} \cup \left\{ \operatorname{arctg}\left(-\frac{2B}{A+C}\right) + k\pi \mid k \in \mathbb{Z} \right\}.$$

iii) $A = B = C = 0$. Then any real number is a solution.

iv) $A = C = 0$ and $B \neq 0$. Then $\sin 2x = 0$ and so

$$x \in \left\{ k\frac{\pi}{2} \mid k \in \mathbb{Z} \right\}.$$

v) $A + C \neq 0$ and $C \neq 0$. The equation is equivalent to

$$(A + C)\tan^2 x + 2B \tan x + C = 0,$$

hence

$$\tan x = \frac{-B \pm \sqrt{B^2 - AC + C^2}}{A + C}$$

for $B^2 + C^2 \geq AC$. It follows that

$$x \in \{\operatorname{arctg} y_1 + k\pi \mid k \in \mathbb{Z}\} \cup \{\operatorname{arctg} y_1 + k\pi \mid k \in \mathbb{Z}\}$$

if $B^2 + C^2 \geq AC$. Otherwise there are no solution.

(*Dorin Andrica*, Revista Matematică Timişoara (RMT), No. 1(1978), pp. 89, Problem 3429)

28. The equation is equivalent to

$$2 \sin x \cos y + 2 \sin y \cos z + 2 \sin z \cos x = 3,$$

or

$$(\sin x - \cos y)^2 + (\sin y - \cos z)^2 + (\sin z - \cos x)^2 = 0.$$

It follows that

$$\sin x = \cos y, \quad \sin y = \cos z, \quad \sin z = \cos x.$$

Hence

$$x + y = (4k_1 + 1)\frac{\pi}{2}, \quad y + z = (4k_2 + 1)\frac{\pi}{2},$$

$$z + x = (4k_3 + 1)\frac{\pi}{2}$$

for some integers k_1, k_2, k_3 and therefore

$$x = [4(k_1 - k_2 + k_3) + 1]\frac{\pi}{4}, \quad y = [4(k_1 + k_2 - k_3) + 1]\frac{\pi}{4},$$

and

$$z = [4(-k_1 + k_2 + k_3) + 1]\frac{\pi}{4}, \quad k_1, k_2, k_3 \in \mathbb{Z}.$$

(*Titu Andreescu*, Gazeta Matematică (GM-B), No. 11(1977), pp. 451, Problem 16931; Revista Matematică Timişoara (RMT), No. 1-2(1979), pp. 52, Problem 3835)

29. Note that

$$\sin x \sin 2x \sin 3x \sin 4x = \frac{1}{4}(\cos 3x - \cos 5x)(\cos x - \cos 5x) =$$

$$= \frac{1}{4}(\cos^2 5x - \cos 3x \cos 5x - \cos 5x \cos x + \cos x \cos 3x) =$$

$$= \frac{1}{8}(2\cos^2 5x - \cos 2x + \cos 8x - \cos 4x + \cos 6x) < \frac{6}{8} = \frac{3}{4},$$

hence the equation has no solution.

(*Titu Andreescu*, Revista Matematică Timişoara (RMT), No. 1(1977), pp. 41, Problem 2923)

30. Squaring both equations and summing up yields

$$4(\sin^2 x + \cos^2 x) + 9(\cos^2 y + \sin^2 y) + 12(\sin x \cos y + \sin y \cos x) = 25,$$

or

$$13 + 12\sin(x + y) = 25.$$

Hence

$$\sin(x + y) = 1,$$

and so

$$x + y = (4k + 1)\frac{\pi}{2}$$

for some integer k. It follows that

$$\sin x = \cos y \quad \text{and} \quad \sin y = \cos x.$$

Turning back to the system we obtain

$$\sin x = \cos y = \frac{3}{5} \text{ and } \sin y = \cos x = \frac{4}{5},$$

hence

$$\tan x = \frac{3}{4}, \quad \tan y = \frac{4}{3}.$$

Note that $\sin x$, $\cos x$, $\sin y$, $\cos y$ are all positive, therefore

$$x = \arctan\frac{3}{4} + 2k\pi$$

and

$$y = \arctan \frac{4}{3} + 2l\pi,$$

for some integers k and l.

(*Titu Andreescu*, Revista Matematică Timişoara (RMT), No. 2(1978), pp. 74, Problem 3694)

31. Observe that $x \in [-1, 1]$ and

$$x = \sin(\arcsin x), \quad \sqrt{1 - x^2} = \cos(\arcsin x).$$

From the first equation we obtain

$$\cos(y - \arcsin x) = \frac{\sqrt{2}}{2},$$

then

$$y - \arcsin x = \pm \frac{\pi}{4} + 2k\pi.$$

Using $x + y = \frac{\pi}{4}$, we get

$$x + \arcsin x = \frac{\pi}{4} \pm \frac{\pi}{4} + 2k\pi,$$

for some integer k.

Case 1. $x + \arcsin x = \frac{\pi}{2} - 2k\pi$. Because $x \in [-1, 1]$ and $\arcsin x \in \left[-\frac{\pi}{2}, \frac{\pi}{2}\right]$, we have $k = 0$, hence

$$x + \arcsin x = \frac{\pi}{2}$$

Therefore

$$\arcsin x = \frac{\pi}{2} - x, \quad \text{or} \quad x = \cos x.$$

For this equation there is only one solution $x_0 \in \left(0, \frac{\pi}{4}\right)$. The system has the solution

$$x = x_0, \quad y = \frac{\pi}{4} - x_0$$

Case 2. $x + \arcsin x = 2k\pi$.

Using similar arguments, $k = 0$, so

$$\arcsin x = -x.$$

This equation has the unique solution $x = 0$ so the system has the solution

$$x = 0, \quad y = \frac{\pi}{4}.$$

(*Titu Andreescu*, Revista Matematică Timişoara (RMT), No. 1(1977), pp 41, Problem 2824)

32. Using the formula

$$\tan(x + y + z) = \frac{\tan x + \tan y + \tan z - \tan x \tan y \tan z}{1 - \tan x \tan y - \tan y \tan z - \tan z \tan x}$$

we have

$$-1 = \tan\frac{3\pi}{4} = \frac{5-1}{1 - \tan x \tan y - \tan y \tan z - \tan z \tan x}$$

Hence

$$\tan x \tan y + \tan y \tan z + \tan z \tan x = 5.$$

The equation

$$t^3 - 5t^2 + 5t - 1 = 0$$

has roots $\tan x$, $\tan y$, $\tan z$, from the relations between the roots and the coefficients.

On the other hand, the equation has the roots $1, 2+\sqrt{3}, 2-\sqrt{3}$, hence $\{x, y, z\} = \left\{\frac{\pi}{4} + k\pi, \frac{5\pi}{12} + h\pi, \frac{\pi}{12} + p\pi\right\}$, for some integers k, l, p.

(*Titu Andreescu*, Revista Matematică Timişoara (RMT), No. 8(1971), pp. 27, Problem 1018)

33. Using the Extended Law of Sines we obtain

$$a\cos A + b\cos B + c\cos C = 2R(\sin A \cos A + \sin B \cos B + \sin C \cos C) =$$

$$= R(\sin 2A + \sin 2B + \sin 2C) = R(2\sin(A+B)\cos(A-B) + \sin 2C) =$$

$$= 2R\sin C(\cos(A-B) + \cos C) = 4R\sin C \cos\frac{A-B+C}{2}\cos\frac{A-B-C}{2} =$$

$$= -4R\sin C \cos\left(\frac{\pi}{2} - B\right)\cos\left(\frac{\pi}{2} - A\right) = 4R\sin A \sin B \sin C = \frac{abc}{2R^2},$$

as desired.

(*Titu Andreescu*, Revista Matematică Timişoara (RMT), No. 2(1977), pp. 65, Problem 3060)

34. Because $A + B + C = \pi$, we have

$$\cos\frac{A}{2} = \sin\frac{B}{2}\cos\frac{C}{2} + \sin\frac{C}{2}\cos\frac{B}{2},$$

$$\cos\frac{B}{2} = \sin\frac{C}{2}\cos\frac{A}{2} + \sin\frac{A}{2}\cos\frac{C}{2},$$

$$\cos\frac{C}{2} = \sin\frac{A}{2}\cos\frac{B}{2} + \sin\frac{B}{2}\cos\frac{A}{2}.$$

Hence

$$\begin{vmatrix} \cos\frac{A}{2} & \sin\frac{B}{2}\cos\frac{C}{2} & \sin\frac{C}{2}\cos\frac{B}{2} \\[2mm] \cos\frac{B}{2} & \sin\frac{C}{2}\cos\frac{A}{2} & \sin\frac{A}{2}\cos\frac{C}{2} \\[2mm] \cos\frac{C}{2} & \sin\frac{A}{2}\cos\frac{B}{2} & \sin\frac{B}{2}\cos\frac{A}{2} \end{vmatrix} = 0,$$

because the first column is the sum of the other two. Computing the determinant, we obtain

$$\sum \cos^3 \frac{A}{2} \sin \frac{B}{2} \sin \frac{C}{2} = \cos \frac{A}{2} \cos \frac{B}{2} \cos \frac{C}{2} \sum \sin^2 \frac{A}{2},$$

as desired.

(*Dorin Andrica*)

35. Denote

$$E_1 = \sum \sin nA \sin nB \cos nC \quad \text{and} \quad E_2 = \sum \cos nA \cos nB \sin nC.$$

Observe that

$$(\cos A + i \sin A)(\cos B + i \sin B)(\cos C + i \sin C) =$$
$$= \cos(A + B + C) + i \sin(A + B + C) =$$
$$= \cos \pi + i \sin \pi = -1.$$

By de Moivre's formula,

$$(\cos nA + i \sin nA)(\cos nB + i \sin nB)(\cos nC + i \sin nC) = (-1)^n.$$

Expanding the brackets yields

$$-E_1 + iE_2 + \cos nA \cos nB \cos nC - i \sin nA \sin nB \sin nC = (-1)^n.$$

Hence

$$E_1 = (-1)^{n+1} + \cos nA \cos nB \cos nC \quad \text{and} \quad E_2 = \sin nA \sin nB \sin nC.$$

(*Dorin Andrica*, Revista Matematică Timişoara (RMT), No. 1(1978), pp. 65, Problem 3278)

36. Subtracting from the second equality the first multiplied by 2 yields

$$(\sin A - 1)(\sin B - 1)(\sin C - 1) = 0.$$

Hence $\sin A, \sin B$ or $\sin C$ is 1, so ABC is a right triangle.

(*Titu Andreescu*, Revista Matematică Timişoara (RMT), No. 2(1978), pp. 49, Problem 3514)

37. Note that

$$a \cos B + b \cos A - c = 0.$$

The system of linear equations

$$\begin{cases} a \cos B + b \cos A - c = 0 \\ a^\lambda \cos B + b^\lambda \cos A - c^\lambda = 0 \\ a^{2\lambda-1} \cos B + b^{2\lambda-1} \cos A - c^{2\lambda-1} = 0 \end{cases}$$

has the solution $(\cos B, \cos A, -1)$ and is homogeneous. Therefore the determinant

$$\Delta = \begin{vmatrix} a & b & c \\ a^\lambda & b^\lambda & c^\lambda \\ a^{2\lambda-1} & b^{2\lambda-1} & c^{2\lambda-1} \end{vmatrix}$$

is zero.

On the other hand,

$$\Delta = abc \begin{vmatrix} 1 & 1 & 1 \\ a^{\lambda-1} & b^{\lambda-1} & c^{\lambda-1} \\ (a^{\lambda-1})^2 & (b^{\lambda-1})^2 & (c^{\lambda-1})^2 \end{vmatrix} =$$

$$= abc(a^{\lambda-1} - b^{\lambda-1})(a^{\lambda-1} - c^{\lambda-1})(b^{\lambda-1} - c^{\lambda-1}).$$

Therefore $a = b$, $b = c$ or $c = a$, hence the triangle is isosceles.

(*Dorin Andrica*, Revista Matematică Timişoara (RMT), No. 2(1977), pp. 89, Problem 3199)

38. The relation is equivalent to

$$\frac{\sqrt{(p-b)(p-c)}}{\sqrt{p(p-a)}} + \frac{\sqrt{(p-c)(p-a)}}{\sqrt{p(p-b)}} + \frac{\sqrt{(p-a)(p-b)}}{\sqrt{p(p-c)}} = \frac{1}{4S}(a^2 + b^2 + c^2)$$

or

$$\frac{1}{S}\sum (p-a)(p-b) = \frac{1}{4S}(a^2 + b^2 + c^2).$$

Expanding the brackets yields

$$-p^2 + ab + bc + ca = \frac{1}{4}(a^2 + b^2 + c^2),$$

then

$$4(ab + bc + ca) = a^2 + b^2 + c^2 + (a + b + c)^2.$$

It follows that

$$(a - b)^2 + (b - c)^2 + (c - a)^2 = 0,$$

hence $a = b = c$.

(*Titu Andreescu*, Revista Matematică Timişoara (RMT), No. 2(1972), pp. 28, Problem 1160)

39. By the Extended Law of Sines,

$$a = 2R\sin A, \quad b = 2R\sin B, \quad c = 2R\sin C.$$

On the other hand,

$$a^2 + 2bc\cos A = b^2 + c^2,$$

so

$$\sin^2 B + \sin^2 C = \sin^2 A + 2\sin B \sin C \cos A.$$

From the hypothesis we have

$$\sin^2 B + \sin^2 C = 1 + 2\sin B \sin C \cos A,$$

therefore $\sin^2 A = 1$. It follows that $A = \dfrac{\pi}{2}$, hence the triangle ABC is right, as desired.

(*Dorin Andrica*, Revista Matematică Timişoara (RMT), No. 1-2(1977), pp. 52, Problem 3838)

40. Because $6^2 + 3^2 + 2^2 = 7^2$ and

$$\frac{s}{r} = \cot \frac{A}{2} + \cot \frac{B}{2} + \cot \frac{C}{2} = \cot \frac{A}{2} \cot \frac{B}{2} \cot \frac{C}{2}, \tag{1}$$

the given relation is equivalent to

$$(6^2 + 3^2 + 2^2)\left[\left(\cot \frac{A}{2}\right)^2 + \left(2\cot \frac{B}{2}\right)^2 + \left(3\cot \frac{C}{2}\right)^2\right] =$$

$$= \left(6\cot \frac{A}{2} + 6\cot \frac{B}{2} + 6\cot \frac{C}{2}\right)^2.$$

This means that we have equality in the Cauchy-Schwarz inequality. It follows that

$$\frac{\cot \dfrac{A}{2}}{6} = \frac{2\cot \dfrac{B}{2}}{3} = \frac{3\cot \dfrac{C}{2}}{2}.$$

Plugging back into (1) gives $\cot \dfrac{A}{2} = 7$, $\cot \dfrac{B}{2} = \dfrac{7}{4}$, and $\cot \dfrac{C}{2} = \dfrac{7}{9}$. Hence by the Double angle formulas, $\sin A = \dfrac{7}{25}$, $\sin B = \dfrac{28}{65}$, and $\sin C = \dfrac{63}{130}$. Thus the side lengths of T are 26, 40, and 45.

(*Titu Andreescu*, USA Mathematical Olympiad, 2002, Problem 2)

41. Summing up the formulas

$$r_a = 4R \sin \frac{A}{2} \cos \frac{B}{2} \cos \frac{C}{2},$$

$$r_b = 4R \sin \frac{B}{2} \cos \frac{C}{2} \cos \frac{A}{2},$$

$$r_c = 4R \sin \frac{C}{2} \cos \frac{B}{2} \cos \frac{A}{2}$$

yields

$$\sum \sin \frac{A}{2} \cos \frac{B}{2} \cos \frac{C}{2} = \frac{r_a + r_b + r_c}{4R}.$$

On the other hand $r_a + r_b + r_c = 4R + r$, hence

$$\sum \sin \frac{A}{2} \cos \frac{B}{2} \cos \frac{C}{2} = \frac{4R + r}{4R} = 1 + \frac{r}{4R}.$$

Because $\dfrac{R}{2} \geq r$, it follows that

$$\sum \sin \frac{A}{2} \cos \frac{B}{2} \cos \frac{C}{2} \leq 1 + \frac{1}{8} = \frac{9}{8},$$

as desired.

(*Dorin Andrica*, Revista Matematică Timişoara (RMT), No. 2(1978), pp. 49, Problem 3510)

42. We have

$$2bc \cos A + a^2 = b^2 + c^2,$$

or

$$2 \cos A + \frac{a^2}{bc} = \frac{b}{c} + \frac{c}{b}.$$

Because $\dfrac{b}{c} + \dfrac{c}{b} \geq 2$, we obtain

$$\frac{a^2}{bc} \geq 2(1 - \cos A) = 4\sin^2 \frac{A}{2}$$

and likewise

$$\frac{b^2}{ac} \geq 4\sin^2 \frac{B}{2}, \quad \frac{c^2}{ab} \geq 4\sin^2 \frac{C}{2}.$$

Summing up these inequalities yields

$$\frac{a^2}{bc} + \frac{b^2}{ca} + \frac{c^2}{ab} \geq 4\left(\sin^2 \frac{A}{2} + \sin^2 \frac{B}{2} + \sin^2 \frac{C}{2}\right),$$

as desired.

(*Dorin Andrica*)

43. We have

$$a^2 + 2bc \cos A = b^2 + c^2,$$

so

$$\frac{2bc \cos A}{a^2} + 1 = \frac{b^2}{a^2} + \frac{c^2}{a^2}.$$

Likewise,

$$\frac{2ac \cos B}{b^2} + 1 = \frac{a^2}{b^2} + \frac{c^2}{b^2}$$

and

$$\frac{2ab \cos C}{c^2} + 1 = \frac{a^2}{c^2} + \frac{b^2}{c^2}.$$

Summing up these equalities implies

$$3 + \frac{2bc \cos A}{a^2} + \frac{2ac \cos B}{b^2} + \frac{2ab \cos C}{c^2} = \left(\frac{b^2}{a^2} + \frac{a^2}{b^2}\right) +$$

$$+ \left(\frac{c^2}{b^2} + \frac{b^2}{c^2}\right) + \left(\frac{a^2}{c^2} + \frac{c^2}{a^2}\right) \geq 2 + 2 + 2 = 6,$$

hence

$$\frac{bc\cos A}{a^2} + \frac{ca\cos B}{b^2} + \frac{ab\cos C}{c^2} \geq \frac{3}{2},$$

and moreover

$$\frac{\cos A}{a^3} + \frac{\cos B}{b^3} + \frac{\cos C}{c^3} \geq \frac{3}{2abc}.$$

By the AM-GM inequality,

$$\frac{3}{2abc} \geq \frac{3}{2}\left(\frac{3}{a+b+c}\right)^3 = \frac{81}{16p^3},$$

therefore

$$\frac{\cos A}{a^3} + \frac{\cos B}{b^3} + \frac{\cos C}{c^3} \geq \frac{81}{16p^3}.$$

(*Dorin Andrica*, Revista Matematică Timişoara (RMT), No. 2(1975), pp. 46, Problem 2134)

44. We have

$$\sec^2\frac{A}{2} = \frac{1}{\cos^2\dfrac{A}{2}} = \frac{bc}{p(p-a)}, \quad \sec^2\frac{B}{2} = \frac{ca}{p(p-b)}, \quad \sec^2\frac{C}{2} = \frac{ab}{p(p-c)},$$

so it suffices to prove that

$$\frac{1}{p-a} + \frac{1}{p-b} + \frac{1}{p-c} \geq \frac{9}{p}.$$

Setting $x = p-a$, $y = p-b$, $z = p-c$ in the inequality

$$(x+y+z)\left(\frac{1}{x} + \frac{1}{y} + \frac{1}{z}\right) \geq 9$$

yields

$$p\left(\frac{1}{p-a} + \frac{1}{p-b} + \frac{1}{p-c}\right) \geq 9,$$

and the solution is complete.

(*Dorin Andrica*)

45. By the AM-GM inequality,

$$p = (p-a) + (p-b) + (p-c) \geq 3\sqrt[3]{(p-a)(p-b)(p-c)},$$

Then

$$p^3 \geq 27(p-a)(p-b)(p-c)$$

so

$$p^4 \geq 27p(p-a)(p-b)(p-c) = 27S^2.$$

It follows that $p^2 \geq 3\sqrt{3}S$, and since $S = pr$, $\dfrac{p}{r} \geq 3\sqrt{3}$, as desired.

(*Titu Andreescu*, Revista Matematică Timişoara (RMT), No. 2(1982), pp. 66, Problem 4993)

46. Let $\alpha = \dfrac{A}{2}, \beta = \dfrac{B}{2}, \gamma = \dfrac{C}{2}$. Then $0° < \alpha, \beta, \gamma < 90°$ and $\alpha + \beta + \gamma = 90°$. We have

$$\sin \frac{3A}{2} - \cos \frac{B-C}{2} = \sin 3\alpha - \cos(\beta - \gamma) = \sin 3\alpha - \sin(\alpha + 2\gamma) =$$

$$= 2\cos(2\alpha + \gamma)\sin(\alpha - \gamma) = -2\sin(\alpha - \beta)\sin(\alpha - \gamma).$$

In exactly the same way, we can show that

$$\sin \frac{3B}{2} - \cos \frac{C-A}{2} = -2\sin(\beta - \alpha)\sin(\beta - \gamma)$$

and

$$\sin \frac{3C}{2} - \cos \frac{A-B}{2} = -2\sin(\gamma - \alpha)\sin(\gamma - \beta).$$

Hence it suffices to prove that

$$\sin(\alpha - \beta)\sin(\alpha - \gamma) + \sin(\beta - \alpha)\sin(\beta - \gamma) + \sin(\gamma - \alpha)\sin(\gamma - \beta) \geq 0.$$

Note that this inequality is symmetric with respect to α, β, γ, we can assume without loss of generality that $0° < \alpha < \beta < \gamma < 90°$. Then regrouping the terms on the left-hand-side gives

$$\sin(\alpha - \beta)\sin(\alpha - \gamma) + \sin(\gamma - \beta)[\sin(\gamma - \alpha) - \sin(\beta - \alpha)],$$

which is positive as function $y = \sin x$ is increasing for $0° < x < 90°$.

Alternative Solution. We keep the notation of the first solution. We have

$$\sin 3\alpha = \sin \alpha \sin 2\alpha + \sin 2\alpha \cos \alpha;$$

$$\cos(\beta - \alpha) = \sin(2\alpha + \gamma) = \sin 2\alpha \cos \gamma + \sin \gamma \cos 2\alpha;$$

$$\cos(\beta - \gamma) = \sin(2\gamma + \alpha) = \sin 2\gamma \cos \alpha + \sin \alpha \cos 2\gamma;$$

$$\sin 3\gamma = \sin \gamma \cos 2\gamma + \sin 2\gamma \cos \gamma.$$

It follows that

$$\sin 3\alpha + \sin 3\gamma - \cos(\beta - \alpha) - \cos(\beta - \gamma) =$$

$$= (\sin \alpha - \sin \gamma)(\cos 2\alpha - \cos 2\gamma) + (\cos \alpha - \cos \gamma)(\sin 2\alpha - \sin 2\gamma) =$$

$$= (\sin \alpha - \sin \gamma)(\cos 2\alpha - \cos 2\gamma) + 2(\cos \alpha - \cos \gamma)\cos(\alpha + \gamma)\sin(\alpha - \gamma).$$

Note that $\sin x$ is increasing and $\cos x$ is decreasing for $0 < x < 90°$. Since $0 < \alpha, \gamma, \alpha + \gamma < 90°$, each of the two products in the last addition is less than or equal to 0. Hence

$$\sin 3\alpha + \sin 3\gamma - \cos(\beta - \alpha) - \cos(\beta - \gamma) \leq 0.$$

In exactly the same way, we can show that

$$\sin 3\beta + \sin 3\alpha - \cos(\gamma - \beta) - \cos(\gamma - \alpha) \leq 0$$

and

$$\sin 3\gamma + \sin 3\beta - \cos(\alpha - \gamma) - \cos(\alpha - \beta) \leq 0.$$

Adding the last three inequalities gives the desired result.

(*Titu Andreescu*, USA IMO Team Selection Test, 2002, Problem 1)

47. Let $z = a + bi$, $\overline{z} = a - bi$, and $|z| = \sqrt{a^2 + b^2}$. The given relation becomes $z^{2002} = \overline{z}$. Note that

$$|z|^{2002} = |z^{2002}| = |\overline{z}| = |z|,$$

from which it follows that

$$|z|(|z|^{2001} - 1) = 0.$$

Hence $|z| = 0$, and $(a, b) = (0, 0)$, or $|z| = 1$. In the case $|z| = 1$, we have $z^{2002} = \overline{z}$, which is equivalent to $z^{2003} = \overline{z} \cdot z = |z|^2 = 1$. Since the equation $z^{2003} = 1$ has 2003 distinct solutions, there are altogether $1 + 2003 = 2004$ ordered pairs that meet the required conditions.

(*Titu Andreescu*, American Mathematics Contest 12A, 2002, Problem 24)

48. Let a, b be real numbers such that $z = a + bi$, $b \neq 0$. Then $\operatorname{Im} z^5 = 5a^4b - 10a^2b^2 + b^5$ and

$$\frac{\operatorname{Im} z^5}{\operatorname{Im}^5 z} = 5\left(\frac{a}{b}\right)^4 - 10\left(\frac{a}{b}\right)^2 + 1.$$

Setting $x = \left(\dfrac{a}{b}\right)^2$ yields

$$\frac{\operatorname{Im} z^5}{\operatorname{Im}^5 z} = 5x^2 - 10x + 1 = 5(x - 1)^2 - 4.$$

The minimum value is -4 and is obtained for $x = 1$ i.e. for $z = a(1 \pm i)$, $a \neq 0$.

(*Titu Andreescu*, Revista Matematică Timişoara (RMT), No. 1(1984), pp. 67, Problem 5221)

49. Let $M_1, M_2, \ldots, M_{2n}$ be the points with the complex coordinates $z_1, z_2, \ldots, z_{2n}$ and let $A_1, A_2, \ldots, A_n$ be the midpoints of segments M_1M_{2n}, $M_2M_{2n-1}, \ldots, M_nM_{n+1}$.

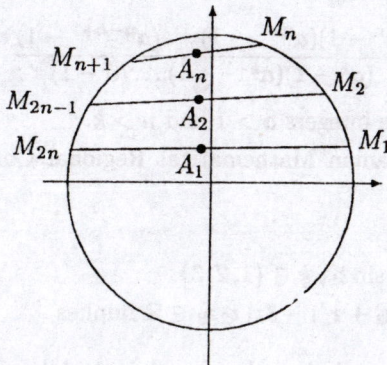

The points M_i, $i = \overline{1, 2n}$ lie on the upper semicircle centered in origin and with radius 1. Moreover, the lengths of the chords $M_1 M_{2n}$, $M_2 M_{2n-1}, \ldots, M_n M_{n+1}$ are in a decreasing order, hence $OA_1, OA_2, \ldots, OA_n$ are increasing. Thus

$$\left| \frac{z_1 + z_{2n}}{2} \right| \leq \left| \frac{z_2 + z_{2n-1}}{2} \right| \leq \cdots \leq \left| \frac{z_n + z_{n+1}}{2} \right|$$

and the conclusion follows.

Alternative Solution. Consider $z_k = r(\cos t_k + i \sin t_k)$, $k = 1, 2, \ldots, 2n$ and observe that for any $j = 1, 2, \ldots, n$, we have

$$|z_j + z_{2n-j+1}|^2 = |r[(\cos t_j + \cos t_{2n-j+1}) + i(\sin t_j + \sin t_{2n-j+1})]|^2 =$$

$$= r^2[(\cos t_j + \cos t_{2n-j+1})^2 + (\sin t_j + \sin t_{2n-j+1})^2] =$$

$$= r^2[2 + 2(\cos t_j \cos t_{2n-j+1} + \sin t_j \sin t_{2n-j+1})] =$$

$$= 2r^2[1 + \cos(t_{2n-j+1} - t_j)] = 4r^2 \cos^2 \frac{t_{2n-j+1} - t_j}{2}.$$

Therefore $|z_j + z_{2n-j+1}| = 2r \cos \dfrac{t_{2n-j+1} - t_j}{2}$ and the inequalities

$$|z_1 + z_{2n}| \leq |z_2 + z_{2n-1}| \leq \cdots \leq |z_n + z_{n+1}|$$

are equivalent to $t_{2n} - t_1 \geq t_{2n-1} - t_2 \geq \cdots \geq t_{n+1} - t_n$. Because $0 \leq t_1 \leq t_2 \leq \cdots \leq t_{2n} \leq \pi$, the last inequalities are obviously satisfied.

(*Dorin Andrica*, Revista Matematică Timişoara (RMT), No. 1(1984), pp. 67, Problem 5222)

50. Let $p = 1, 2, \ldots, m$ and let $z \in A_p$. Then $z^p = 1$.

Note that $n - m + 1, n - m + 2, \ldots, n$ are m consecutive integers, and, since $p \leq m$, there is an integer $k \in \{n - m + 1, n - m + 2, \ldots, n\}$ such that p divides k.

Let $k = k'p$. It follows that $z^k = (z^p)^{k'} = 1$, so $z \in A_k \subset A_{n-m+1} \cup A_{n-m+2} \cup \cdots \cup A_n$, as claimed.

Remark. An alternative solution can be obtained by using the fact that

$$\frac{(a^n - 1)(a^{n-1} - 1) \ldots (a^{n-k+1} - 1)}{(a^k - 1)(a^{k-1} - 1) \ldots (a - 1)}$$

is an integer for all positive integers $a > 1$ and $n > k$.

(*Dorin Andrica*, Romanian Mathematical Regional Contest "Grigore Moisil", 1997)

51. Let $z_k = \cos t_k + i \sin t_k$, $k \in \{1, 2, 3\}$.

The condition $2(z_1 + z_2 + z_3) - 3z_1 z_2 z_3 \in \mathbb{R}$ implies

$$2(\sin t_1 + \sin t_2 + \sin t_3) = 3 \sin(t_1 + t_2 + t_3). \qquad (1)$$

Assume by way of contradiction that $\max(t_1, t_2, t_3) < \dfrac{\pi}{6}$, hence $t_1, t_2, t_3 < \dfrac{\pi}{6}$. Let $t = \dfrac{t_1 + t_2 + t_3}{3} \in \left(0, \dfrac{\pi}{6}\right)$. The sine function is concave on $\left[0, \dfrac{\pi}{6}\right)$, so

$$\frac{1}{3}(\sin t_1 + \sin t_2 + \sin t_3) \leq \sin \frac{t_1 + t_2 + t_3}{3}. \tag{2}$$

From the relations (1) and (2) we obtain

$$\frac{\sin(t_1 + t_2 + t_3)}{2} \leq \sin \frac{t_1 + t_2 + t_3}{3},$$

then

$$\sin 3t \leq 2 \sin t.$$

It follows that

$$4 \sin^3 t - \sin t \geq 0,$$

i.e. $\sin^2 t \geq \dfrac{1}{4}$. Hence $\sin t \geq \dfrac{1}{2}$, then $t \geq \dfrac{\pi}{6}$, which contradicts that $t \in \left(0, \dfrac{\pi}{6}\right)$. Therefore $\max(t_1, t_2, t_3) \geq \dfrac{\pi}{6}$, as desired.

(*Titu Andreescu*, Revista Matematică Timişoara (RMT), No. 1(1986), pp. 91, Problem 5862)

52. Let $n = 2(2s + 1)$ and $b \neq 0$, otherwise the claim is obvious. Consider a complex number α such that $\alpha^2 = \dfrac{a}{b}$ and the polynomial

$$f = X^n - 1 = (X - \varepsilon_0)(X - \varepsilon_1) \ldots (X - \varepsilon_{n-1}).$$

We have

$$f\left(\frac{\alpha}{i}\right) = \left(\frac{1}{i}\right)^a (\alpha - i\varepsilon_0) \ldots (\alpha - i\varepsilon_{n-1})$$

and

$$f\left(-\frac{\alpha}{i}\right) = \left(\frac{-1}{i}\right)^a (\alpha + i\varepsilon_0) \ldots (\alpha + i\varepsilon_{n-1}),$$

hence

$$f\left(\frac{\alpha}{i}\right) f\left(-\frac{\alpha}{i}\right) = (\alpha^2 + \varepsilon_0^2) \ldots (\alpha^2 + \varepsilon_{n-1}^2).$$

Therefore

$$\prod_{k=0}^{n-1}(a + b\varepsilon_k^2) = b^n \prod_{k=0}^{n-1} \left(\frac{a}{b} + \varepsilon_k^2\right) = b^n \prod_{k=0}^{n-1} (\alpha^2 + \varepsilon_k^2) =$$

$$= b^n f\left(\frac{\alpha}{i}\right) f\left(-\frac{\alpha}{i}\right) = b^n[(\alpha^2)^{2s+1} + 1]^2 = b^n \left[\left(\frac{a}{b}\right)^{2s+1} + 1\right]^2 =$$

$$= b^{2(2s+1)} \left(\frac{a^{2s+1} + b^{2s+1}}{b^{2s+1}}\right)^2 = (a^{\frac{n}{2}} + b^{\frac{n}{2}})^2.$$

(*Dorin Andrica*, Romanian Mathematical Olympiad - second round, 2000)

53. If $ab = 0$, then claim is obvious, so consider the case when $a \neq 0$ and $b \neq 0$. We start with a useful lemma.

Lemma. *If $\varepsilon_0, \varepsilon_1, \ldots, \varepsilon_{n-1}$ are the complex roots of unity of order n, where n is an odd integer, then*

$$\prod_{k=0}^{n-1}(A + B\varepsilon_k) = A^n + B^n,$$

for all complex numbers A and B.

Proof. Using the identity

$$x^n - 1 = \prod_{k=0}^{n-1}(x - \varepsilon_k)$$

for $x = -\dfrac{A}{B}$ yields

$$-\left(\frac{A^n}{B^n} + 1\right) = -\prod_{k=0}^{n-1}\left(\frac{A}{B} + \varepsilon_k\right),$$

and the conclusion follows. $\square$

Consider the equation $bx^2 + a = 0$ with roots x_1 and x_2. Since

$$bx^2 + a = b(x - x_1)(x - x_2),$$

we have

$$\prod_{k=0}^{n-1}(a + b\varepsilon_k^2) = b^n \prod_{k=0}^{n-1}(\varepsilon_k - x_1)(\varepsilon_k - x_2) = b^n \prod_{k=0}^{n-1}(\varepsilon_k - x_1) \prod_{k=0}^{n-1}(\varepsilon_k - x_2)$$

Using the lemma for $A = -x_1$, $B = 1$ and then for $A = -x_2$, $B = 1$ gives

$$\prod_{k=0}^{n-1}(\varepsilon_k - x_1) = (-x_1)^n + 1 = 1 - x_1^n,$$

$$\prod_{k=0}^{n-1}(\varepsilon_k - x_2) = (-x_2)^n + 1 = 1 - x_2^n.$$

Hence

$$\prod_{k=0}^{n-1}(a + b\varepsilon_k^n) = b^n(1 - x_1^n)(1 - x_2^n) =$$

$$= b^n[1 + (x_1 x_2)^n - (x_1^n + x_2^n)] = b^n\left[1 + \left(\frac{a}{b}\right)^n\right] = a^n + b^n,$$

since $x_1 x_2 = \dfrac{a}{b}$ and $x_1^n + x_2^n = x_1^n + (-x_1)^n = 0$.

(*Dorin Andrica*, Romanian Mathematical Olympiad - second round, 2000)

54. Consider the triangle with vertices of complex coordinates z_1, z_2, z_3 and the circumcenter in the origin of the complex plane. Then the circumradius R equals $|z_1| = |z_2| = |z_3| = r$ and the side lengths are

$$a = |z_2 - z_3|, \quad b = |z_1 - z_3|, \quad c = |z_1 - z_2|.$$

The desired inequality is equivalent to

$$\frac{1}{ab} + \frac{1}{bc} + \frac{1}{ca} \geq \frac{1}{R^2}$$

i.e.

$$a + b + c \geq \frac{abc}{R^2} = \frac{4S}{R} = \frac{4pr}{R}$$

or $R \geq 2r$, which is Euler's inequality for a triangle.

(*Dorin Andrica*, Revista Matematică Timişoara (RMT), No. 2(1985), pp. 82, Problem 5720)

55. Let A_1, A_2, A_3 and A be the points of complex coordinates z_1, z_2, z_3 and let $z = az_2 + (1 - a)z_3$, $a \in \mathbb{R}$. Hence point A lies on the line $A_2 A_3$ and the triangle $A_1 A_2 A_3$ has its circumcenter in the origin of the complex plane.

Point B is the foot of the altitude from A_1 in the triangle $A_1 A_2 A_3$. It follows that $A_1 A \geq A_1 B$, so

$$\min_{a \in \mathbb{R}} |z - z_1| = \min_{a \in \mathbb{R}} |az_2 + (1 - a)z_3 - z_1| = A_1 B = h.$$

We have

$$S_{A_1 A_2 A_3} = \frac{|z_2 - z_3|h}{2} = \frac{|z_1 - z_2||z_1 - z_3| \sin A_1}{2} = \frac{|z_1 - z_2||z_1 - z_3| \cdot \dfrac{|z_2 - z_3|}{2r}}{2},$$

therefore

$$h = \frac{|z_1 - z_2||z_1 - z_3|}{2r},$$

as desired.

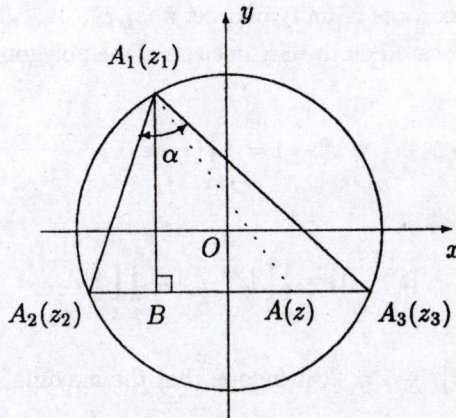

(*Dorin Andrica*, Romanian Mathematical Olympiad - final round, 1984)

56. Denote $|z + 1/z|$ by r. From the hypothesis,

$$\left|\left(z + \frac{1}{z}\right)^3\right| = \left|z^3 + \frac{1}{z^3} + 3\left(z + \frac{1}{z}\right)\right| \leq \left|z^3 + \frac{1}{z^3}\right| + \left|3\left(z + \frac{1}{z}\right)\right| \leq 2 + 3r.$$

Hence $r^3 \leq 2 + 3r$, which by factorization gives $(r - 2)(r + 1)^2 \leq 0$. This implies $r \leq 2$, as desired.

(*Titu Andreescu*, Romanian Mathematical Olympiad - first round, 1987; Revista Matematică Timişoara (RMT), No. 1(1987), pp. 75, Problem 6191)

57. Denote $t = \dfrac{z_1}{z_2}$, $t \in \mathbb{C}^*$. The relation $z_1^2 - az_1z_2 + z_2^2 = 0$ is equivalent to $t^2 - at + 1 = 0$. We have $\Delta = a^2 - 4 \leq 0$, hence $t = \dfrac{a \pm i\sqrt{4 - a^2}}{2}$ and $|t| = \sqrt{\dfrac{a^2}{4} + \dfrac{4 - a^2}{4}} = 1$. If $t = \cos\alpha + i\sin\alpha$, then $\dfrac{z_1^n}{z_2^n} = t^n = \cos n\alpha + i\sin n\alpha$ and we can write $z_1^{2n} - a_n z_1^n z_2^n + z_2^{2n} = 0$, where $a_n = 2\cos n\alpha \in [-2, 2]$.

Alternative Solution. Because $a \in [-2, 2]$, we can write $a = 2\cos\alpha$. The relation $z_1^2 - az_1z_2 + z_2^2 = 0$ is equivalent to

$$\frac{z_1}{z_2} + \frac{z_2}{z_1} = 2\cos\alpha \tag{1}$$

and, by a simple inductive argument, from (1) it follows that

$$\frac{z_1^n}{z_2^n} + \frac{z_2^n}{z_1^n} = 2\cos n\alpha, \quad n = 1, 2, \ldots$$

(*Dorin Andrica*, Romanian Mathematical Olympiad - second round, 2001; Gazeta Matematică (GM-B), No. 4(2001), pp. 166)

58. Rotate the polygon $A_1 A_2 \ldots A_n$ such that the complex coordinates of its vertices are the complex roots of unity of order n, $\varepsilon_1, \varepsilon_2, \ldots, \varepsilon_n$. Let z be the complex coordinate of point P located on the circumcircle of the polygon and note that $|z| = 1$.

The equality

$$z^n - 1 = \prod_{j=1}^{n} (z - \varepsilon_j)$$

yields

$$|z^n - 1| = \prod_{j=1}^{n} |z - \varepsilon_j| = \prod_{j=1}^{n} PA_j.$$

Since $|z^n - 1| \leq |z|^n + 1 = 2$, it follows that the maximal value of $\prod_{j=1}^{n} PA_j^2$ is 2 and is attained for $z^n = -1$, i.e. for middle points of arcs $A_j A_{j+1}$, $j = 1, \ldots, n$, where $A_{n+1} = A_1$.

(*Dorin Andrica*, Romanian Mathematical Regional Contest "Grigore Moisil", 1992)

59. We will use the following auxiliary result:

Lemma. (IMO 1973, Problem 1) *Let* C *be a semicircle of unit radius and* $P_1, P_2, \ldots, P_n$ *points on* C, *where* $n \geq 1$ *is an odd integer. Then*

$$|\overrightarrow{OP_1} + \overrightarrow{OP_2} + \cdots + \overrightarrow{OP_n}| \geq 1,$$

where O *is the center of* C.

Proof. The key idea is to show that the orthogonal projection of the vector sum $\overrightarrow{OP_1} + \overrightarrow{OP_2} + \cdots + \overrightarrow{OP_n}$ onto some line has length not less than 1 (see S. Savchev, T. Andreescu, "Mathematical Miniatures", The Mathematical Association of America, 2003, pp. 75). Let $n = 2k - 1$. From the considerations of symmetry, the line l containing the middle vector $\overrightarrow{OP_k}$ is a natural candidate for such a line (here we use the fact that n is odd!).

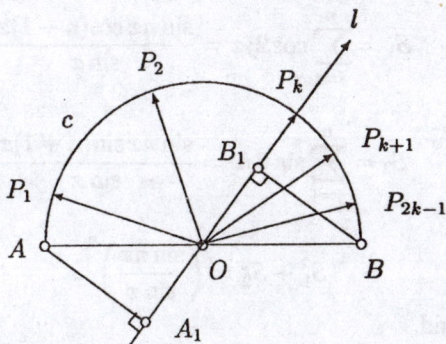

It is technically convenient to consider l as an axis with positive direction determined by $\overrightarrow{OP_k}$. As is well known, the projection of the sum of several vectors is equal to the sum of their projections. Hence it suffices to prove that the sum of the signed lengths $\overline{OP_1}, \overline{OP_2}, \ldots, \overline{OP_{2k-1}}$ of the projections of $\overrightarrow{OP_1}, \overrightarrow{OP_2}, \ldots, \overrightarrow{OP_{2k-1}}$ onto l is greater than or equal to 1. Denote the diameter of C by AB and the orthogonal projections of A and B onto l by A_1 and B_1. We have $\overline{OP_k} = 1$ and also

$$\overline{OP_1} + \overline{OP_2} + \cdots + \overline{OP_{k-1}} \geq (k-1)\overline{OA_1},$$

$$\overline{OP_{k+1}} + \overline{OP_{k+2}} + \cdots + \overline{OP_{2k-1}} \geq (k-1)\overline{OB_1}.$$

This is because $\overline{OP_j} \geq \overline{OA_1}$ for $j = 1, \ldots, k-1$ and $\overline{OP_j} \geq \overline{OB_1}$ for $j = k+1, \ldots, 2k-1$. Since $\overline{OA_1} + \overline{OB_1} = 0$, the proof is complete. $\square$

Consider the complex numbers

$$z_k = \cos \alpha_k + i \sin \alpha_k, \quad k = 1, 2, \ldots, n$$

and the points $P_1, P_2, \ldots, P_n$ with complex coordinates $z_1, z_2, \ldots, z_n$.

Using the above Lemma we have $|\overrightarrow{OP_1} + \overrightarrow{OP_2} + \cdots + \overrightarrow{OP_n}| \geq 1$, hence $|z_1 + z_2 + \cdots + z_n| \geq 1$, or

$$\left| \sum_{k=1}^{n} \cos \alpha_k + i \sum_{k=1}^{n} \sin \alpha_k \right| \geq 1.$$

It follows that

$$\sum_{1 \leq i < j \leq n} \cos(\alpha_i - \alpha_j) \geq \frac{1-n}{2},$$

as desired.

(*Dorin Andrica*, Revista Matematică Timişoara (RMT), No. 2(1983), pp. 90, Problem C:58)

60. Using the identities

$$S_1 = \sum_{j=1}^{n} \cos 2jx = \frac{\sin nx \cos(n+1)x}{\sin x}$$

and

$$S_2 = \sum_{j=1}^{n} \sin 2jx = \frac{\sin nx \sin(n+1)x}{\sin x}$$

we obtain

$$S_1^2 + S_2^2 = \left(\frac{\sin nx}{\sin x} \right)^2.$$

On the other hand,

$$S_1^2 + S_2^2 = (\cos 2x + \cos 4x + \cdots + \cos 2nx)^2 +$$

$$+ (\sin 2x + \sin 4x + \cdots + \sin 2nx)^2 =$$

$$= n + \sum_{1 \leq l < k \leq n} (\cos 2kx \cos 2lx + \sin 2kx \sin 2lx) =$$

$$= x + 2 \sum_{1 \leq l < k \leq n} \cos 2(k-l)x,$$

hence

$$\left(\frac{\sin nx}{\sin x} \right)^2 = n + \sum_{1 \leq l < k \leq n} \cos 2(k-l)x.$$

Set $a_0 = n$ and $a_{kl} = 2$, $1 \leq l < k \leq n$, and the problem is solved.

(*Dorin Andrica*, Romanian Mathematical Regional Contest "Grigore Moisil" 1995)

Chapter 5
MATHEMATICAL ANALYSIS

PROBLEMS

1. Let $1 \leq \alpha < \beta$ be real numbers. Prove that there are integers $m, n > 1$ such that $\alpha < \sqrt[n]{m} < \beta$.

2. Let $(a_n)_{n \geq 0}$ and $(b_n)_{n \geq 0}$ be the sequences of integers defined by

$$\left(1 + \sqrt{3}\right)^{2n+1} = a_n + b_n\sqrt{3}, \quad n \in \mathbb{N}.$$

Find a recursive relation for each of the sequences $(a_n)_{n \geq 0}$ and $(b_n)_{n \geq 0}$.

3. Study the convergence of the sequence $(x_n)_{n \geq 0}$ satisfying the following properties:

1) $x_n > 1, \ n = 0, 1, 2, \ldots$

2) $\dfrac{1}{2}\left(x_{n+1} - \dfrac{1}{x_{n+1}}\right) = \dfrac{x_n + 1}{x_n - 1}, \quad n = 0, 1, 2, \ldots$

4. Study the convergence of the sequence $(x_n)_{n \geq 1}$ defined by $x_1 \in (0, 2)$ and

$$x_{n+1} = 1 + \sqrt{2x_n - x_n^2}$$

for $n \geq 1$.

5. Consider the sequence of real numbers $(x_n)_{n \geq 1}$ such that

$$\lim_{n \to \infty} \frac{x_1^2 + x_2^2 + \cdots + x_n^2}{n} = 0.$$

Prove that

$$\lim_{n \to \infty} \frac{x_1 + x_2 + \cdots + x_n}{n} = 0.$$

Is the converse true?

6. Let $(a_n)_{n \geq 1}$ and $(b_n)_{n \geq 1}$ be sequences of positive numbers such that $a_n > nb_n$ for all $n > 1$.

Prove that if $(a_n)_{n \geq 1}$ is increasing and $(b_n)_{n \geq 1}$ is unbounded, then the sequence $(c_n)_{n \geq 1}$, given by $c_n = a_{n+1} - a_n$, is also unbounded.

7. Let $0 < a < \alpha$ be real numbers and let $(x_n)_{n \geq 1}$ be defined by $x_1 = a$ and

$$x_n = \frac{(\alpha + 1)x_{n-1} + \alpha^2}{x_{n-1} + (\alpha + 1)}, \quad n \geq 2.$$

Prove that the sequence is convergent and find its limit.

8. Find a sequence $(a_n)_{n\geq 1}$ of positive real numbers such that

$$\lim_{n\to\infty} (a_{n+1} - a_n) = \infty$$

and

$$\lim_{n\to\infty} \left(\sqrt{a_{n+1}} - \sqrt{a_n}\right) = 0.$$

9. Let $(x_n)_{n\geq 1}$ be an increasing sequence of positive real numbers such that

$$\lim_{n\to\infty} \frac{x_n}{n^2} = 0.$$

Prove that there is a sequence $(n_k)_{k\geq 1}$ of positive integers such that

$$\lim_{k\to\infty} \frac{x_{n_k+1} - x_{n_k}}{n_k} = 0.$$

10. Let α, β be real numbers and let $(x_n)_{n\geq 1}, (y_n)_{n\geq 1}, (z_n)_{n\geq 1}$ be real sequences such that

$$\max\{x_n^2 + \alpha y_n, y_n^2 + \beta x_n\} \leq z_n \text{ for all } n \geq 1.$$

a) Prove that $z_n \geq -\frac{1}{8}(\alpha^2 + \beta^2)$ for all $n \geq 1$.

b) If $\lim_{n\to\infty} z_n = -\frac{1}{8}(\alpha^2 + \beta^2)$, prove that the sequences $(x_n)_{n\geq 1}$, $(y_n)_{n\geq 1}$ are convergent and find their limits.

11. The sequences $(x_n)_{n\geq 1}$ and $(y_n)_{n\geq 1}$ are defined by $x_1 = 2$, $y_1 = 1$ and $x_{n+1} = x_n^2 + 1$, $y_{n+1} = x_n y_n$ for all $n \geq 1$.

a) Prove that $x_n/y_n < \sqrt{7}$ for all $n \geq 1$.

b) Prove that the sequence $(z_n)_{n\geq 1}$, $z_n = x_n/y_n$, is convergent and $\lim_{n\to\infty} z_n < \sqrt{7}$.

12. Let $\alpha \geq 0$ and $a \neq 0$ be real numbers and let $(x_n)_{n\geq 1}$ be an increasing sequence of real numbers such that

$$\lim_{n\to\infty} n^\alpha (x_{n+1} - x_n) = a.$$

Prove that the sequence is bounded if and only if $\alpha > 1$.

13. Evaluate

$$\lim_{n\to\infty} \sum_{k=0}^{n} \frac{k(n-k)! + (k+1)}{(k+1)!(n-k)!}$$

14. Evaluate

$$\lim_{n\to\infty} \sum_{k=1}^{n} \left(\frac{k}{n^2}\right)^{\frac{k}{n^2}+1}$$

15. Evaluate

(i) $\displaystyle\sum_{n=1}^{\infty} \frac{1}{nq^n}$, $q > 1$;   (ii) $\displaystyle\sum_{n=1}^{\infty} \frac{1}{(4n+1)q^{n+1}}$, $q > 1$.

16. Let $(x_n)_{n\geq 1}$ be an increasing sequence of positive integers such that $x_{n+2} + x_n > 2x_{n+1}$ for all $n \geq 1$.

Prove that the number

$$\theta = \sum_{n=1}^{\infty} \frac{1}{10^{x_n}}$$

is irrational.

17. Prove that

$$\lambda_n = \sum_{k=1}^{\infty} \frac{1}{(k!)^n}$$

is irrational for all $n \geq 1$.

18. Let k, s be positive integers and let $a_1, a_2, \ldots, a_k, b_1, b_2, \ldots, b_s$ be positive real numbers such that

$$\sqrt[n]{a_1} + \sqrt[n]{a_2} + \cdots + \sqrt[n]{a_k} = \sqrt[n]{b_1} + \sqrt[n]{b_2} + \cdots + \sqrt[n]{b_s}$$

for infinitely many integers $n \geq 2$.

Prove that

1) $k = s$;

2) $a_1 a_2 \ldots a_k = b_1 b_2 \ldots b_s$.

19. Let $(x_n)_{n\geq 1}$ be a sequence with $x_1 = 1$ and let x be a real number such that

$$x_{n+1} = x^n + nx_n, \quad n \geq 1.$$

Prove that

$$\prod_{n=1}^{\infty} \left(1 - \frac{x^n}{x_{n+1}}\right) = e^{-x}.$$

20. Let $\lambda \neq \pm 1$ be a real number. Find all functions $f : \mathbb{R} \to \mathbb{R}$ and $g : (0, \infty) \to \mathbb{R}$ such that

$$f(\ln x + \lambda \ln y) = g\left(\sqrt{x}\right) + g\left(\sqrt{y}\right) \text{ for all } x, y \in (0, \infty).$$

21. Let f be a continuous real-valued function on the interval $[a, b]$ and let m_1, m_2 be real numbers such that $m_1 m_2 > 0$. Prove that the equation

$$f(x) = \frac{m_1}{a - x} + \frac{m_2}{b - x}$$

has at least a solution in the interval (a, b).

22. Let a and b be real numbers in the interval $(0, 1/2)$, and let g be a continuous real-valued function such that $g(g(x)) = ag(x) + bx$ for all real x. Prove that $g(x) = cx$ for some constant c.

23. Find all continuous functions $f : \mathbb{R} \to [0, \infty)$ such that

$$f^2(x + y) - f^2(x - y) = 4f(x)f(y)$$

for all real numbers x, y.

24. (i) Prove that if the continuous functions $f : \mathbb{R} \to (-\infty, 0]$ and $g : \mathbb{R} \to [0, \infty)$ have a fixed point, then $f + g$ has a fixed point.

(ii) Prove that if the continuous functions $\varphi : \mathbb{R} \to [0, 1]$ and $\psi : \mathbb{R} \to [1, \infty)$ have a fixed point, then $\varphi\psi$ has a fixed point.

25. Let $\varphi : \mathbb{R} \to \mathbb{R}$ be a differentiable function at the origin and satisfying $\varphi(0) = 0$. Evaluate

$$\lim_{x \to 0} \frac{1}{x} \left[\varphi(x) + \varphi\left(\frac{x}{2}\right) + \cdots + \varphi\left(\frac{x}{n}\right) \right],$$

where n is a positive integer.

26. Let a be a positive real number. Prove that there is a unique positive real number μ such that

$$\frac{\mu^x}{x^\mu} \geq a^{\mu - x} \text{ for all } x > 0.$$

27. Let $f : [a, b] \to \mathbb{R}$ be a twice differentiable function on $[a, b]$ such that $f(a) = f(b)$ and $f'(a) = f'(b)$.

Prove that for any real number λ the equation

$$f''(x) - \lambda(f'(x))^2 = 0$$

has at least a solution in the interval (a, b).

28. Find all functions $f : [0, 2] \to (0, 1]$ that are differentiable at the origin and satisfies

$$f(2x) = 2f^2(x) - 1, \quad x \in [0, 1]$$

29. Let λ be a positive integer. Prove that there is a unique positive real number θ such that

$$\theta^{x^\lambda} \geq x^{\theta^\lambda}$$

for all real number $x > 0$.

30. Let $f : \mathbb{R} \to \mathbb{R}$ be a function continuous at the origin and let λ, μ be two distinct positive real numbers.

Prove that the limit

$$\lim_{x \to 0} \frac{f(\lambda x) - f(\mu x)}{x}$$

exists and is finite if and only if f is differentiable at the origin.

31. The sequence $(x_n)_{n \geq 1}$ is defined by

$$x_1 < 0, \quad x_{n+1} = e^{x_n} - 1, \quad n \geq 1.$$

Prove that $\lim_{n \to \infty} n x_n = -2$.

32. Let $x_0 \in (0, 1]$ and $x_{n+1} = x_n - \arcsin(\sin^3 x_n)$, $n \geq 0$. Evaluate $\lim_{n \to \infty} \sqrt{n} x_n$.

33. Let $f : \mathbb{R} \to \mathbb{R}$ be a twice differentiable function with the second derivative nonnegative.
Prove that

$$f(x + f'(x)) \geq f(x), \quad x \in \mathbb{R}.$$

34. Let $a < b$ be positive real numbers. Prove that the equation

$$\left(\frac{a+b}{2}\right)^{x+y} = a^x b^y$$

has at least a solution in the interval (a, b).

35. Find with proof if there are differentiable functions $\varphi : \mathbb{R} \to \mathbb{R}$ such that $\varphi(x)$ and $\varphi'(x)$ are integers only if x is integer.

36. Let $f : [a, b] \to \mathbb{R}$ be a differentiable function.
Prove that for any positive integer n there are numbers $\theta_1 < \theta_2 < \cdots < \theta_n$ in the interval (a, b) such that

$$\frac{f(b) - f(a)}{b - a} = \frac{f'(\theta_1) + f'(\theta_2) + \cdots + f'(\theta_n)}{n}$$

37. Let $f, g : \mathbb{R} \to \mathbb{R}$ be differentiable functions with continuous derivatives such that

$$f(x) + g(x) = f'(x) - g'(x)$$

for all $x \in \mathbb{R}$.
Prove that if x_1, x_2 are two consecutive real solutions of the equation $f(x) - g(x) = 0$, then the equation $f(x) + g(x) = 0$ has at least a solution in the interval (x_1, x_2).

38. Let $f : \left[-\frac{\pi}{2}, \frac{\pi}{2}\right] \to (-1, 1)$ be a differentiable function whose derivative f' is continuous and nonnegative. Prove that there exists x_0 in $\left[-\frac{\pi}{2}, \frac{\pi}{2}\right]$ such that

$$(f(x_0))^2 + (f'(x_0))^2 \leq 1.$$

39. Prove that there are no positive real numbers x and y such that

$$x2^y + y2^{-x} = x + y.$$

40. a) Prove that if $x \geq y \geq \left(\dfrac{n}{n+1}\right)^{n(n+1)}$ for some integer $n \geq 2$, then

$$\sqrt[n]{x} + \sqrt[n+1]{y} \geq \sqrt[n]{y} + \sqrt[n+1]{x}.$$

b) Prove that

$$n\sqrt[n]{n} + \frac{n+1}{\sqrt[n+1]{n+1}} \geq 2n+1, \quad n \geq 3.$$

41. Let $x_1, x_2, \ldots, x_n$ be positive real numbers such that $x_1 + x_2 + \cdots + x_n = 1$. Prove that

$$x_1^{x_1} x_2^{x_2} \ldots x_n^{x_n} \geq \frac{1}{n}.$$

42. Let $f : \mathbb{R} \to \mathbb{R}$ be a function with a noninjective antiderivative. Prove that $f(c) = 0$ for some $c \in \mathbb{R}$.

43. Let $f_1, f_2, \ldots, f_n : \mathbb{R} \to \mathbb{R}$ be continuous functions. Prove that

$$\max(f_1(x), f_2(x), \ldots, f_n(x))dx$$

is a derivative and evaluate

$$\int \max(1, x, x^2, \ldots, x^n)dx.$$

44. Evaluate

$$\int \frac{x^2 e^{\arctg x}}{\sqrt{1+x^2}}dx.$$

45. Let p be a polynomial of odd degree such that p' has no multiple zero and let $f : \mathbb{R} \to \mathbb{R}$ be a function such that $f \circ p$ is a derivative.
Prove that f is a derivative.

46. Let $I = (0, \infty)$ and let $f : I \to I$ be a function with an antiderivative F that satisfies the condition

$$F(x)f\left(\frac{1}{x}\right) = x,$$

for all x in I. Prove that $g : I \to \mathbb{R}$, $g(x) = F(x)F\left(\frac{1}{x}\right)$ is a constant function and then find f.

47. Let $n > 1$ be an integer and let $f : [0,1] \to \mathbb{R}$ be a continuous function such that

$$\int_0^1 f(x)dx = 1 + \frac{1}{2} + \cdots + \frac{1}{n}.$$

Prove that there is a real number $x_0 \in (0,1)$, such that

$$f(x_0) = \frac{1 - x_0^n}{1 - x_0}.$$

48. Consider the continuous functions $f, g : [a,b] \to \mathbb{R}$.
Prove that the equation

$$f(x) \int_a^x g(t)dt = g(x) \int_x^b f(t)dt$$

has at least a solution in the interval (a,b).

49. Let $f : [a,b] \to \mathbb{R}$ be a continuous function such that

$$\int_a^b f(x)dx \neq 0.$$

Prove that there are numbers $a < \alpha < \beta < b$ such that

$$\int_a^\alpha f(x)dx = (b - \alpha)f(\beta).$$

50. Let a, c be nonnegative real numbers and let $f : [a,b] \to [c,d]$ be a bijective increasing function.
Prove that there is a unique real number $\mu \in (a,b)$ such that

$$\int_a^b f(t)dt = (\mu - a)c + (b - \mu)d.$$

51. Let $\varphi : \mathbb{R} \to \mathbb{R}$ be a continuous function such that

$$\int_x^{x+y} \varphi(t)dt = \int_{x-y}^x \varphi(t)dt,$$

for all $x, y \in \mathbb{R}$.
Prove that φ is a constant function.

52. Let $f : \mathbb{R} \to \mathbb{R}$ be a differentiable function such that

$$\int_x^{\frac{x+y}{2}} f(t)dt \leq \int_{\frac{x+y}{2}}^y f(t)dt$$

for all real number $x < y$.
Prove that f is a nondecreasing function.

53. Let $f : \mathbb{R} \to \mathbb{R}$ be an injective and differentiable function.

Prove that the function $F : (0, \infty) \to \mathbb{R}$,

$$F(x) = \frac{1}{x} \int_0^x f(t)dt$$

is monotone.

54. Prove that

$$\lim_{n \to \infty} n^2 \int_0^{\frac{1}{n}} x^{x+1} dx = \frac{1}{2}.$$

55. Prove that there are no Riemann integrable functions $f : \mathbb{R} \to \mathbb{R} \setminus \{0\}$ such that

$$\int_x^y f(t)dt = \frac{f(x)}{f(y)},$$

for all real numbers $x \neq y$.

56. Let $f : [0, 1] \to \mathbb{R}$ be a differentiable function with continuous derivative such that

$$\int_0^1 [f'(x)]^2 dx = 1.$$

Prove that $|f(1) - f(0)| < 1$.

57. Find all continuous functions $f : [0, 1] \to \mathbb{R}$ such that

$$\int_0^1 f(x)(x - f(x))dx = \frac{1}{12}.$$

58. Let $f_0 : [0, 1] \to \mathbb{R}$ be a continuous function and let the sequence $(f_n)_{n \geq 1}$ be defined by

$$f_n(x) = \int_0^x f_{n-1}(t)dt, \quad x \in [0, 1].$$

Prove that if there is an integer $m \geq 0$ such that

$$\int_0^1 f_m(t)dt = \frac{1}{(m + 1)!},$$

then the function f_0 has a fixed point.

59. Let $f : [-1, 1] \to \mathbb{R}$ be a differentiable function with nondecreasing derivative. Prove that

$$\frac{1}{2} \int_{-1}^1 f(x)dx \leq f(-1) + f'(1).$$

60. Let $f, g : [a, b] \to \mathbb{R}$ be continuous functions. Prove that there is a real number $c \in (a, b)$ such that

$$\int_a^c f(x)dx + (c - a)g(c) = \int_c^b g(x)dx + (b - c)f(c).$$

SOLUTIONS

1. We prove that there is an integer $n > 1$ such that

$$\beta^n - \alpha^n > 1.$$

Let $c = \beta - \alpha$. Then

$$\beta^n - \alpha^n = (\alpha + c)^n - \alpha^n = \binom{n}{1}\alpha^{n-1}c + \cdots + c^n > n\alpha^{n-1}c > nc,$$

because $\alpha > 1$.

Take an integer $n > \dfrac{1}{c}$. Then $\beta^n - \alpha^n > 1$.

The interval (α^n, β^n) has length greater than 1, hence there is an integer $m > 1$ such that $\alpha^n < m < \beta^n$, or $\alpha < \sqrt[n]{m} < \beta$, as desired.

(*Dorin Andrica*, Revista Matematică Timişoara (RMT), No. 1(1982), pp. 90, Problem 4955)

2. Note that

$$\left(1 + \sqrt{3}\right)^{2(n+1)+1} = \left(1 + \sqrt{3}\right)^{2n+3} = \left(1 + \sqrt{3}\right)^{2n+1}\left(1 + \sqrt{3}\right)^2 =$$

$$= \left(a_n + b_n\sqrt{3}\right)\left(4 + 2\sqrt{3}\right) = 4a_n + 6b_n + (2a_n + 4b_n)\sqrt{3}.$$

On the other hand,

$$\left(1 + \sqrt{3}\right)^{2(n+1)+1} = a_{n+1} + b_{n+1}\sqrt{3},$$

and since a_n, b_n are integers we derive that

(i) $a_{n+1} = 4a_n + 6b_n$; (ii) $b_{n+1} = 2a_n + 4b_n$.

From relation (i) we obtain $b_n = \dfrac{a_{n+1} - 4a_n}{6}$. Substituting in relation (ii) implies

$$\frac{a_{n+2} - 4a_{n+1}}{6} = 2a_n + 4\frac{a_{n+1} - 4a_n}{6},$$

or

$$a_{n+2} = 8a_{n+1} - 4a_n.$$

On the other hand, $a_n = \dfrac{b_{n+1} - 4b_n}{2}$, and the first relation gives

$$\frac{b_{n+2} - 4b_{n+1}}{2} = 4\frac{b_{n+1} - 4b_n}{2} + 6b_n.$$

Thus

$$b_{n+2} = 8b_{n+1} - 4b_n.$$

It follows that the sequences $(a_n)_{n \geq 1}$, $(b_n)_{n \geq 1}$ are given by

$$a_1 = 10, \quad a_2 = 76 \text{ and } a_{n+2} = 8a_{n+1} - 4a_n,$$

$$b_1 = 6, \quad b_2 = 44 \text{ and } b_{n+2} = 8b_{n+1} - 4b_n,$$

for all $n \geq 1$.

(*Dorin Andrica*, Revista Matematică Timişoara (RMT), No. 2(1981), pp. 71, Problem 4648)

3. Solving the quadratic equation in x_{n+1} and taking into account condition 1) yields

$$x_{n+1} = \frac{x_n + 1 + \sqrt{2(x_n^2 + 1)}}{x_n - 1}, \quad n = 0, 1, 2, \ldots \tag{1}$$

That is $x_{n+1} = f(x_n)$, $n = 0, 1, 2, \ldots$, where $f : (1, \infty) \to \mathbb{R}$ is the function given by

$$f(x) = \frac{x + 1 + \sqrt{2(x^2 + 1)}}{x - 1}.$$

It is not difficult to check that f is decreasing and $f(2 + \sqrt{3}) = 2 + \sqrt{3}$. We distinguish three cases:

Case 1. If $x_0 = 2 + \sqrt{3}$, then $x_n = 2 + \sqrt{3}$ for all n.

Case 2. If $x_0 \in (1, 2 + \sqrt{3})$, then from the monotonicity of function f it follows that

$$x_0 < x_2 < x_4 < \cdots < 2 + \sqrt{3} < \cdots < x_5 < x_3 < x_1.$$

Case 3. If $x_0 \in (2 + \sqrt{3}, \infty)$, then

$$x_1 < x_3 < x_5 < \cdots < 2 + \sqrt{3} < \cdots < x_4 < x_2 < x_0.$$

In all cases the sequence $(x_n)_{n \geq 0}$ is convergent and $\lim_{n \to \infty} x_n = 2 + \sqrt{3}$.

(*Titu Andreescu* and *Dorin Andrica*, Romanian Mathematical Regional Contest "Grigore Moisil", 2003)

4. Note that

$$x_{n+2} = 1 + \sqrt{x_{n+1}(2 - x_{n+1})} =$$

$$= 1 + \sqrt{\left(1 + \sqrt{2x_n - x_n^2}\right)\left(1 - \sqrt{2x_n - x_n^2}\right)} =$$

$$= 1 + \sqrt{1 - 2x_n + x_n^2} = 1 + |x_n - 1|,$$

hence $x_n \geq 1$ for all $n \geq 2$.

We study three cases.

i) If $x_1 < 1$, then

$$x_n = \begin{cases} x_1 & \text{if } n = 1 \\ x_2 & \text{if } n \text{ is even} \\ x_3 & \text{if } n \text{ is odd and } n > 1 \end{cases}$$

So the sequence converges if and only if $x_2 = x_3$. The equation

$$x_2 = 1 + \sqrt{2x_2 - x_2^2}$$

has only the solution $x_2 = \dfrac{2 + \sqrt{2}}{2}$. In all other cases the sequence is divergent.

ii) If $x_1 = 1$, then

$$x_n = \begin{cases} 1 & \text{if } n \text{ is odd} \\ 2 & \text{if } n \text{ is even} \end{cases}$$

and the sequence is divergent.

iii) If $x_1 > 1$, then

$$x_n = \begin{cases} x_1 & \text{if } n \text{ is odd} \\ x_2 & \text{if } n \text{ is even.} \end{cases}$$

It follows that the sequence is convergent if and only if $x_1 = x_2$ i.e. $x_1 = \dfrac{2 + \sqrt{2}}{2}$.

(*Titu Andreescu*, Revista Matematică Timişoara (RMT), No. 1-2(1979), pp. 56, Problem 3865)

5. We prove a more general statement: If p is a positive integer and $(x_n)_{n \geq 1}$ is a sequence such that

$$\lim_{n \to \infty} \frac{x_1^{2p} + x_2^{2p} + \cdots + x_n^{2p}}{n} = 0, \tag{1}$$

then

$$\lim_{n \to \infty} \frac{x_1 + x_2 + \cdots + x_n}{n} = 0. \tag{2}$$

For this, recall the inequality

$$\left(\frac{x_1 + x_2 + \cdots + x_n}{n} \right)^{2p} \leq \frac{x_1^{2p} + x_2^{2p} + \cdots + x_n^{2p}}{n}.$$

It follows that

$$\left| \frac{x_1 + x_2 + \cdots + x_n}{n} \right| \leq \sqrt[2p]{\frac{x_1^{2p} + x_2^{2p} + \cdots + x_n^{2p}}{n}}.$$

Using the squeeze theorem and the hypothesis (1), the conclusion (2) follows. For $p = 1$ we obtain the initial problem.

The converse is not true. Take $x_n = (-1)^n$ and observe that

$$\frac{x_1 + x_2 + \cdots + x_n}{n} = \begin{cases} 0 & \text{if } n \text{ is even} \\ \dfrac{-1}{n} & \text{if } n \text{ is odd} \end{cases}$$

Hence

$$\lim_{n \to \infty} \frac{x_1 + x_2 + \cdots + x_n}{n} = 0$$

but

$$\lim_{n \to \infty} \frac{x_1^2 + x_2^2 + \cdots + x_n^2}{n} = 1.$$

(*Dorin Andrica*, Revista Matematică Timişoara (RMT), **No. 2(1977)**, pp. **47**, Problem 2570)

6. Assume by way of contradiction that there is $M > 0$ such that $a_{n+1} - a_n < M$ for all n. Summing up these inequalities from 1 to n yields

$$a_{n+1} - a_1 < nM,$$

or

$$\frac{a_{n+1}}{n} < \frac{a_1}{n} + M. \tag{1}$$

From $a_n \geq nb_n$ it follows that

$$\frac{a_{n+1}}{n} \geq \frac{n+1}{n} b_{n+1}$$

Since the sequence $(b_n)_{n \geq 1}$ is not bounded from above we obtain that the sequence $\left(\dfrac{a_n + 1}{n} \right)_{n \geq 1}$ is not bounded from above, which contradicts (1).

(*Dorin Andrica*, Revista Matematică Timişoara (RMT), **No. 1(1978)**, pp. **91**, Problem 3441)

7. Note that $0 < x_2 = \dfrac{(\alpha + 1)x_1 + \alpha^2}{x_1 + (\alpha + 1)} < \alpha$. The left inequality is obvious and the right inequality is equivalent to $x_1 < \alpha$. Since $0 < x_2 < \alpha$ we obtain – likewise – $0 < x_3 < \alpha$ and then $x_n \in (0, \alpha)$ by inducting on n.

On the other hand,

$$x_n - x_{n-1} = \frac{(\alpha + 1)x_{n-1} + \alpha^2}{x_{n-1} + (\alpha + 1)} - x_{n-1} = \frac{\alpha^2 - x_{n-1}^2}{x_{n-1} + (\alpha + 1)} > 0,$$

therefore the sequence is increasing and bounded. It follows that the sequence is convergent and let $l = \lim_{n \to \infty} x_n$. Then

$$l = \frac{(\alpha + 1)l + \alpha^2}{l + (\alpha + 1)}$$

so $l = \alpha$.

(*Dorin Andrica*, Revista Matematică Timişoara (RMT), **No. 2(1976)**, pp. **53**, Problem 2567)

8. We prove that $a_n = n \ln n$, $n \geq 1$, satisfies the conditions.

First,

$$a_{n+1} - a_n = (n+1)\ln(n+1) - n\ln n = \ln(n+1) + \ln\left(1 + \frac{1}{n}\right)^n$$

so

$$\lim_{n\to\infty}(a_{n+1} - a_n) = \infty.$$

Second,

$$\sqrt{a_{n+1}} - \sqrt{a_n} = \sqrt{(n+1)\ln(n+1)} - \sqrt{n\ln n} =$$

$$= \frac{(n+1)\ln(n+1) - n\ln n}{\sqrt{(n+1)\ln(n+1)} + \sqrt{n\ln n}} =$$

$$= \frac{\ln(n+1)}{\sqrt{(n+1)\ln(n+1)} + \sqrt{n\ln n}} + \frac{\ln\left(1 + \frac{1}{n}\right)^n}{\sqrt{(n+1)\ln(n+1)} + \sqrt{n\ln n}} =$$

$$= \sqrt{\frac{\ln(n+1)}{n+1}} \frac{1}{1 + \sqrt{\frac{n\ln n}{(n+1)\ln(n+1)}}} + \frac{\ln\left(1 + \frac{1}{n}\right)^n}{\sqrt{(n+1)\ln(n+1)} + \sqrt{n\ln n}}.$$

Because

$$\lim_{n\to\infty} \ln\left(1 + \frac{1}{n}\right)^n = 1,$$

we have

$$\lim_{n\to\infty} \frac{\ln\left(1 + \frac{1}{n}\right)^n}{\sqrt{(n+1)\ln(n+1)} + \sqrt{n\ln n}} = 0.$$

Because $\lim\limits_{n\to\infty} \dfrac{\ln(n+1)}{n+1} = 0$ and $\lim\limits_{n\to\infty} \dfrac{n\ln n}{(n+1)\ln(n+1)} = 1$, it follows that

$$\lim_{n\to\infty}\left(\sqrt{a_{n+1}} - \sqrt{a_n}\right) = 0,$$

as desired.

Remark. Another such sequence is given by $a_n = n\sqrt{n}$, $n \geq 1$.

(*Dorin Andrica*, Revista Matematică Timişoara (RMT), No. 2(1977), pp. 70, Problem 3087)

9. Assume by way of contradiction that there is no sequence $(n_k)_{k\geq 1}$ with the desired property. Then there is $\alpha > 0$ such that

$$\frac{x_{n+1} - x_n}{n} \geq \alpha > 0$$

hence

$$x_{n+1} - x_n \geq \alpha n, \text{ for all } n \geq 1.$$

It follows that

$$x_n - x_1 \geq \alpha(1 + 2 + \cdots + (n-1)) = \alpha\frac{(n-1)n}{2},$$

then
$$\frac{x_n}{n^2} \geq \alpha \frac{n-1}{2n} + \frac{x_1}{n^2} > \frac{\alpha}{3}$$

for all $n \geq 1$. This is in contradiction with

$$\lim_{n \to \infty} \frac{x_n}{n^2} = 0,$$

and we are done.

(*Dorin Andrica*, Romanian Mathematical Olympiad - final round, 1984)

10. a) Summing the inequalities $x_n^2 + \alpha y_n \leq z_n$ and $y_n^2 + \beta x_n \leq z_n$ we obtain

$$0 \leq \left(x_n + \frac{\beta}{2}\right)^2 + \left(y_n + \frac{\alpha}{2}\right)^2 \leq 2\left(z_n + \frac{\alpha^2 + \beta^2}{8}\right), \text{ for all } n \geq 1.$$

The conclusion follows immediately.

b) Notice that

$$\left|x_n + \frac{\beta}{2}\right| \leq \sqrt{2}\left(z_n + \frac{\alpha^2 + \beta^2}{8}\right)^{\frac{1}{2}} \quad \text{and} \quad \left|y_n + \frac{\alpha}{2}\right| \leq \sqrt{2}\left(z_n + \frac{\alpha^2 + \beta^2}{8}\right)^{\frac{1}{2}}$$

From the squeeze theorem follows that

$$\lim_{n \to \infty} x_n = -\frac{\beta}{2} \quad \text{and} \quad \lim_{n \to \infty} y_n = -\frac{\alpha}{2}.$$

(*Dorin Andrica*, Romanian Mathematical Regional Contest "Grigore Moisil", 1997)

11. By induction on n we obtain $y_n = x_1 x_2 \ldots x_{n-1}$ and

$$z_n = x_1 + \frac{1}{x_1} + \frac{1}{x_1 x_2} + \cdots + \frac{1}{x_1 x_2 \ldots x_{n-1}}$$

for all $n \geq 1$.

Since $x_{n+1} - x_n = x_n^2 - x_n + 1 > 0$, the sequence $(x_n)_{n \geq 1}$ is increasing. From $x_2 = 5$ we obtain

$$x_1 x_2 \ldots x_k \geq 2 \cdot 5^{k-1}, \quad k \in \mathbb{N}^*$$

hence

$$\frac{1}{x_1 x_2 \ldots x_k} \leq \frac{1}{2 \cdot 5^{k-1}}, \quad k \in \mathbb{N}^*.$$

It follows that

$$z_n < 2 + \frac{1}{2} + \frac{1}{2 \cdot 5} + \cdots + \frac{1}{2 \cdot 5^{n-2}} = 2 + \frac{1}{2} \cdot \frac{1 - \left(\frac{1}{5}\right)^{n-1}}{1 - \frac{1}{5}} =$$

$$= 2 + \frac{5}{8}\left[1 - \left(\frac{1}{5}\right)^{n-1}\right] < 2 + \frac{5}{8} = \frac{21}{8} < \sqrt{7},$$

as desired.

On the other hand,

$$\frac{z_{n+1}}{z_n} = \frac{\frac{x_{n+1}}{y_{n+1}}}{\frac{x_n}{y_n}} = \frac{x_{n+1} y_n}{x_n y_{n+1}} = \frac{x_{n+1} y_n}{x_n x_n y_n} =$$

$$\frac{x_{n+1}}{x_n^2} = \frac{x_n^2 + 1}{x_n^2} = 1 + \frac{1}{x_n^2} > 1,$$

so $(z_n)_{n\geq 1}$ is an increasing and bounded sequence. Then $(z_n)_{n\geq 1}$ is convergent and

$$\lim_{n\to\infty} z_n \leq \frac{21}{8} < \sqrt{7},$$

as claimed.

(*Dorin Andrica* and *Şerban Buzeţeanu*, Romanian Mathematical Regional Contest "Grigore Moisil", 1992)

12. Let $\varepsilon > 0$ such that $a - \varepsilon > 0$. From

$$\lim_{n\to\infty} n^\alpha (x_{n+1} - x_n) = a$$

it follows that there is an integer n_1 such that

$$\frac{1}{n^\alpha}(a - \varepsilon) < x_{n+1} - x_n < (a + \varepsilon)\frac{1}{n^\alpha} \tag{1}$$

for all $n \geq n_1$.

Summing up inequality (1) from $n = n_1$ to $n = n_1 + p - 1$, $p > 0$ implies

$$(a - \varepsilon)\sum_{k=0}^{p-1} \frac{1}{(n_1 + k)^\alpha} < x_{n_1+p} - x_{n_1} < (a + \varepsilon)\sum_{k=0}^{p-1} \frac{1}{(n_1 + k)^\alpha} \tag{2}$$

The series $\displaystyle\sum_{k=0}^{\infty} \frac{1}{(n_1 + k)^\alpha}$ converges if and only if $\alpha > 1$, therefore applying the squeeze theorem to the inequality (2) leads to the conclusion.

(*Dorin Andrica*, Gazeta Matematică (GM-B), No. 11(1979), pp. 422, Problem 18011)

13. Note that

$$\sum_{k=0}^{n} \frac{k(n-k)! + (k+1)}{(k+1)!(n-k)!} = \sum_{k=0}^{n} \frac{k}{(k+1)!} + \sum_{k=0}^{n} \frac{1}{k!(n-k)!} =$$

$$= \sum_{k=0}^{n} \frac{k}{(k+1)!} + \frac{1}{n!}\sum_{k=0}^{n} \frac{n!}{k!(n-k)!} = \sum_{k=0}^{n}\left(\frac{1}{k!} - \frac{1}{(k+1)!}\right) + \frac{1}{n!}\sum_{k=0}^{n}\binom{n}{k} =$$

$$= 1 - \frac{1}{(n+1)!} + \frac{2^n}{n!}.$$

Since

$$\lim_{n\to\infty} \frac{1}{(n+1)!} = \lim_{n\to\infty} \frac{2^n}{n!} = 0,$$

it follows that

$$\lim_{n\to\infty} \sum_{k=0}^{n} \frac{k(n-k)! + (k+1)}{(k+1)!(n-k)!} = 1.$$

(*Dorin Andrica*, Revista Matematică Timişoara (RMT), No. 2(1975), pp. 52, Problem 2281)

14. Note that
$$\lim_{\substack{x\to 0 \\ x>0}} x^x = 1.$$

Indeed,
$$\lim_{\substack{x\to 0 \\ x>0}} x^x = \lim_{\substack{x\to 0 \\ x>0}} e^{x\ln x} = e^{\lim_{\substack{x\to 0 \\ x>0}} \frac{\ln x}{\frac{1}{x}}} = e^{\lim_{\substack{x\to 0 \\ x>0}} (-x)} = 1,$$

after applying L'Hospital rule.

Then
$$\lim_{\substack{x\to 0 \\ x>0}} \frac{x^{x+1}}{x} = 1.$$

Let $\varepsilon > 0$. There is an integer $n(\varepsilon) > 0$ such that for any integer $n \geq n(\varepsilon)$, we have

$$1-\varepsilon < \frac{\left(\frac{k}{n^2}\right)^{\frac{k}{n^2}+1}}{\frac{k}{n^2}} < 1+\varepsilon, \quad k = 1, 2, \ldots, n.$$

Summing up from $k=1$ to $k=n$ and using algebraic manipulations yields

$$1-\varepsilon < \frac{\sum_{k=1}^{n} \left(\frac{k}{n^2}\right)^{\frac{k}{n^2}+1}}{\sum_{k=1}^{n} \frac{k}{n^2}} < 1+\varepsilon, \quad n \geq n(\varepsilon),$$

or

$$\frac{1}{2} - \frac{1}{2}\left(\varepsilon - \frac{1}{n} + \frac{\varepsilon}{n}\right) < \sum_{k=1}^{n}\left(\frac{k}{n^2}\right)^{\frac{k}{n^2}+1} < \frac{1}{2} + \frac{1}{2}\left(\varepsilon + \frac{1}{n} + \frac{\varepsilon}{n}\right),$$

for any integer $n \geq n(\varepsilon)$.

Therefore
$$\lim_{n\to\infty} \sum_{k=1}^{n}\left(\frac{k}{n^2}\right)^{\frac{k}{n^2}+1} = \frac{1}{2}.$$

(*Dorin Andrica*)

15. (i) We have
$$1 + x + x^2 + \cdots + x^n + \cdots = \frac{1}{1-x}, \quad |x| < 1.$$

Hence

$$\int_0^{1/q} (1 + x + x^2 + \dots)dx = \int_0^{1/q} \frac{dx}{1-x},$$

so

$$\sum_{n=1}^{\infty} \frac{1}{nq^n} = \ln \frac{q}{q-1}, \quad q > 1.$$

(ii) For any $|x| < 1$ we have

$$1 + x^4 + x^8 + \dots + x^{4n} + \dots = \frac{1}{1-x^4}.$$

Hence

$$\int_0^{1/q} (1 + x^4 + x^8 + \dots)dx = \int_0^{1/q} \frac{dx}{1-x^4},$$

so

$$\sum_{n=1}^{\infty} \frac{1}{(4n+1)q^{4n+1}} = -\frac{1}{q} + \frac{1}{4}\ln\left(1 - \frac{1}{q^2}\right) + \frac{1}{2}\text{arctg}\frac{1}{q}.$$

(*Dorin Andrica*, Revista Matematică Timişoara (RMT), No. 2(1977), pp. 70, Problem 3091; Gazeta Matematică (GM-B), No. 1(1981), pp. 40, Problem 18608)

16. The number θ has the decimal representation

$$\theta = 0.0\dots01\underbrace{0\dots0}_{k_1}1\underbrace{0\dots0}_{k_2}1\dots1\underbrace{0\dots0}_{k_n}1$$

where $k_1, k_2, \dots, k_n$ are the number of zeros between two consecutive ones.
Because

$$x_{n+2} - x_{n+1} > x_{n+1} - x_n, \quad n \geq 1$$

we have

$$k_1 < k_2 < k_3 < \dots < k_n < \dots,$$

hence θ does not have a periodical decimal representation.

It follows that θ is irrational, as claimed.

(*Dorin Andrica*, Revista Matematică Timişoara (RMT), No. 2(1981), pp. 73, Problem 4661)

17. Note that

$$\lambda_n = 1 + \sum_{k=2}^{\infty} \frac{1}{(k!)^n} > 1$$

and that

$$\lambda_n = -1 + \sum_{k=0}^{\infty} \frac{1}{(k!)^n} < -1 + \sum_{k=0}^{\infty} \frac{1}{k!} = -1 + e < 2.$$

Hence $1 < \lambda_n < 2$ for all $n \geq 1$. So λ_n is not an integer.

Assume by way of contradiction that there are positive integers n, p, q with $q \neq 1$ such that $\frac{p}{q} = \lambda_n$. Then

$$pq^{n-1}(q-1)! = A + \frac{1}{(q+1)^n} + \frac{1}{(q+1)^n(q+2)^n} + \cdots <$$

$$< A + \frac{1}{(q+1)^n} + \frac{1}{(q+1)^n(q+1)^n} + \cdots =$$

$$= A + \frac{1}{(q+1)^n}\left(1 + \frac{1}{(q+1)^n} + \frac{1}{(q+1)^{2n}} + \cdots\right) = A + \frac{1}{(q+1)^n - 1},$$

for some integer $A \geq 0$. It follows that

$$B = \frac{1}{(q+1)^n} + \frac{1}{(q+1)^n(q+2)^n} + \cdots < 1,$$

so $A + B$ is not integer, which is false.

Therefore λ_n is irrational for all $n \geq 1$.

(*Dorin Andrica*)

18. 1) Using the limit

$$\lim_{n \to \infty} \sqrt[n]{a} = 1$$

and taking the limits in both sides of the equality, we obtain

$$\underbrace{1 + 1 + \cdots + 1}_{k \text{ times}} = \underbrace{1 + 1 + \cdots + 1}_{s \text{ times}},$$

so $k = s$.

2) Using the limit

$$\lim_{n \to \infty} n\left(\sqrt[n]{a} - 1\right) = \ln a$$

and the relation

$$n\left(\sqrt[n]{a_1} - 1\right) + n\left(\sqrt[n]{a_2} - 1\right) + \cdots + n\left(\sqrt[n]{a_k} - 1\right) =$$

$$= n\left(\sqrt[n]{b_1} - 1\right) + n\left(\sqrt[n]{b_2} - 1\right) + \cdots + n\left(\sqrt[n]{b_k} - 1\right)$$

we obtain after taking limits:

$$\ln a_1 + \ln a_2 + \cdots + \ln a_k = \ln b_1 + \ln b_2 + \cdots + \ln b_k.$$

This implies

$$a_1 \cdot a_2 \ldots a_k = b_1 \cdot b_2 \cdot b_k,$$

as desired.

(*Dorin Andrica*, Romanian Mathematical Regional Contest "Grigore Moisil", 1999)

19. Let $P_n = \displaystyle\prod_{k=1}^{n} \left(1 - \frac{x^k}{x_{k+1}}\right)$. Then

$$P_n = \prod_{k=1}^{n} \left(\frac{x_{k+1} - x^k}{x_{k+1}}\right) = \prod_{k=1}^{n} \frac{kx_k}{x_{k+1}} = \frac{n!}{x_{n+1}},$$

hence

$$\frac{1}{P_{n+1}} - \frac{1}{P_n} = \frac{x_{n+2}}{(n+1)!} - \frac{x_{n+1}}{n!} = \frac{x_{n+2} - (n+1)x_{n+1}}{(n+1)!} = \frac{x^{n+1}}{(n+1)!}.$$

It follows that

$$\frac{1}{P_{n+1}} = \frac{1}{P_1} + \frac{x^2}{2!} + \frac{x^3}{3!} + \cdots + \frac{x^{n+1}}{(n+1)!} =$$

$$= 1 + \frac{x}{1!} + \frac{x^2}{2!} + \cdots + \frac{x^{n+1}}{(n+1)!}.$$

Because

$$\lim_{n\to\infty} \left(1 + \frac{x}{1!} + \frac{x^2}{2!} + \cdots + \frac{x^{n+1}}{(n+1)!}\right) = e^x,$$

it follows that $\lim_{n\to\infty} P_{n+1} = e^{-x}$, as desired.

(*Titu Andreescu* and *Dorin Andrica*, Revista Matematică Timişoara (RMT), No. 1(1977), pp. 49, Problem 2843)

20. Interchanging x and y we obtain

$$f(\ln x + \lambda \ln y) = g\left(\sqrt{x}\right) + g\left(\sqrt{y}\right), \quad x, y \in (0, \infty)$$

so

$$f(\ln y + \lambda \ln x) = g\left(\sqrt{x}\right) + g\left(\sqrt{y}\right), \quad x, y > 0.$$

Let

$$a = \ln x + \lambda \ln y \text{ and } b = \ln y + \lambda \ln x.$$

Then

$$x = e^{\frac{\lambda b - a}{\lambda^2 - 1}} \text{ and } y = e^{\frac{\lambda a - b}{\lambda^2 - 1}},$$

hence

$$f(a) = f(b) = g\left(e^{\frac{\lambda b - a}{2(\lambda^2 - 1)}}\right) + g\left(e^{\frac{\lambda a - b}{2(\lambda^2 - 1)}}\right), \quad a, b \in \mathbb{R}.$$

It follows that f is a constant and let $f(x) = C$. Then for $x = y$ we have $g(\sqrt{x}) = \frac{C}{2}$, so g is a constant and $g(x) = \frac{C}{2}$.

(*Dorin Andrica*, Revista Matematică Timişoara (RMT), No. 1-2(1979), pp. 51, Problem 3827)

21. Consider the function $F : I \to \mathbb{R}$,

$$F(x) = (x - a)(x - b)f(x) + m_1(x - b) + m_2(x - a).$$

Note that F is continuous and

$$F(a)F(b) = m_1(a - b)m_2(b - a) = -m_1 m_2(a - b)^2 < 0,$$

hence there is $c \in (a, b)$ such that $F(c) = 0$. It follows that

$$f(c) = \frac{m_1}{a - c} + \frac{m_2}{b - c}$$

and the solution is complete.

(*Dorin Andrica*)

22. Note that $g(x) = g(y)$ implies that $g(g(x)) = g(g(y))$ and hence $x = y$ from the given equation. That is, g is injective. Since g is also continuous, g is either strictly increasing or strictly decreasing. Moreover, g cannot tend to a finite limit L as $x \to \infty$, or else we'd have $g(g(x)) - ag(x) = bx$, with the left side bounded and the right side unbounded. Similarly, g cannot tend to a finite limit as $x \to -\infty$. Together with monotonicity, this yields that g is also surjective.

Pick x_0 arbitrary, and define x_n for all $n \in \mathbb{Z}$ recursively by $x_{n+1} = g(x_n)$ for $n > 0$, and $x_{n-1} = g^{-1}(x_n)$ for $n < 0$. Let $r_1 = (1 + \sqrt{a^2 + 4b})/2$ and $r_2 = (a - \sqrt{a^2 + 4b})/2$ be the roots of $x^2 - ax - b = 0$, so that $r_1 > 0 > r_2$ and $1 > |r_1| > |r_2|$. Then there exist $c_1, c_2 \in \mathbb{R}$ such that $x_n = c_1 r_1^n + c_2 r_2^n$ for all $n \in \mathbb{Z}$.

Suppose g is strictly increasing. If $c_2 \neq 0$ for some choice of x_0, then x_n is dominated by r_2^n for n sufficiently negative. But taking x_n and x_{n+2} for n sufficiently negative of the right parity, we get $0 < x_n < x_{n+2}$ but $g(x_n) > g(x_{n+2})$, contradiction. Thus $c_2 = 0$. Since $x_0 = c_1$ and $x_1 = c_1 r_1$, we have $g(x) = r_1 x$ for all x. Analogously, if g is strictly decreasing, then $c_2 = 0$ or else x_n is dominated by r_1^n for n sufficiently positive. But taking x_n and x_{n+2} for n sufficiently positive of the right parity, we get $0 < x_{n+2} < x_n$ but $g(x_{n+2}) < g(x_n)$, contradiction. Thus in that case, $g(x) = r_2 x$ for all x.

(*Titu Andreescu*, The "William Lowell Putnam" Mathematical Competition, 2001, Problem B-5)

23. Setting $x = y = 0$ yields $f(0) = 0$. For $x = y$ we obtain $f^2(2x) = 4f^2(x)$ and then $f(2x) = 2f(x)$, since $f(x) \geq 0$.

We prove that

$$f(nx) = nf(x), \quad n \geq 1.$$

Assume that $f(kx) = kf(x)$ for all $k = 1, 2, \ldots, n$. We have

$$f^2((n + 1)x) - f^2((n - 1)x) = 4f(nx)f(x),$$

then

$$f^2((n + 1)x) = [(n - 1)^2 + 4n]f^2(x),$$

hence

$$f((n+1)x) = (n+1)f(x),$$

as desired.

It follows that if p, q are positive integers then

$$qf\left(\frac{p}{q}\right) = f(p) = pf(1),$$

so

$$f\left(\frac{p}{q}\right) = \frac{p}{q}f(1)$$

and $f(r) = rf(1)$ for any positive rational r.

Setting $x = 0$ in the initial condition gives

$$f^2(y) - f^2(-y) = 0,$$

then

$$f(y) = f(-y),$$

for all real y, hence

$$f(r) = |r|f(1),$$

for all rational numbers r.

We prove that $f(x) = |x|f(1)$ for all real numbers x. Let x be an arbitrary real number and let $(r_n)_{n\geq 1}$ be a sequence of rational numbers with $\lim_{n\to\infty} r_n = x$. Because

$$f(r_n) = |r_n|f(1)$$

and f is a continuous function, it follows that

$$\lim_{n\to\infty} f(r_n) = \lim_{n\to\infty} |r_n|f(1) = f\left(\lim_{n\to\infty} r_n\right),$$

hence

$$f(x) = f(1)|x|.$$

Note that $a = f(1) \geq 0$, therefore the desired functions are $f(x) = a|x|$ for some $a \geq 0$.

(*Titu Andreescu*, Revista Matematică Timişoara (RMT), No. 2(1977), pp. 90, Problem 3203)

24. (i) Let a and b be fixed points for f and g, respectively. We have

$$a - f(a) \leq 0, \quad b = g(b) \geq 0$$

so $a \leq b$.

Consider the function $\varphi : \mathbb{R} \to \mathbb{R}$, $\varphi(x) = f(x) + g(x) - x$.

The function φ is continuous because functions f and g are continuous. Moreover,

$$\varphi(a) = f(a) + g(a) - a = g(a) \geq 0$$

and
$$\varphi(b) = f(b) + g(b) - b = f(b) \leq 0.$$

By the Intermediate Value Theorem, there is an $x_0 \in (a, b)$ such that $\varphi(x_0) = 0$, hence
$$(f + g)(x_0) = x_0,$$

as desired.

(ii) Let α and β be fixed points of the functions φ and ψ, respectively. We have
$$0 \leq \alpha = \varphi(\alpha) \leq 1, \quad \beta = \psi(\beta) \geq 1 \text{ so } \alpha \leq \beta.$$

Consider the function $\omega : \mathbb{R} \to \mathbb{R}$, $\omega(x) = \varphi(x)\psi(x) - x$.

The function ω is continuous because functions φ and ψ are continuous. Moreover,
$$\omega(\alpha) = \varphi(\alpha)\psi(\alpha) - \alpha = \alpha(\psi(\alpha) - 1) \geq 0,$$
$$\omega(\beta) = \varphi(\beta)\psi(\beta) - \beta = \beta(\varphi(\beta) - 1) \leq 0.$$

Likewise, there is an $\gamma_0 \in [\alpha, \beta]$ such that $\omega(\gamma_0) = 0$, hence $(\varphi\psi)(\gamma_0) = \gamma_0$, as desired.

(*Titu Andreescu*, "Asupra unor funcţii cu punct fix", Revista Matematică Timişoara (RMT), No. 1(1977), pp. 5-10)

25. We have
$$\lim_{x \to 0} \frac{1}{x}\left(\varphi(x) + \varphi\left(\frac{x}{2}\right) + \cdots + \varphi\left(\frac{x}{n}\right)\right) =$$
$$= \lim_{x \to 0}\left(\frac{\varphi(x) - \varphi(0)}{x - 0} + \frac{1}{2}\frac{\varphi\left(\frac{x}{2}\right) - \varphi(0)}{\frac{x}{2} - 0} + \cdots + \frac{1}{n}\frac{\varphi\left(\frac{x}{n}\right) - \varphi(0)}{\frac{x}{n} - 0}\right) =$$
$$= \varphi'(0)\left(1 + \frac{1}{2} + \cdots + \frac{1}{n}\right),$$

since $\varphi(0) = 0$ and φ is differentiable at the origin.

(*Titu Andreescu*, Revista Matematică Timişoara (RMT), No. 2(1977), pp. 71, Problem 3095; Gazeta Matematică (GM-B), No. 3(1979), pp. 111, Problem 17671)

26. Consider the function $f : (0, \infty) \to \mathbb{R}$, $f(x) = \dfrac{\ln ax}{x}$.

We have
$$f'(x) = \frac{1 - \ln ax}{x^2}$$

so
$$f'(x) = 0 \text{ if and only if } x = \frac{e}{a}.$$

It follows that $\mu = \dfrac{e}{a}$ is the maximum point of the function f so μ is the only point such that $f(x) \leq f(\mu)$ for all positive real numbers x.

Hence
$$\frac{\mu^x}{x^\mu} \geq a^{\mu - x}$$

for all $x > 0$, as desired.

(*Dorin Andrica*, Revista Matematică Timişoara (RMT), No. 2(1978), pp. 54, Problem 3547)

27. Consider the function $F : [a, b] \to \mathbb{R}$,

$$F(x) = f(x)e^{-\lambda f(x)}, \quad \lambda \in \mathbb{R}.$$

Function F is differentiable, since f and f' are differentiable, and $F(a) = F(b)$. By Rolle's theorem it follows that there is $c \in (a, b)$ such that $F'(c) = 0$.

On the other hand,

$$F'(x) = e^{-\lambda f(x)}(f''(x) - \lambda(f'(x))^2),$$

hence $f''(c) - \lambda(f'(c))^2 = 0$, as desired.

(*Dorin Andrica*, Revista Matematică Timişoara (RMT), No. 2(1981), pp. 76, Problem 4677)

28. Let $g : [0, 2] \to \left[0, \dfrac{\pi}{2}\right)$, $g(x) = \arccos f(x)$. Then

$$f(x) = \cos g(x)$$

for all $x \in [0, 2]$ and the condition is equivalent to

$$\cos g(2x) = \cos 2g(x).$$

It follows that

$$g(2x) = 2g(x) + k(x)\pi$$

for all $x \in [0, 1]$, where $k : [0, 1] \to \mathbb{Z}$.

On the other hand, $0 \le g(x) < \dfrac{\pi}{2}$ for all $x \in [0, 2]$, hence $k(x) = 0$ and

$$g(2x) = 2g(x), \quad x \in [0, 1]$$

By induction on n we obtain

$$g(x) = 2^n g\left(\frac{x}{2^n}\right).$$

Because $f(0) = 1$, $g(0) = \arccos 1 = 0$, so

$$\frac{g(x)}{x} = \frac{g\left(\dfrac{x}{2^n}\right) - g(0)}{\dfrac{x}{2^n}}$$

for all $x \in (0, 2]$.

Since f is differentiable at the origin g is differentiable at the origin and

$$\frac{g(x)}{x} = \lim_{n \to \infty} \frac{g\left(\dfrac{x}{2^n}\right) - g(0)}{\dfrac{x}{2^n}} - = g'(0)$$

for all $x \in (0, 2]$.

It follows that $g(x) = \mu x$, where $\mu = g'(0) \in \left[0, \frac{\pi}{4}\right)$, because $0 \le g(x) < \frac{\pi}{2}$ for all $x \in [0, 2]$.

Therefore the desired functions are

$$f_\mu(x) = \cos \mu x, \quad \mu \in \left[0, \frac{\pi}{4}\right).$$

(*Titu Andreescu*, Revista Matematică Timişoara (RMT), No. 1(1977), pp. 45, Problem 2852)

29. Consider the function $f : (0, \infty) \to \mathbb{R}$, $f(x) = \dfrac{\ln x}{x^\lambda}$.

Then

$$f'(x) = \frac{1 - \lambda \ln x}{x^{\lambda+1}},$$

and $f'(x) = 0$ for $x = e^{\frac{1}{\lambda}}$.

It follows that $\theta = e^{1/\lambda}$ is the only maximum point of the function, so

$$f(x) \le f(e^{\frac{1}{\lambda}}), \quad x > 0.$$

Hence

$$\frac{\ln x}{x^\lambda} \le \frac{\ln \theta}{\theta^\lambda} \text{ or } x^{\theta^\lambda} \le \theta^{x^\lambda},$$

only for $\theta = e^{\frac{1}{\lambda}}$.

(*Dorin Andrica*, Gazeta Matematică (GM-B), No. 3(1976), pp. 104, Problem 15768; Revista Matematică Timişoara (RMT), No. 1-2(1979), pp. 57, Problem 3870)

30. a) Let $\lambda > \mu$ and let $y = x\mu$. Then

$$\lim_{x \to 0} \frac{f(\lambda x) - f(\mu x)}{x} = \lim_{y \to 0} \frac{f\left(\dfrac{\lambda}{\mu}y\right) - f(y)}{\dfrac{y}{\mu}} = A,$$

so

$$\lim_{y \to 0} \frac{f(\alpha y) - f(y)}{y} = \frac{A}{\mu} = a,$$

where $\alpha = \dfrac{\lambda}{\mu} > 1$.

Let $\varepsilon > 0$. Then there is a $\delta > 0$ such that for any $|y| < \delta$, we have

$$a - \varepsilon < \frac{f(\alpha y) - f(y)}{y} < a + \varepsilon. \tag{1}$$

Substituting y with $\dfrac{y}{\alpha^k}$, $k = 1, 2, \ldots, n$, in the relation (1) we obtain

$$\frac{1}{\alpha}(a - \varepsilon) < \frac{f(y) - f\left(\dfrac{y}{\alpha}\right)}{y} < \frac{1}{\alpha}(a + \varepsilon),$$

$$\frac{1}{\alpha^2}(a - \varepsilon) < \frac{f\left(\dfrac{y}{\alpha}\right) - f\left(\dfrac{y}{\alpha^2}\right)}{y} < \frac{1}{\alpha^2}(a + \varepsilon),$$

$$\cdots$$

$$\frac{1}{\alpha^n}(a-\varepsilon) < \frac{f\left(\frac{y}{\alpha^{n-1}}\right) - f\left(\frac{y}{\alpha^n}\right)}{y} < \frac{1}{\alpha^n}(a+\varepsilon).$$

Summing up these inequalities yields

$$\frac{1}{\alpha}\frac{1-\frac{1}{\alpha^n}}{1-\frac{1}{\alpha}}(a-\varepsilon) < \frac{f(y) - f\left(\frac{y}{\alpha^n}\right)}{y} < \frac{1}{\alpha}\frac{1-\frac{1}{\alpha^n}}{1-\frac{1}{\alpha}}(a+\varepsilon).$$

Because f is continuous at the origin

$$\lim_{n\to\infty} f\left(\frac{y}{\alpha^n}\right) = f(0),$$

and so

$$\frac{1}{\alpha-1}(a-\varepsilon) \le \frac{f(y) - f(0)}{y} \le \frac{1}{\alpha-1}(a+\varepsilon).$$

It follows that

$$f'(0) = \lim_{y\to 0} \frac{f(y) - f(0)}{y} = \frac{a}{\alpha-1} = \frac{A}{\lambda-\mu},$$

so the function f is differentiable at the origin.

Conversely, if f is differentiable at the origin, then

$$\lim_{x\to 0} \frac{f(\lambda x) - f(0)}{\lambda x} = f'(0) \quad \text{and} \quad \lim_{x\to 0} \frac{f(\mu x) - f(0)}{\mu x} = f'(0).$$

Hence

$$\lim_{x\to 0} \frac{f(\lambda x) - f(\mu x)}{x} = (\lambda-\mu)f'(0),$$

as desired.

(*Dorin Andrica*, Revista Matematică Timişoara (RMT), No. 2(1978), pp. 76, Problem 3708)

31. Since $e^x > 1 + x$ for all real $x \ne 0$, we have $x_{n+1} - x_n = e^{x_n} - 1 - x_n > 0$ so the sequence $(x_n)_{n\ge 1}$ is increasing. By induction on n we obtain $x_n < 0$ for all $n \ge 1$, so the sequence $(x_n)_{n\ge 1}$ is bounded. Therefore the sequence converges and let l be its limit. The equation $e^l = l + 1$ has the unique solution $l = 0$, hence $\lim_{n\to\infty} x_n = 0$.

Using $\lim_{x\to 0} \left(\frac{1}{x} - \frac{1}{e^x - 1}\right) = \frac{1}{2}$, it follows that

$$\lim_{n\to\infty} \frac{\frac{1}{x_{n+1}} - \frac{1}{x_n}}{(n+1) - n} = \lim_{n\to\infty} \frac{\frac{1}{e^{x_n} - 1} - \frac{1}{x_n}}{1} = -\frac{1}{2}.$$

Cesaro-Stolz's Theorem implies

$$\lim_{n\to\infty} \frac{1}{nx_n} = -\frac{1}{2},$$

hence $\lim_{n\to\infty} nx_n = -2$, as desired.

(*Dorin Andrica*, Revista Matematică Timisoara (RMT), No. 2(1982), pp. 68, Problem 5004)

32. We first prove by induction that $x_n > 0$. This is true for $n = 0$ and assuming $x_k > 0$ for some positive integer k yields $0 < \sin x_k < 1$, hence $\sin^3 x_k < \sin x_k$, which implies $x_{k+1} > x_k - \arcsin(\sin x_k) = 0$.

It is not difficult to see that $(x_n)_{n \geq 0}$ is convergent and $\lim\limits_{n \to \infty} x_n = 0$. We have

$$(\sqrt{n} \sin x_n)^2 = \frac{n}{\dfrac{1}{\sin^2 x_n}}$$

and

$$\lim_{n \to \infty} \frac{n+1-n}{\dfrac{1}{\sin^2 x_{n+1}} - \dfrac{1}{\sin^2 x_n}} = \lim_{n \to \infty} \frac{\sin^2 x_{n+1} \sin^2 x_n}{\sin^2 x_n - \sin^2 x_{n+1}} =$$

$$= \lim_{n \to \infty} \frac{\sin^2 x_{n+1} \sin^2 x_n}{\sin(x_n - x_{n+1}) \sin(x_n + x_{n+1})} = \lim_{n \to \infty} \frac{\sin^2 x_{n+1} \sin^2 x_n}{x_n^3 \sin(x_n + x_{n+1})} =$$

$$= \lim_{n \to \infty} \left(\frac{\sin x_{n+1}}{x_{n+1}} \right)^2 \lim_{n \to \infty} \left(\frac{\sin x_n}{x_n} \right)^2 \lim_{n \to \infty} \frac{x_n + x_{n+1}}{\sin(x_n + x_{n+1})} \cdot$$

$$\cdot \lim_{n \to \infty} \frac{x_n}{x_{n+1}} \lim_{n \to \infty} \frac{1}{1 + \dfrac{x_{n+1}}{x_n}} = \frac{1}{2}.$$

From Cesaro-Stolz Theorem we obtain

$$\lim_{n \to \infty} \frac{n}{\dfrac{1}{\sin^2 x_n}} = \frac{1}{2},$$

hence

$$\lim_{n \to \infty} (\sqrt{n} x_n)^2 = \lim_{n \to \infty} \frac{n}{\dfrac{1}{\sin^2 x_n}} \lim_{n \to \infty} \left(\frac{x_n}{\sin x_n} \right)^2 = \frac{1}{2}.$$

Thus $\lim\limits_{n \to \infty} \sqrt{n} x_n = \dfrac{\sqrt{2}}{2}$.

Alternative Solution. We have seen above that $(x_n)_{n \geq 0}$ is convergent, $\lim\limits_{n \to \infty} x_n = 0$ and $x_n > 0$ for all $n = 0, 1, 2, \ldots$ We will calculate

$$\lim_{n \to \infty} \frac{n+1-n}{\dfrac{1}{x_{n+1}^2} - \dfrac{1}{x_n^2}} = \lim_{n \to \infty} \frac{1}{\dfrac{1}{(x_n - \arcsin(\sin^3 x_n))^2} - \dfrac{1}{x_n^2}}. \tag{1}$$

It is clear that the last limit is obtained from

$$\lim_{t \to 0} \left[\frac{1}{(\arcsin t - \arcsin t^3)^2} - \frac{1}{\arcsin^2 t} \right] = \lim_{t \to 0} \frac{(\arcsin t^3)(2 \arcsin t - \arcsin t^3)}{(\arcsin t - \arcsin t^3)^2 \arcsin^2 t} =$$

$$= \lim_{t \to 0} \frac{t(2\arcsin t - \arcsin t^3)}{(\arcsin t - \arcsin t^3)^2} = \lim_{t \to 0} \frac{\left(2\dfrac{\arcsin t}{t} - t^2\dfrac{\arcsin t^3}{t^3}\right)}{\left(\dfrac{\arcsin t}{t} - t^2\dfrac{\arcsin t^3}{t^3}\right)^2} = 2.$$

It follows that the limit (1) is $\dfrac{1}{2}$ and the conclusion is obtained via Cesaro-Stoltz Theorem.

(*Titu Andreescu*, Gazeta Matematică (GM-B), No. 10(2002), pp. 409, Problem C:2557)

33. Let x be a zero of f'. Then $f(x + f'(x)) = f(x)$ and the conclusion follows.

Let x be a real number such that $f'(x) < 0$. Applying the Mean Value Theorem on the interval $[x + f'(x), x]$ we obtain

$$f(x) - f(x + f'(x)) = -f'(x)f'(c),$$

for some $c \in (x + f'(x), x)$. Because the second derivative is nonnegative, f' is non-decreasing, hence

$$f'(c) < f'(x) < 0,$$

and

$$f(x) - f(x + f'(x)) < 0,$$

as desired.

Let x be a real number such that $f'(x) > 0$. Likewise,

$$f(x + f'(x)) - f(x) = f'(x)f'(c),$$

for some $c \in (x, x + f'(x))$ and $f'(c) > f'(x) > 0$. Hence $f(x + f'(x)) \geq f(x)$ for all real numbers x, as claimed.

(*Dorin Andrica*, Revista Matematică Timişoara (RMT), No. 1-2(1989), pp. 67, Problem 6143)

34. Applying the Mean Value Theorem for the function $f(t) = \ln t$ on the interval $\left[a, \dfrac{a+b}{2}\right]$ yields

$$\frac{\ln\dfrac{a+b}{2} - \ln a}{\dfrac{b-a}{2}} = \frac{1}{x}, \quad x \in \left(a, \frac{a+b}{2}\right).$$

Hence

$$\ln\left(\frac{a+b}{2a}\right)^x = \frac{b-a}{2}. \tag{1}$$

Using the same argument for the interval $\left[\dfrac{a+b}{2}, b\right]$ gives

$$\frac{\ln b - \ln \dfrac{a+b}{2}}{\dfrac{b-a}{2}} = \frac{1}{y}, \quad y \in \left(\frac{a+b}{2}, b\right),$$

hence

$$\ln \left(\frac{2b}{a+b}\right)^y = \frac{b-a}{2}. \tag{2}$$

From the equalities (1) and (2) we obtain

$$\left(\frac{a+b}{2a}\right)^x = \left(\frac{2b}{a+b}\right)^y.$$

Then

$$\left(\frac{a+b}{2}\right)^{x+y} = a^x b^y,$$

as desired.

(*Dorin Andrica*, Revista Matematică Timişoara (RMT), No. 2(1978), pp. 54, Problem 3548)

35. We prove that no such function exists. Assume the contrary and let k be an integer. From the Mean Value Theorem we obtain

$$\varphi(k+1) - \varphi(k) = \varphi'(\xi), \quad \xi \in (k, k+1).$$

Since $\varphi(k)$ and $\varphi(k+1)$ are integers, $\varphi(k+1) - \varphi(k)$ is also an integer and so is $\varphi'(\xi)$.

On the other hand, ξ is not an integer, hence $\varphi'(\xi)$ is not integer, a contradiction.

(*Dorin Andrica*, Revista Matematică Timişoara (RMT), No. 2(1978), pp. 67, Problem 3618)

36. Define $x_k = a + \dfrac{k}{n}(b-a)$, $k = 0, 1, \dots, n$ and note that

$$x_{k+1} - x_k = \frac{b-a}{n}, \quad k = 0, 1, \dots, n.$$

The Mean Value Theorem yields

$$f(x_1) - f(x_0) = \frac{b-a}{n} f'(\theta_1), \quad \theta_1 \in (x_0, x_1)$$

$$f(x_2) - f(x_1) = \frac{b-a}{n} f'(\theta_2), \quad \theta_2 \in (x_1, x_2)$$

$$\cdots$$

$$f(x_n) - f(x_{n-1}) = \frac{b-a}{n} f'(\theta_n), \quad \theta_n \in (x_{n-1}, x_n)$$

Summing up these equalities implies

$$f(x_n) - f(x_0) = \frac{b-a}{n} \sum_{i=1}^{n} f'(\theta_i),$$

or

$$\frac{f(b) - f(a)}{b-a} = \frac{1}{n} \sum_{i=1}^{n} f'(\theta_i),$$

as desired.

(*Dorin Andrica*, Revista Matematică Timişoara (RMT), No. 1-2(1979), pp. 58, Problem 3878)

37. Let $F : \mathbb{R} \to \mathbb{R}$, $F(x) = f(x) - g(x)$ and note that F is differentiable. Since $F(x_1) = F(x_2) = 0$ from Rolle's Theorem there is $c \in (x_1, x_2)$ such that $F'(c) = 0$.

On the other hand, $F'(x) = f'(x) - g'(x) = f(x) + g(x)$, and therefore

$$f(c) + g(c) = 0,$$

as desired.

(*Dorin Andrica*, Revista Matematică Timişoara (RMT), No. 2(1977), pp. 74, Problem 3113)

38. Assume that $(f(x))^2 + (f'(x))^2 > 1$ for all x in $\left[-\frac{\pi}{2}, \frac{\pi}{2}\right]$. Then

$$\frac{f'(x)}{\sqrt{1 - (f(x))^2}} > 1$$

for all $x \in \left[-\frac{\pi}{2}, \frac{\pi}{2}\right]$. Integrating from $-\frac{\pi}{2}$ to $\frac{\pi}{2}$ yields $\arcsin f\left(\frac{\pi}{2}\right) - \arcsin f\left(-\frac{\pi}{2}\right) > \pi$. On the other hand, it is clear that $\arcsin f\left(\frac{\pi}{2}\right) - \arcsin f\left(-\frac{\pi}{2}\right) \le \frac{\pi}{2} + \frac{\pi}{2} = \pi$. contradicting the previous inequality.

(*Titu Andreescu*, Mathematical Horizons, 2000)

39. If $x = y$, then $x = y = 0$, which is impossible, because x and y are positive. Assume that there are $x \ne y > 0$ such that

$$x \cdot 2^y + y \cdot 2^{-x} = x + y,$$

and let $y = x_1 - x_2$, $x = x_2 - x_3$ for some $x_1 > x_2 > x_3 > 0$.

Then

$$\frac{2^{x_1 - x_2} - 1}{1 - 2^{x_3 - x_2}} = \frac{x_1 - x_2}{x_2 - x_3},$$

or

$$\frac{2^{x_1} - 2^{x_2}}{x_1 - x_2} = \frac{2^{x_2} - 2^{x_3}}{x_2 - x_3}.$$

By the Mean Value Theorem there are $\theta_1 \in (x_2, x_1)$ and $\theta_2 \in (x_3, x_2)$ such that

$$\frac{2^{x_1} - 2^{x_2}}{x_1 - x_2} = 2^{\theta_1} \ln 2, \ \theta_1 \in (x_2, x_1) \quad \text{and} \quad \frac{2^{x_2} - 2^{x_3}}{x_2 - x_3} = 2^{\theta_2} \ln 2, \ \theta_2 \in (x_3, x_2)$$

Hence $2^{\theta_1} \ln 2 = 2^{\theta_2} \ln 2$, that implies $\theta_1 = \theta_2$, a contradiction.

(*Dorin Andrica*, Revista Matematică Timişoara (RMT), No. 1-2(1980), pp. 70, Problem 4152)

40. a) Consider the differentiable function $f : (0, \infty) \to \mathbb{R}$,

$$f(t) = \sqrt[n]{t} - \sqrt[n+1]{t}.$$

We have

$$f'(t) = \frac{1}{n} t^{\frac{1}{n+1}-1} \left(t^{\frac{1}{n(n+1)}} - \frac{n}{n+1} \right),$$

so, if $t \geq \left(\dfrac{n}{n+1} \right)^{n(n+1)}$, then $f'(t) \geq 0$. Hence f is increasing on $\left[\left(\dfrac{n}{n+1} \right)^{n(n+1)}, \infty \right)$ and for $x \geq y \geq \left(\dfrac{n}{n+1} \right)^{n(n+1)}$, we have $f(x) \geq f(y)$. Therefore

$$\sqrt[n]{x} + \sqrt[n+1]{y} \geq \sqrt[n]{y} + \sqrt[n+1]{x},$$

as desired.

b) We prove that

$$n^{n+1} \geq (n+1)^n$$

for all $n \geq 3$.

The inequality is equivalent to

$$\left(1 + \frac{1}{n} \right)^n \leq n,$$

which is clearly true, because

$$\left(1 + \frac{1}{n} \right)^n < e < 3$$

for all $n \geq 1$.

Setting $x = n^{n+1}$ and $y = (n+1)^n$, $x \geq y$ in the inequality from a) yields

$$n \sqrt[n]{n} + \frac{n+1}{\sqrt[n+1]{n+1}} \geq 2n+1, \quad n \geq 3$$

as desired.

(*Dorin Andrica*, Revista Matematică Timişoara (RMT), No. 2(1981), pp. 74, Problem 4668)

41. Recall Jensen's inequality for a concave function f:

$$\frac{\displaystyle\sum_{i=1}^{n} \lambda_i f(x_i)}{\displaystyle\sum_{i=1}^{n} \lambda_i} \underset{(\leq)}{\geq} f\left(\frac{\displaystyle\sum_{i=1}^{n} \lambda_i x_i}{\displaystyle\sum_{i=1}^{n} \lambda_i} \right)$$

Consider $f(x) = \ln x$, $y_i = \dfrac{1}{x_i}$, $p = y_1 y_2 \ldots y_n$ and $\lambda_i = \dfrac{p}{y_i}$ for $i = 1, 2, \ldots, n$. We have

$$\frac{\displaystyle\sum_{i=1}^{n} \frac{p}{y_i} \ln y_i}{\displaystyle\sum_{i=1}^{n} \frac{p}{y_i}} \leq \ln \left(\frac{\displaystyle\sum_{i=1}^{n} p}{\displaystyle\sum_{i=1}^{n} \frac{p}{y_i}} \right),$$

so

$$\ln \left(y_1^{\frac{1}{y_1}} y_2^{\frac{1}{y_2}} \ldots y_n^{\frac{1}{y_n}} \right) \leq \ln \left(\frac{n}{\displaystyle\sum_{i=1}^{n} \frac{1}{y_i}} \right)^{\sum_{i=1}^{n} \frac{1}{y_i}}.$$

Hence

$$y_1^{\frac{1}{y_1}} y_2^{\frac{1}{y_2}} \ldots y_n^{\frac{1}{y_n}} \leq \ln \left(\frac{n}{\displaystyle\sum_{i=1}^{n} \frac{1}{y_i}} \right)^{\sum_{i=1}^{n} \frac{1}{y_i}},$$

and since $y_i = \dfrac{1}{x_i}$, $i = 1, 2, \ldots n$, it follows that

$$\frac{1}{x_1^{x_1} x_2^{x_2} \ldots x_n^{x_n}} \leq \left(\frac{n}{\displaystyle\sum_{i=1}^{n} x_i} \right)^{\sum_{i=1}^{n} x_i} = n,$$

thus

$$x_1^{x_1} x_2^{x_2} \ldots x_n^{x_n} \geq \frac{1}{n},$$

as desired.

(*Dorin Andrica*, Revista Matematică Timişoara (RMT), No. 2(1977), pp. 74, Problem 3111)

42. Let F be an antiderivative of the function f. Since F is noninjective, there are real numbers $x_1 < x_2$ such that $F(x_1) = F(x_2)$. Applying Rolle's Theorem on the interval $[x_1, x_2]$ we obtain $f(c) = F'(c) = 0$ for some $c \in (x_1, x_2)$, as desired.

(*Titu Andreescu*)

43. Because

$$\max(f_1(x), f_2(x)) = \frac{f_1(x) + f_2(x) + |f_1(x) - f_2(x)|}{2}$$

and f_1, f_2 are continuous, $\max(f_1, f_2)$ is also continuous. Assume that if $f_1, f_2, \ldots, f_{k-1}$ are continuous, then $\max(f_1, f_2, \ldots, f_{k-1})$ is continuous. It follows that

$$\max(f_1, f_2, \ldots f_k) = \max(\max(f_1, \ldots, f_{k-1}), f_k)$$

and according to the first step, the function $\max(f_1, \ldots, f_k)$ is continuous. Hence $\max(f_1, \ldots, f_n)$ is continuous and furthermore a derivative function.

Note that if n is even, then

$$\max(1, x, \ldots, x^n) = \begin{cases} x^n, & x \in (-\infty, -1) \\ 1, & x \in [-1, 1] \\ x^n, & x \in (1, \infty), \end{cases}$$

and

$$\int \max(1, x, \ldots, x^n) dx = \begin{cases} \dfrac{x^{n+1} - n}{n+1} + C, & x \in (-\infty, -1) \\ x + C, & x \in [-1, 1] \\ \dfrac{x^{n+1} + n}{n+1} + C, & x \in (1, \infty). \end{cases}$$

On the other hand, if n is odd, then

$$\max(1, x, \ldots, x^n) = \begin{cases} x^{n-1}, & x \in (-\infty, -1) \\ 1, & x \in [-1, 1] \\ x^n, & x \in (1, \infty), \end{cases}$$

and

$$\int \max(1, x, \ldots, x^n) dx = \begin{cases} \dfrac{x^n - n + 1}{n} + C, & x \in (-\infty, -1) \\ x + C, & x \in [-1, 1] \\ \dfrac{x^{n+1} + n}{n+1} + C, & x \in (1, \infty). \end{cases}$$

(*Dorin Andrica*, Revista Matematică Timişoara (RMT), No. 2(1983), pp. 62 Problem 5185)

44. Denote

$$I_1 = \int \frac{e^{\operatorname{arctg}x}}{\sqrt{1 + x^2}} dx \text{ and } I_2 = \int \frac{x e^{\operatorname{arctg}x}}{\sqrt{1 + x^2}} dx.$$

We have

$$I_1 = \int \frac{e^{\operatorname{arctg}x}}{\sqrt{1 + x^2}} dx = \int \frac{\sqrt{1 + x^2} e^{\operatorname{arctg}x}}{1 + x^2} dx =$$

$$= \int \sqrt{1 + x^2} d(e^{\operatorname{arctg}x}) = \sqrt{1 + x^2} e^{\operatorname{arctg}x} - \int \frac{x e^{\operatorname{arctg}x}}{\sqrt{1 + x^2}} dx =$$

$$= \sqrt{1 + x^2} e^{\operatorname{arctg}x} - I_2,$$

hence

$$I_1 + I_2 = \sqrt{1 + x^2} e^{\operatorname{arctg}x}.$$

On the other hand,

$$I_2 = \int \frac{x e^{\operatorname{arctg} x}}{\sqrt{1+x^2}} dx = \int \frac{x 1 + x^2 e^{\operatorname{arctg} x}}{1+x^2} dx = \int x\sqrt{1+x^2} d(e^{\operatorname{arctg} x}) =$$

$$= x\sqrt{1+x^2} e^{\operatorname{arctg} x} - I_1 - 2 \int \frac{x^2 e^{\operatorname{arctg} x}}{\sqrt{1+x^2}} dx,$$

so

$$\int \frac{x^2 e^{\operatorname{arctg} x}}{\sqrt{1+x^2}} dx = \frac{x\sqrt{1+x^2} e^{\operatorname{arctg} x} - (I_1 + I_2)}{2} =$$

$$= \frac{(x-1)\sqrt{1+x^2} e^{\operatorname{arctg} x}}{2} + C.$$

(*Dorin Andrica*, Romanian Mathematical Olympiad - final round, 1975; Revista Matematică Timişoara (RMT), No. 2(1978), pp. 35, Problem 2125)

45. We start with the following lemma.

Lemma. *Let $g, h : \mathbb{R} \to \mathbb{R}$ be functions such that:*

1) h is a derivative;

2) g is differentiable with a continuous derivative.

Then $g \cdot h$ is a derivative function.

Proof. Let H be an antiderivative of h and define $u : \mathbb{R} \to \mathbb{R}$, $u(x) = g(x)H(x)$. Then

$$u'(x) = g(x)h(x) + g'(x)H(x),$$

or $g(x)h(x) = u'(x) - g'(x)H(x)$.

The function u' is a derivative and $g' \cdot H$ is continuous, hence the function $g \cdot h$ is a derivative, as claimed. $\square$

Applying the lemma for $h = f \circ p$ and $g(x) = x^k$ for a nonnegative integer k, it follows that $x^k (f \circ p)(x)$ is a derivative, hence $p'(f \circ p)$ is a derivative. Since the degree of p is odd, $p(\mathbb{R}) = \mathbb{R}$. Assuming that $\lim_{x \to -\infty} p(x) = -\infty$, there are real numbers $x_1, x_1', x_2', \ldots, x_m, x_m'$ such that p is increasing on each of the interval $(-\infty, x_1], [x_1', x_2], \ldots, [x_{m-1}', x_m], [x_m', \infty)$ and $p(x_1) = p(x_1') = M_1$, $p(x_2) = p(x_2') = M_2, \ldots, p(x_m) = p(x_m') = M_m$. Let $F_1, H_1, \ldots, H_m$ be an antiderivative of $p(f \circ p)$ on the interval $(-\infty, x_1], [x_1', x_2], \ldots, [x_m', \infty)$, respectively. It follows that $F_1 \circ p^{-1}, H_1 \circ p^{-1}, \ldots, H_m \circ p^{-1}$ are antiderivative of f on the intervals $(-\infty, M_1], [M_1, M_2], \ldots, [M_m, \infty)$, respectively, hence f is a derivative function on all $\mathbb{R}$.

(*Dorin Andrica*, Revista Matematică Timişoara (RMT), No. 2(1985), pp. 76, Problem 2)

46. Substituting $x \to \dfrac{1}{x}$ in the given condition yields

$$F\left(\frac{1}{x}\right) f(x) = \frac{1}{x}, \tag{1}$$

for all x in I. We have

$$g'(x) = F'(x)F\left(\frac{1}{x}\right) + F(x)F'\left(\frac{1}{x}\right)\left(-\frac{1}{x^2}\right) = f(x)F\left(\frac{1}{x}\right) - \frac{1}{x^2}f\left(\frac{1}{x}\right)F(x) \overset{(1)}{=\!=\!=}$$

$$= \frac{1}{x} - \frac{1}{x^2} \cdot x = 0$$

for all x in I, so g is constant. Then there is a constant $c > 0$ such that $F(x)F\left(\frac{1}{x}\right) = c$ for all x in I, and from (1) we obtain

$$\frac{f(x)}{F(x)} = \frac{1}{cx}, \quad x \in I.$$

Integrating gives $\ln F(x) = \frac{1}{c}\ln x + \ln d$, where $d > 0$. It follows that $F(x) = dx^{\frac{1}{c}}$, for all x in I. The relation $F(x)F\left(\frac{1}{x}\right) = c$ becomes $d^2 = c$, so $d = \sqrt{c}$.

Finally,

$$f(x) = \frac{1}{xF\left(\frac{1}{x}\right)} = \frac{1}{\sqrt{c}}x^{\frac{1}{c}-1}, \quad x \in I,$$

where c is any positive real constant.

(*Titu Andreescu*, Romanian Mathematical Olympiad - final round, 1987; Revista Matematică Timişoara (RMT), No. 2(1987), pp. 86, Problem 6307)

47. Consider the function $g : [0,1] \to \mathbb{R}$,

$$g(x) = f(x) - (1 + x + \cdots + x^{n-1})$$

and note that g is continuous. We have

$$\int_0^1 g(x)dx = \int_0^1 g(x)dx - \int_0^1 (1 + x + \cdots + x^{n-1})dx =$$

$$= \int_0^1 f(x)dx - \left(1 + \frac{1}{2} + \cdots + \frac{1}{n}\right) = 0.$$

From the Mean Value Theorem there is $x_0 \in (0,1)$ such that

$$g(x_0) = \int_0^1 g(x)dx = 0,$$

hence

$$f(x_0) = 1 + x_0 + \cdots + x_0^{n-1} = \frac{1 - x_0^n}{1 - x_0},$$

as desired.

(*Titu Andreescu*, Revista Matematică Timişoara (RMT), No. 1-2(1979), pp. 33, Problem 3444)

48. Consider the function $F : [a, b] \to \mathbb{R}$,

$$F(x) = \int_a^x g(t)dt \int_x^b f(t)dt.$$

Note that F is differentiable and $F(a) = F(b) = 0$. Applying Rolle's Theorem, we obtain $c \in (a, b)$ such that $F'(c) = 0$ hence

$$f(c) \int_a^c g(t)dt = g(c) \int_c^b f(t)dt,$$

as desired.

(*Dorin Andrica*)

49. Consider the function $F : [a, b] \to \mathbb{R}$,

$$F(t) = \int_a^t f(x)dx - \int_t^b f(x)dx$$

and observe that F is continuous and $F(a)F(b) < 0$. Then there is $\alpha \in (a, b)$ such that $F(\alpha) = 0$ so

$$\int_a^\alpha f(x)dx = \int_\alpha^b f(x)dx.$$

From the Mean Value Theorem there is $\beta \in (\alpha, b)$ such that

$$\int_\alpha^b f(x)dx = (b - \alpha)f(\beta),$$

therefore there are numbers $\alpha, \beta \in (a, b)$, $\alpha < \beta$, with

$$\int_a^\alpha f(x)dx = (b - \alpha)f(\beta),$$

as claimed.

(*Dorin Andrica*, Revista Matematică Timişoara (RMT), No. 1-2(1979), pp. 61, Problem 3897)

50. Since f is an increasing bijective function, f is continuous.

Denote

$$S_1 = \int_a^b f(x)dx, \quad S_2 = \int_c^d f^{-1}(y)dy,$$

and note from the diagram below that

$$S_1 + S_2 = bc - ac. \tag{1}$$

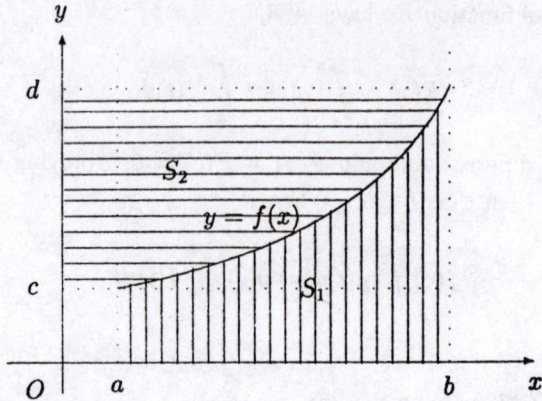

From the Mean Value Theorem there is $\xi \in (c, d)$ such that

$$\int_c^d f^{-1}(y)dy = (d - c)f^{-1}(\xi).$$

Observe that ξ is unique and let $\mu = f^{-1}(\xi)$. The relation (1) gives

$$\int_a^b f(t)dt = (\mu - a)c + (b - \mu)d, \quad \mu \in (a, b),$$

as desired.

(*Dorin Andrica*, Revista Matematică Timişoara (RMT), No. 2(1978), pp. 56, Problem 3556)

51. Consider the function $F : \mathbb{R} \to \mathbb{R}$,

$$F(s) = \int_0^s \varphi(t)dt,$$

and note that F is differentiable.

From the hypothesis we obtain $F(x + y) - F(x) = F(x) - F(x - y)$, so

$$F(x + y) + F(x - y) = 2F(x), \quad x, y \in \mathbb{R}.$$

Differentiating with respect to y it follows that

$$F'(x + y) = F'(x - y), \quad x, y \in \mathbb{R}.$$

Setting $x = y = \dfrac{z}{2}$, $z \in \mathbb{R}$, we obtain $F'(z) = F'(0)$, so $\varphi(z) = F'(0)$ for all $z \in \mathbb{R}$. Hence φ is a constant function, as desired.

(*Titu Andreescu*, Revista Matematică Timişoara (RMT), No. 1(1977), pp. 47, Problem 2865)

52. Consider the function $\varphi : \mathbb{R} \to \mathbb{R}$, $\varphi(s) = \int_0^s f(t)dt$. The condition is equivalent to

$$\int_0^x f(t)dt + \int_0^y f(t)dt \geq 2 \int_0^{\frac{x+y}{2}} f(t)dt,$$

hence

$$\frac{\varphi(x) + \varphi(y)}{2} \geq \varphi\left(\frac{x+y}{2}\right) \tag{1}$$

for all $x, y \in \mathbb{R}$.

Since f is differentiable, φ is twice differentiable and moreover is concave up, from relation (1). Hence $\varphi''(x) \geq 0$ or $f'(x) \geq 0$ for all x, so f is a nondecreasing function.

(*Titu Andreescu*, Revista Matematică Timişoara (RMT), No. 1(1976), pp. 56, Problem 2349; Gazeta Matematică (GM-B), No. 2(1980), pp. 68, Problem 18154)

53. Consider the function $h : [0, \infty) \to \mathbb{R}$,

$$h(x) = x f(x) - \int_0^x f(t) dt.$$

Because f is differentiable, h is differentiable and

$$h(x) = x f'(x), \quad x \geq 0. \tag{1}$$

Since f is injective and continuous, f is either increasing or decreasing, so $f'(x) \leq 0$ for all x or $f'(x) \geq 0$ for all real numbers x.

Case 1. If $f'(x) \leq 0$ for all x, then from (1) we deduce that $h'(x) \leq 0$, $x \geq 0$, hence h is nondecreasing. It follows that $h(x) \leq h(0) = 0$, $x \geq 0$.

Case 2. If $f'(x) \geq 0$ for all x, then $h'(x) \geq 0$, $x \geq 0$, and h is nonincreasing. It follows that $h(x) \geq h(0) = 0$, $x \geq 0$.

Since F is differentiable and

$$F'(x) = \frac{x f(x) - \int_0^x f(t) dt}{x^2} = \frac{h(x)}{x^2},$$

we derive that $F'(x) \leq 0$ for all $x > 0$ or $F'(x) \geq 0$ for all $x > 0$, hence F is a monotonic function, as desired.

(*Titu Andreescu*, Revista Matematică Timişoara (RMT), No. 2(1978), pp. 76, Problem 3709; Gazeta Matematică (GM-B), No. 1(1980), pp. 38, Problem 18115)

54. Recall from Problem 14 that

$$\lim_{\substack{x \to 0 \\ x > 0}} x^x = 1,$$

and let $\varepsilon > 0$. There is $\delta > 0$ such that for all $x < \delta$, $|x^x - 1| < \varepsilon$.

Then for $n > \frac{1}{\delta}$ we obtain

$$\left| n^2 \int_0^{\frac{1}{n}} (x^{x+1} - x) dx \right| \leq n^2 \int_0^{\frac{1}{n}} |x^{x+1} - x| dx =$$

$$= n^2 \int_0^{\frac{1}{n}} x |x^x - 1| dx < \varepsilon n^2 \int_0^{\frac{1}{n}} x dx = \frac{\varepsilon}{2}.$$

It follows that

$$\lim_{n\to\infty} n^2 \int_0^{\frac{1}{n}} (x^{x+1} - x)dx = 0,$$

hence

$$\lim_{n\to\infty} n^2 \int_0^{\frac{1}{n}} x^{x+1} dx = \frac{1}{2},$$

as desired.

Alternative Solution. Consider the function $F(t) = \int_0^t x^{x+1} dx$. Then $F(0) = 0$ and we can write

$$\lim_{n\to\infty} n^2 \int_0^{\frac{1}{n}} x^{x+1} dx = \lim_{n\to\infty} n^2 F\left(\frac{1}{n}\right) = \lim_{u\to 0} \frac{F(u)}{u^2} = \lim_{u\to 0} \frac{F'(u)}{2u} =$$

$$= \lim_{u\to 0} \frac{u^{u+1}}{2u} = \frac{1}{2} \lim_{u\to 0} u^u = \frac{1}{2}.$$

(*Dorin Andrica*, Gazeta Matematică (GM-B), No. 11(1979), pp. 424, Problem 18025; Revista Matematică Timişoara (RMT), No. 1-2(1980), pp. 71, Problem 4160)

55. Assume the contrary and let $x \neq y$ be real numbers. Then

$$\int_x^y f(t)dt = \frac{f(x)}{f(y)} \quad \text{and} \quad \int_y^x f(t)dt = \frac{f(y)}{f(x)},$$

hence

$$\frac{f(x)}{f(y)} = -\frac{f(y)}{f(x)}.$$

It follows that $f^2(x) + f^2(y) = 0$, so $f(x) = f(y) = 0$, which is absurd since $f(x) \neq 0$ for all x.

(*Titu Andreescu*, Revista Matematică Timişoara (RMT), No. 2(1978), pp. 35, Problem 3126)

56. It is clear that

$$\int_0^1 (|f'(x)| - 1)^2 dx \geq 0.$$

Hence

$$\int_0^1 (f'(x))^2 dx - 2\int_0^1 |f'(x)|dx + \int_0^1 dx \geq 0,$$

and

$$1 \geq \int_0^1 |f'(x)|dx \geq \left|\int_0^1 f'(x)dx\right|,$$

as desired.

(*Titu Andreescu*, Revista Matematică Timişoara (RMT), No. 2(1977), pp. 77, Problem 3130)

57. The relation is equivalent to

$$\int_0^1 (xf(x) - f^2(x))dx = \int_0^1 \frac{x^2}{4}dx.$$

Hence

$$\int_0^1 \left(f^2(x) - xf(x) + \frac{x^2}{4} \right) dx = 0,$$

or

$$\int_0^1 \left(f(x) - \frac{x}{2} \right)^2 dx = 0.$$

Because f is continuous, $f(x) - \frac{x}{2} = 0$, for all $x \in [0,1]$, so $f(x) = \frac{x}{2}$, $x \in [0,1]$.

(*Titu Andreescu*, Revista Matematică Timişoara (RMT), No. 1(1978), pp. 72, Problem 3319)

58. The relation

$$\int_0^1 f_m(t)dt = \frac{1}{(m+1)!},$$

is equivalent to

$$\int_0^1 \left(f_m(t) - \frac{t^m}{m!} \right) dt = 0.$$

Since f_m is continuous by the Mean Value Theorem there is $x_0 \in (0,1)$ such that

$$f_m(x_0) = \frac{x_0^m}{m!},$$

or

$$\int_0^{x_0} \left(f_{m-1}(t) - \frac{t^{m-1}}{(m-1)!} \right) dt = 0.$$

Using the same argument, we obtain $x_1 \in (0, x_0)$ such that

$$f_{m-1}(x_1) = \frac{x_1^{m-1}}{(m-1)!}.$$

Continuing this procedure, we obtain $x_m \in (0, x_{m-1})$ such that

$$f_0(x_m) = x_m,$$

as desired.

(*Titu Andreescu*, Revista Matematică Timişoara (RMT), No. 1(1978), pp. 72 Problem 3320)

59. From the Mean Value Theorem we deduce that for any $x \in [-1,1]$ there i $c_x \in (-1, x)$ such that

$$f(x) - f(-1) = (x+1)f'(c_x).$$

Since $f'(c_x) \leq f'(1)$, $f(x) - f(-1) \leq (x+1)f'(1)$, hence

$$\int_{-1}^1 f(x)dx - 2f(-1) \leq \frac{(x+1)^2}{2}\Big|_{-1}^1 f'(1)$$

and the conclusion follows.

(*Titu Andreescu*, Revista Matematică Timişoara (RMT), No. 2(1981), pp. 77, Problem 4686)

60. Consider the function $h : [a, b] \to \mathbb{R}$,

$$h(t) = (b - t) \int_a^t f(x)dx + (t - a) \int_t^b g(x)dx$$

and note that h is differentiable and

$$h'(t) = -\int_a^t f(x)dx + (b - t)f(t) + \int_t^b g(x)dx - (t - a)g(t).$$

Since $h(a) = h(b) = 0$, from Rolle's Theorem it follows that there is a real number $c \in (a, b)$ such that $h'(c) = 0$. Then

$$-\int_a^c f(x)dx - (c - a)g(c) + (b - c)f(c) + \int_c^b g(x)dx = 0,$$

and the conclusion follows.

(*Titu Andreescu*, Revista Matematică Timişoara (RMT), No. 2(1985), pp. 56, Problem 5628)

Chapter 6
COMPREHENSIVE PROBLEMS

PROBLEMS

1. Let A be a set with n elements and let B be a subset of A with $m \geq 1$ elements. Find the number of functions $f : A \to A$ such that $f(B) \subseteq B$.

2. Let A be a set with n elements and let X, Y be subsets of A with $p \geq 1$ and $q \geq 1$ elements respectively. Find the number of functions $f : A \to A$ such that $Y \subset f(X)$.

3. Let A be a set with n elements and let X be a subset of A with $k \geq 1$ elements. Find the number of functions $f : A \to A$ such that $f(X) = X$.

4. Consider the sets $A = \{1, 2, \ldots, n\}$, $B = \{1, 2, \ldots, m\}$ and let $k \leq \min\{n, m\}$. Find the number of functions $f : A \to B$ having exactly k fixed points.

5. Let $a_1, a_2, \ldots, a_n$ be positive real numbers and let $m \geq 1$. Prove that

$$\left(1 + \frac{a_1}{a_2}\right)^m + \left(1 + \frac{a_2}{a_3}\right)^m + \cdots + \left(1 + \frac{a_n}{a_1}\right)^m \geq n \cdot 2^m.$$

6. Let $a_1, a_2, \ldots, a_n$ be positive real numbers and let $k \geq 0$. Prove that

$$k + \sqrt[n]{\prod_{i=1}^{n} a_i} \leq \sqrt[n]{\prod_{i=1}^{n} (k + a_i)} \leq k + \frac{1}{n} \sum_{i=1}^{n} a_i.$$

7. Let a, b, c be positive real numbers such that $abc = 1$. Prove that

$$\left(a - 1 + \frac{1}{b}\right) \left(b - 1 + \frac{1}{c}\right) \left(c - 1 + \frac{1}{a}\right) \leq 1.$$

8. Let α, β, γ be positive real numbers and let $[a, b]$ be an interval. Find the numbers $x, y, z \in [a, b]$ such that

$$E(x, y, z) = \alpha(x - y)^2 + \beta(y - z)^2 + \gamma(z - x)^2$$

is maximum.

9. Find the maximum number of nonzero terms of the sum

$$\sum_{i,j=1}^{n} |f(i) - f(j)|$$

where $f : \{1, 2, \ldots, n\} \to \{a, b, c\}$ is one of the 3^n possible functions.

10. Let $a_1, a_2, \ldots, a_n$, $b_1 \leq b_2 \leq \cdots \leq b_n$ be positive numbers such that

$$a_1 \leq b_1, \ a_1 + a_2 \leq b_1 + b_2, \ldots, a_1 + a_2 + \cdots + a_n \leq b_1 + b_2 + \cdots + b_n.$$

Prove that

$$\sqrt{a_1} + \sqrt{a_2} + \cdots + \sqrt{a_n} \leq \sqrt{b_1} + \sqrt{b_2} + \cdots + \sqrt{b_n}.$$

11. Define $S(n, p) = \displaystyle\sum_{i=1}^{n} (n + 1 - 2i)^{2p}$ for all positive integers n and p. Prove that for all positive real numbers a_i, $i = \overline{1, n}$ the following inequality holds

$$\min_{1 \leq i < j \leq n} (a_i - a_j)^{2p} \leq \frac{4^p}{S(n, p)} \sum_{i=1}^{n} a_i^{2p}.$$

12. Prove that

$$\sqrt[n]{n} < 1 + \sqrt[k]{(n - 1)\binom{n}{k}^{-1}},$$

for all integers $n \geq k \geq 2$.

13. a) Consider the real numbers a_{ij}, $i = 1, 2, \ldots, n - 2$, $j = 1, 2, \ldots, n$, $n \geq 3$, and the determinants A_k, $k = 1, 2, \ldots, n$

$$A_k = \begin{vmatrix} 1 & \cdots & 1 & 1 & \cdots & 1 \\ a_{11} & \cdots & a_{1,k-1} & a_{1,k+1} & \cdots & a_{1n} \\ \cdots & \cdots & \cdots & \cdots & \cdots & \cdots \\ a_{n-2,1} & \cdots & a_{n-2,k-1} & a_{n-2,k+1} & \cdots & a_{n-2,n} \end{vmatrix}$$

Prove that

$$A_1 + A_3 + A_5 + \cdots = A_2 + A_4 + A_6 + \ldots$$

b) Let $x_1, x_2, \ldots, x_n$ be distinct real numbers and let

$$p_k = \prod_{i=0}^{n-(k+1)} (x_{n-i} - x_k), \quad q_k = \prod_{i=1}^{k-1} (x_k - x_i),$$

for $k = 1, 2, \ldots, n$.

Prove that

$$\sum_{k=1}^{n} \frac{(-1)^k}{p_k q_k} = 0.$$

c) Prove that

$$\sum_{k=1}^{n} \frac{(-1)^k k^2}{(n-k)!(n+k)!} = 0,$$

for all integers $n \geq 3$.

14. Let $P(x) = x^n + a_1 x^{n-1} + \cdots + a_n$ be a polynomial with all zeros positive real numbers.

Prove that if there are $m \neq p \in \{1, 2, \ldots, n\}$ such that

$$a_m = (-1)^m \binom{n}{m} \quad \text{and} \quad a_p = (-1)^p \binom{n}{p},$$

then $P(x) = (x-1)^n$.

15. Define the polynomials $P_0, P_1, \ldots, P_n$ by

$$P_0(x) = 1 \text{ and } P_{k+1}(x) = (n-k+x)P_k(x) + xP_k'(x)$$

for all $k = 0, 1, \ldots, n-1$. Prove that $\deg P_k = k$ for all k and find the polynomial P_n.

16. Let $(P_n)_{n \geq 0}$ be a sequence of polynomials defined by

$$P_{n+1}(x) = -2xP_n'(x) + P_n(x) \text{ and } P_0(x) = 1.$$

Find $P_n(0)$.

17. Consider the polynomial

$$P(x) = \sum_{k=0}^{n} \frac{1}{n+k+1} x^k.$$

Prove that the equation $P(x^2) = P^2(x)$ has no real roots.

18. Let P be a polynomial with real coefficients. Find all functions $f : \mathbb{R} \to \mathbb{R}$ such that there is a real number t such that

$$f(x+t) - f(x) = P(x)$$

for all $x \in \mathbb{R}$.

19. Find the real numbers $a, b, c, d, e \in [-2, 2]$ such that

$$a + b + c + d + e = 0$$

$$a^3 + b^3 + c^3 + d^3 + e^3 = 0$$

and

$$a^5 + b^5 + c^5 + d^5 + e^5 = 10.$$

20. Let p be an odd prime. The sequence $(a_n)_{n \geq 0}$ is defined as follows: $a_0 = 0$, $a_1 = 1, \ldots, a_{p-2} = p-2$ and, for all $n \geq p-1$, a_n is the least integer greater than a_{n-1} that does not form an arithmetic progression of length p with any of the preceding terms. Prove that, for all n, a_n is the number obtained by writing n in base $p-1$ and reading it in base p.

21. i) Let a, c be nonnegative real numbers and let $f : [a, b] \to [c, d]$ be a bijective increasing function.

Prove that

$$\sum_{a \leq k \leq b} [f(k)] + \sum_{c \leq k \leq d} [f^{-1}(k)] - n(G_f) = [b][d] - \alpha(a)\alpha(c)$$

where k is integer, $n(G_f)$ is the number of points with nonnegative integer coordinates on the graph of f and $\alpha : \mathbb{R} \to \mathbb{Z}$ is defined by

$$\alpha(x) = \begin{cases} [x] & \text{if } x \in \mathbb{R} \setminus \mathbb{Z} \\ 0 & \text{if } x = 0 \\ x - 1 & \text{if } x \in \mathbb{Z} \setminus \{0\} \end{cases}$$

ii) Evaluate

$$S_n = \sum_{k=1}^{\frac{n(n+1)}{2}} \left[\frac{-1 + \sqrt{1 + 8k}}{2} \right]$$

22. i) Let a, c be nonnegative real numbers and let $f : [a, b] \to [c, d]$ be a bijective decreasing function.

Prove that

$$\sum_{a \leq k \leq b} [f(k)] - \sum_{c \leq k \leq d} [f^{-1}(k)] = [b]\alpha(c) - [d]\alpha(a),$$

where k is integer and α is the function defined in previous problem.

ii) Prove that

$$\sum_{k=1}^{n} \left[\frac{n^2}{k^2} \right] = \sum_{k=1}^{n^2} \left[\frac{n}{\sqrt{k}} \right]$$

for all integers $n \geq 1$.

23. Let $1 < n_1 < n_2 < \cdots < n_k < \ldots$ be a sequence of integers such that no two are consecutive.

Prove that for all positive integers m between $n_1 + n_2 + \cdots + n_m$ and $n_1 + n_2 + \cdots + n_{m+1}$ there is a perfect square.

24. Let $(x_n)_{n \geq 1}$ be a sequence defined by $x_1 = 3$ and $x_{n+1} = x_n^2 - 2$ for all positive integers n.

Taking into account that $(x_n, x_{n+1}) = 1$ for all $n \geq 1$, there are sequences $(u_n)_{n \geq 1}$, $(v_n)_{n \geq 1}$ of positive integers such that

$$u_n x_{n+1} - v_n x_n = 1, \quad n \geq 1.$$

Prove that

$$t_n = v_n^2 + 8u_n^2 + 4u_n$$

is a perfect square for all $n \geq 1$.

25. Find the sum of the series

$$\sum_{n=1}^{\infty} \frac{\varphi(n)}{2^n - 1}.$$

26. In a coordinate system xOy consider the points $A_k(k, n-1)$, $k = 0, 1, \ldots, n-1$ for a given positive integer n.

Find the number of open segments OA_k that do not contain a point with integral coordinates.

27. Let $(a_n)_{n \geq 1}$, $(b_n)_{n \geq 1}$, $(c_n)_{n \geq 1}$ be sequences of positive integers defined by

$$(1 + \sqrt[3]{2} + \sqrt[3]{4})^n = a_n + b_n \sqrt[3]{2} + c_n \sqrt[3]{4}, \quad n \geq 1.$$

Prove that

$$2^{-\frac{n}{3}} \sum_{k=0}^{n} \binom{n}{k} a_k = \begin{cases} a_n, & \text{if } n \equiv 0 \pmod{3} \\ b_n \sqrt[3]{2}, & \text{if } n \equiv 2 \pmod{3} \\ c_n \sqrt[3]{4}, & \text{if } n \equiv 1 \pmod{3} \end{cases}$$

and find similar relations for $(b_n)_{n \geq 1}$ and $(c_n)_{n \geq 1}$.

28. Consider the sequences $(a_n)_{n \geq 1}$, $(b_n)_{n \geq 1}$, $(c_n)_{n \geq 1}$, $(d_n)_{n \geq 1}$ defined by $a_1 = 0$, $b_1 = 1$, $c_1 = 1$, $d_1 = 0$ and $a_{n+1} = 2b_n + 3c_n$, $b_{n+1} = a_n + 3d_n$, $c_{n+1} = a_n + 2d_n$, $d_{n+1} = b_n + c_n$, $n \geq 1$.

Find a closed formula for the general term of these sequences.

29. Let $f : \mathbb{N}^* \times \mathbb{N}^* \to \mathbb{N}^*$ be a function such that $f(1,1) = 2$,

$$f(m+1, n) = f(m, n) + m \quad \text{and} \quad f(m, n+1) = f(m, n) - n$$

for all $m, n \in \mathbb{N}^*$. Find all pairs (p, q) such that $f(p, q) = 2001$.

30. Determine all functions $f : \mathbb{Z} \to \mathbb{Z}$ satisfying

$$f(x^3 + y^3 + z^3) = (f(z))^3 + (f(y))^3 + (f(z))^3$$

for all integers x, y, z.

31. 1981 points lie inside a cube of side 9. Prove that there are two points within a distance less than 1.

32. The squares of a chessboard are randomly labeled from 1 to 64. On the first 63 there is a knight. After some moves, the 64's square, initially unoccupied, is also unoccupied. Let n_k be the square number of the knight who was initially on the k's square.

Prove that

$$\sum_{k=1}^{63} |n_k - k| \leq 1984.$$

33. The Fibonacci sequence $(F_n)_{n\geq 1}$ is given by

$$F_1 = F_2 = 1, \quad F_{n+2} = F_{n+1} + F_n, \quad n \geq 1.$$

Prove that

$$F_{2n} = \frac{F_{2n+2}^3 + F_{2n-2}^3}{9} - 2F_{2n}^3$$

for all $n \geq 2$.

34. Let n be a positive integer and let N_k be the number of increasing arithmetic progressions with k terms from the set $\{1, 2, \ldots, n\}$.

Prove that

$$N_k \leq -\frac{1}{2}q^2 + \left(n + \frac{1}{2}\right)q + 1 - k,$$

where $q = \left[\dfrac{n-1}{k-1}\right]$.

35. Let F_n be the nth Fibonacci number (that is, $F_1 = F_2 = 1$, $F_{n+1} = F_n + F_{n-1}$ for $n \geq 2$), and let $P(x)$ be the polynomial of degree 990 such that $P(k) = F_k$ for $k = 992, 993, \ldots, 1982$. Prove that $P(1983) = F_{1983} - 1$.

36. Let x_1, x_2, α, β be real numbers and let the sequence $(x_n)_{n\geq 1}$ be given by

$$x_{n+2} = \alpha x_{n+1} + \beta x_n, \quad n \geq 1.$$

If $x_m^2 - x_{m+1}x_{m-1} \neq 0$ for all $m > 1$, prove that there are real numbers λ_1, λ_2 such that

$$\frac{x_n^2 - x_{n+1}x_{n-1}}{x_{n-1}^2 - x_n x_{n-2}} = \lambda_1$$

and

$$\frac{x_n x_{n-1} - x_{n+1}x_{n-2}}{x_{n-1}^2 - x_n x_{n-2}} = \lambda_2$$

for all $n > 2$.

37. Consider $b \in [0, 1)$ and the sequence $(a_n)_{n \geq 1}$ defined by $a_1 = a_2 = \cdots = a_{k-1} = 0$, $k \geq 3$, and

$$a_{n+1} = \frac{1}{k}(b + a_n + a_{n-1}^2 + \cdots + a_{n-k+2}^{k-1}) \text{ for all } k.$$

Prove that the sequence is convergent.

38. Let $(a_n)_{n \geq 1}$ and $(b_n)_{n \geq 1}$ be sequences such that

i) $(b_n)_{n \geq 1}$ is strictly monotonic and unbounded;

ii) there exists $\lim\limits_{n \to \infty} \dfrac{a_n}{b_n}$;

iii) $\dfrac{a_{n+1}}{a_n} + \dfrac{b_{n+1}}{b_n} = 2$, $n \geq 1$.

Prove that $\lim\limits_{n \to \infty} \dfrac{a_n}{b_n} = 0$.

39. Let $(u_n)_{n \geq 1}$, be a sequence defined by $u_1 \in \mathbb{R} \setminus \{0, 1\}$ and

$$u_{n+1} = \begin{vmatrix} 0 & u_1 & u_2 & \cdots & u_n \\ u_1 & 0 & u_2 & \cdots & u_n \\ \cdots & \cdots & \cdots & \cdots & \cdots \\ u_1 & u_2 & u_3 & \cdots & 0 \end{vmatrix}, \quad n \geq 1.$$

If the sequence converges, evaluate

$$\lim_{n \to \infty} \frac{1}{n} \prod_{k=2}^{n} (1 + u_1 \ldots u_k).$$

40. Let $(a_n)_{n \geq 1}$ and $(b_n)_{n \geq 1}$ be sequences such that

i) $0 < b_1 < b_2 < \cdots < b_n < \ldots$;

ii) $\dfrac{b_{n+1}}{b_n} \geq k > 1$, $n \geq 1$;

iii) there exists $\lim\limits_{n \to \infty} \dfrac{a_n}{b_n}$.

Prove that $\lim\limits_{n \to \infty} \dfrac{a_{n+1} - a_n}{b_{n+1} - b_n}$ exists and is equal to $\lim\limits_{n \to \infty} \dfrac{a_n}{b_n}$.

41. Let k be a positive integer and let

$$a_n = \left[\left(k + \sqrt{k^2 + 1} \right)^n + \left(\frac{1}{2} \right)^n \right], \quad n \geq 0$$

Prove that

$$\sum_{n=1}^{\infty} \frac{1}{a_{n-1} a_{n+1}} = \frac{1}{8k^2}.$$

42. Let $f : \mathbb{R} \to \mathbb{R}$

$$f(x) = \sum_{k=1}^{n} \sin a_k x,$$

where a_k are real numbers. Prove that if $|a_i| \neq |a_j|$ for $i \neq j$, then there is a real number x_0 such that $f(x_0) \neq 0$.

43. Let $f : \mathbb{R} \to \mathbb{R}$ be a differentiable function with continuous derivative such that
$$\lim_{x \to \infty} f(x) = \lim_{x \to \infty} f'(x) = \infty.$$
Prove that the function $g : \mathbb{R} \to \mathbb{R}$,
$$g(x) = \sin f(x),$$
is not periodical.

44. Let a be a real number and let $f : \mathbb{N} \to [0, 1)$, $f(n) = \{an\}$ i.e. the fractional part of the number an.
  i) Prove that f is injective if and only if a is irrational.
  ii) If a is rational, find the number of elements of the set
$$M = \{f(n)|\; n \in \mathbb{N}\}.$$

45. Let $f : \mathbb{R} \to \mathbb{R}$ be a function such that
  i) f has a period $T > 0$;
  ii) $f(x) \leq M$ for all x;
  iii) $f(x) = M$ if and only if $x = kT$, for some integer k.
Prove that, for any irrational θ the function $g : \mathbb{R} \to \mathbb{R}$,
$$g(x) = f(x) + f(\theta x),$$
is not periodical.

46. Let $f : \mathbb{R} \to \mathbb{R}$ be a continuous function with a period $T > 0$.
  a) Prove that if T is irrational, then for any $\lambda \in \left[\min_{x \in \mathbb{R}} f(x), \max_{x \in \mathbb{R}} f(x)\right]$ there is a sequence $(x_n)_{n \geq 1}$ of integers such that
$$\lim_{n \to \infty} f(x_n) = \lambda.$$

  b) Prove that if T is rational, then for any $\lambda \in \left[\min_{x \in \mathbb{R}} f(x), \max_{x \in \mathbb{R}} f(x)\right]$ and for any irrational number θ, there is a sequence $(x_n)_{n \geq 1}$ of integers such that
$$\lim_{n \to \infty} f(\theta x_n) = \lambda.$$

47. i) Let x, y, z, v be distinct positive integers such that $x + y = z + v$. Prove that there is no $\lambda > 1$ such that
$$x^\lambda + y^\lambda = z^\lambda + v^\lambda.$$

ii) Let p be a prime number and let a, b, c, d be distinct positive integers such that

$$a^p + b^p = c^p + d^p.$$

Prove that

$$|a - c| + |b - d| \geq p$$

48. i) Prove that

$$(ey)^{x-y} \leq \frac{x^x}{y^y} \leq (ex)^{x-y}$$

for any $x \geq y > 0$.

ii) Prove that

$$\frac{(n+1)^n}{e^n} < n! < \frac{(n+1)^{n+1}}{e^n}, \quad n \geq 1.$$

49. Let a, c be nonnegative real numbers and let $f : [a, b] \to [c, d]$, be a bijective function.

i) If f is increasing, prove that

$$\int_a^b f(t)dt + \int_c^d f^{-1}(t)dt = bd - ac.$$

ii) If f is decreasing, prove that

$$\int_a^b f(t)dt - \int_c^d f^{-1}(t)dt = bc - ad.$$

50. i) Let $\mu : (0, \infty) \to \mathbb{R}$ be a continuous function such that $\lim\limits_{x \to \infty} \mu(x) = 0$. Prove that

$$\lim_{x \to \infty} e^{-x} \int_0^x e^t \mu(t)dt = 0$$

ii) Let $f : [0, \infty) \to \mathbb{R}$ be an n-time differentiable function with the n-derivative continuous such that there exists

$$\lim_{x \to \infty} \sum_{k=0}^n C_n^k f^{(k)}(x) = A.$$

Prove that $\lim\limits_{x \to \infty} f(x)$ exists and

$$\lim_{x \to \infty} f(x) = A.$$

51. Let $f : [a, b] \to [c, d]$ be a continuous function such that

$$\frac{1}{a - b} \int_a^b f^2(x)dx = cd.$$

Prove that if $c + d \neq 0$, then

$$0 \leq \frac{1}{c + d} \int_a^b f(x)dx \leq \frac{b - a}{4} \left(\frac{c - d}{c + d} \right)^2.$$

52. Let $f : [a, b] \to \mathbb{R}$ be a continuous monotonic function and let $F : [a, b] \to \mathbb{R}$,

$$F(x) = (x - a) \int_x^b f(t)dt + (x - b) \int_a^x f(t)dt.$$

Prove that all values of F have the same sign.

53. a) Consider the functions $f : (0, \infty) \to \mathbb{R}$ and $g : [1, \infty) \to \mathbb{R}$ such that
1) g is differentiable with continuous derivative;
2) f is continuous and the function $h : [1, \infty) \to \mathbb{R}$, $h(x) = g'(x) - f(g(x))$ is nonincreasing.

Denote

$$a_n = \sum_{k=1}^n h(x).$$

Prove that

$$a_{n+1} - h(1) \leq \int_{g(1)}^{g(n+1)} f(x)dx \leq a_n, \quad n \geq 1.$$

b) Prove that

$$\lim_{n \to \infty} \sum_{k=1}^n \frac{1}{k^2} \cot \frac{1}{k} = \infty.$$

54. Let a be a positive real number and let $f : [0, 1] \to \mathbb{R}_+^*$ be an integrable function.

Evaluate

$$\lim_{n \to \infty} \left(\sum_{k=1}^n a^{\frac{1}{n} f\left(\frac{k}{n}\right)} - n \right).$$

55. Consider the functions $f_n : \mathbb{R} \to \mathbb{R}$,

$$f_n(x) = \begin{cases} \left(\dfrac{\sin \dfrac{n}{x}}{\sin \dfrac{1}{x}} \right)^2, & x \neq 0,\ x \neq \dfrac{1}{k\pi},\ k \in \mathbb{Z}^* \\ a_{n,k}, & x = \dfrac{1}{k\pi},\ k \in \mathbb{Z}^* \\ a_n, & x = 0 \end{cases}$$

for all integers $n \geq 0$.
1) Find the numbers $a_{n,k}$ such that f_n is continuous on $\mathbb{R}^*$.
2) Find the number a_n such that f_n is a derivative function.

56. Let $p, q \geq 0$ be integers. Find the numbers $c_{p,q}$ such that $f_{p,q} : \mathbb{R} \to \mathbb{R}$,

$$f_{p,q}(x) = \begin{cases} \sin^p \dfrac{1}{x} \cdot \cos^q \dfrac{1}{x}, & \text{if } x \neq 0 \\ c_{p,q}, & \text{if } x = 0 \end{cases}$$

s a derivative function.

57. Let q be a positive integer. Find the number $a_n(q)$ such that $f_n : \mathbb{R} \to \mathbb{R}$,

$$f_n(x) = \begin{cases} \cos \dfrac{1}{x} \cos \dfrac{q}{x} \ldots \cos \dfrac{q^{n-1}}{x}, & x \neq 0 \\ a_n(q), & x = 0 \end{cases}, \quad n \in \mathbb{N}^*,$$

is a derivative function for any integer $n > 0$.

58. 1) Let $f : \mathbb{R} \to \mathbb{R}$ be a continuous function such that

$$\lim_{|y| \to \infty} \frac{1}{y} \int_0^y f(x)dx = M(f).$$

Prove that the function

$$g(x) = \begin{cases} f\left(\dfrac{1}{x}\right), & x \neq 0 \\ M(f), & x = 0 \end{cases}$$

is a derivative function.

2) Let $f : \mathbb{R} \to \mathbb{R}$ be a continuous function with a period $T > 0$. Prove that

$$M(f) = \lim_{|t| \to \infty} \frac{1}{t} \int_0^t f(x)dx = \frac{1}{T} \int_0^T f(x)dx$$

59. If $f : \mathbb{R} \to \mathbb{R}$ is a derivative function, then is $g : \mathbb{R} \to \mathbb{R}$, $g(x) = |f(x)|$ also a derivative function?

60. If $f_1, f_2 : \mathbb{R} \to \mathbb{R}$ are derivative functions then $f = \max\{f_1, f_2\}$ is also a derivative function?

SOLUTIONS

1. There are m^m functions $h : B \to B$. Each of them can be extended in n^{n-m} ways to a function $f : A \to A$ which satisfies $f(B) \subseteq B$.

Hence the required number is $m^m \cdot n^{n-m}$.

(*Dorin Andrica*, Revista Matematică Timişoara (RMT), No. 1-2(1981), pp. 81, Problem C1:1)

2. Let X_q be a subset with q elements of X. Since Y has q elements, it follows that there are $q!$ bijective functions $g : X_q \to Y$. Each of them can be extended in n^{n-q} ways to a function $f : A \to A$ which satisfies $Y \subseteq f(X)$.

The number of subsets X_q of X is $\binom{p}{q}$, hence the requested number is $\binom{p}{q} n^{n-p}$.

Remark. If $q > p$, consider $\binom{p}{q} = 0$.

(*Dorin Andrica*, Romanian Mathematical Regional Contest "Grigore Moisil", 2000)

3. Since $f(X) = X$, it follows that f is bijective on X. There are $k!$ such bijections and each of them can be extended in n^{n-k} ways to a function $f : A \to A$. Hence the desired number is $k! n^{n-k}$.

(*Dorin Andrica*)

4. We consider two cases.

i) $n \leq m$. Let A_k be a subset with k elements of the set A. There is only one function $h : A_k \to A_k$ that has the property $h(i) = i$ for all $i \in A_k$. This function can be extended in $(m-1)^{n-k}$ ways to a function $f : A \to B$ such that $f(i) \neq i$ for all $i \in A \setminus A_k$.

The number of the subsets A_k of A is $\binom{n}{k}$, hence the desired number is $\binom{n}{k}(m-1)^{n-k}$.

ii) $m \leq n$. Let B_k be a subset with k elements of the set B. There is only one function $h : B_k \to B_k$ such that $h(i) = i$ for all $i \in B_k$. This function can be extended in $(m-1)^{m-k}$ ways to a function $g : B \to B$ such that $g(i) \neq i$ for all $i \in B \setminus B_k$.

Moreover, each function g can be extended in m^{n-m} ways to a function $f : A \to B$, that clearly has exactly k fixed points.

The number of the subsets B_k of B is $\binom{m}{k}$ hence the desired number is $\binom{m}{k} m^{n-m} (m-1)^{m-k}$.

Therefore the number of functions $f : A \to B$ with k fixed points is $\binom{n}{k}(m-1)^{n-k}$ if $n \leq m$ and $\binom{m}{k} m^{n-m}(m-1)^{m-k}$ if $m \leq n$.

(*Dorin Andrica*, Romanian Mathematical Regional Contest "Marian Ţarină, 2001)

5. Using the inequality

$$x_1^m + x_2^m + \cdots + x_n^m \geq \frac{1}{n^{m-1}}(x_1 + x_2 + \cdots + x_n)^m$$

for

$$x_1 = 1 + \frac{a_1}{a_2}, \ x_2 = 1 + \frac{a_2}{a_3}, \ldots, x_n = 1 + \frac{a_n}{a_1},$$

we obtain

$$\left(1 + \frac{a_1}{a_2}\right)^m + \left(1 + \frac{a_2}{a_3}\right)^m + \cdots + \left(1 + \frac{a_n}{a_1}\right)^m \geq$$

$$\geq \frac{1}{n^{m-1}}\left(n + \frac{a_1}{a_2} + \frac{a_2}{a_3} + \cdots + \frac{a_n}{a_1}\right)^m.$$

On the other hand,

$$\frac{a_1}{a_2} + \frac{a_2}{a_3} + \cdots + \frac{a_n}{a_1} \geq n \sqrt[n]{\frac{a_1}{a_2} \cdot \frac{a_2}{a_3} \cdots \frac{a_n}{a_1}} = n$$

from the AM-GM inequality. Therefore

$$\left(1 + \frac{a_1}{a_2}\right)^m + \left(1 + \frac{a_2}{a_3}\right)^m + \cdots + \left(1 + \frac{a_n}{a_1}\right)^m \geq \frac{1}{n^{m-1}}(2n)^m = n \cdot 2^m,$$

as desired.

(*Titu Andreescu*, Revista Matematică Timişoara (RMT), No. 1(1974), pp. 7, Problem 1564; Gazeta Matematică (GM-B), No. 2(1976), pp. 65)

6. We have

$$\prod_{i=1}^{n}(k + a_i) = k^n + \sum a_1 k^{n-1} + \sum a_1 a_2 k^{n-2} + \cdots + a_1 a_2 \ldots a_n.$$

Using the AM-GM inequality gives

$$\sum a_1 a_2 \ldots a_j \geq C_n^k \left(\prod_{i=1}^{n} a_i\right)^{\frac{\binom{n-1}{j-1}}{\binom{n}{j}}} = \binom{n}{j}\left(\prod_{i=1}^{n} a_i\right)^{\frac{j}{n}}.$$

From the previous relation we deduce

$$\prod_{i=1}^{n}(k+a_i) \geq k^n + \binom{n}{1}\left(\prod_{i=1}^{n}a_i\right)^{\frac{1}{n}}k^{n-1} + \binom{n}{2}\left(\prod_{i=1}^{n}a_i\right)^{\frac{2}{n}}k^{n-2}+$$

$$+\cdots+\binom{n}{n}\left(\prod_{i=1}^{n}\right)^{\frac{n}{n}} = \left(k+\sqrt[n]{\prod_{i=1}^{n}a_i}\right)^n.$$

Thus

$$k+\sqrt[n]{\prod_{i=1}^{n}a_i} \leq \sqrt[n]{\prod_{i=1}^{n}(k+a_i)}. \tag{1}$$

Using again the AM-GM inequality, we obtain

$$\frac{1}{n}\sum_{i=1}^{n}(k+a_i) \geq \sqrt[n]{\prod_{i=1}^{n}(k+a_i)},$$

so

$$\sqrt[n]{\prod_{i=1}^{n}(k+a_i)} \leq k+\frac{1}{n}\sum_{i=1}^{n}a_i. \tag{2}$$

(*Titu Andreescu*, Revista Matematică Timişoara (RMT), No. 2(1977), pp. 63, Problem 3045)

7. *First Solution.* Since $abc = 1$, this non-homogeneous inequality can be transformed into a homogeneous one by a suitable change of variables. In fact, there exist positive real numbers p, q, r such that

$$a = \frac{p}{q}, \quad b = \frac{q}{r}, \quad c = \frac{r}{p}.$$

Rewriting the inequality in terms of p, q, r, we obtain

$$(p-q+r)(q-r+p)(r-p+q) \leq pqr, \tag{1}$$

where $p, q, r > 0$.

At most one of the numbers $u = p-q+r$, $v = q-r+p$, $w = r-p+q$ is negative, because any two of them have a positive sum. If exactly one of the numbers u, v, w is negative, then $uvw \leq 0 < pqr$. If they are all nonnegative, then by the AM-GM inequality,

$$\sqrt{uv} \leq \frac{1}{2}(u+v) = p.$$

Likewise, $\sqrt{vw} \leq q$ and $\sqrt{wu} \leq r$. Hence $uvw \leq pqr$, as desired.

Second Solution. Expanding out the left-hand side of (1) gives

$$(p-q+r)(q-r+p)(r-p+q) = [p(p-r)+(r-q)(p-q)+q(r-q)+pq][r+(q-p)] =$$

$$= pr(p-r) + r(r-q)(p-r) + rq(r-q) + pqr + p(p-r)(q-p)+$$

$$+(r-q)(p-r)(q-p) + q(r-q)(q-p) + pq(q-p).$$

Note that

$$pr(p - r) + rq(r - q) + pq(q - p) + (r - q)(p - r)(q - p) = 0.$$

Thus (1) is equivalent to

$$0 \le p(p - q)(p - r) + q(q - r)(q - p) + r(r - p)(r - q),$$

which is a special case of Schur's inequality.

Third Solution. Denoting the left-hand side of the desired inequality by L, we have

$$L = abcL = b\left(a - 1 + \frac{1}{b}\right) c\left(b - 1 + \frac{1}{c}\right) a\left(c - 1 + \frac{1}{a}\right) =$$
$$= (ab - b + 1)(bc - c + 1)(ca - a + 1) = L_1.$$

Also, since $1/b = ac$, $1/c = ab$, $1/a = bc$,

$$L = \left(a - 1 + \frac{1}{b}\right) \left(b - 1 + \frac{1}{c}\right) \left(c - 1 + \frac{1}{a}\right) =$$
$$= (a - 1 + ac)(b - 1 + ab)(c - 1 + bc) = L_2.$$

If $u = a - 1 + 1/b \le 0$, then $a < 1$ and $b > 1$, implying that

$$v = b - 1 + 1/c > 0 \quad \text{and} \quad w = c - 1 + 1/a > 0.$$

Then $L = uvw \le 0$, as desired. Similarly, either $u \le 0$ or $v \le 0$ yields the same result. If $u, v, w > 0$, then all factors of L_1 and L_2 are positive. The AM-GM inequality gives

$$\sqrt{(ab - b + 1)(b - 1 + ab)} \le \frac{1}{2}[(ab - b + 1) + (b - 1 + ab)] = ab.$$

Likewise,

$$\sqrt{(bc - c + 1)(c - 1 + bc)} \le bc,$$
$$\sqrt{(ca - a + 1)(a - 1 + ac)} \le ca.$$

Hence $L = \sqrt{L_1 L_2} \le (ab)(bc)(ca) = (abc)^2 = 1$.

Fourth Solution. Using the notations established in the third solution, it is easy to verify the equalities

$$bcu + vc = 2, \quad cav + aw = 2, \quad abw + bu = 2.$$

As in the third solution, we only need to consider the case when $u, v, w > 0$. The AM-GM inequality gives

$$2 \ge 2c\sqrt{buv}, \quad 2 \ge 2a\sqrt{cvw}, \quad \text{and} \quad 2 \ge 2a\sqrt{awu},$$

from which $uvw \le 1$.

Fifth Solution. Let $u_1 = ab - b + 1$, $v_1 = bc - c + 1$, $w_1 = ca - a + 1$; $u_2 = 1 - bc + c$, $v_2 = 1 - ca + a$, and $w_2 = 1 - ab + b$. As in the third solution, we only need to consider the case in which $u_i, v_i, w_i > 0$ for $i = 1, 2$. Again, we have

$$L = u_1 v_1 w_1 = u_2 v_2 w_2.$$

Let $X = a + b + c$ and $Y = ab + bc + ca$. Then

$$u_1 + v_1 + w_1 = Y - X + 3 \quad \text{and} \quad u_2 + v_2 + w_2 = X - Y + 3.$$

Hence either $u_1 + v_1 + w_1 \leq 3$ or $u_2 + v_2 + w_2 \leq 3$. In either case $L \leq 1$ follows from the AM-GM inequality.

(*Titu Andreescu*, IMO 2000, Problem 2)

8. Without loss of generality we can assume that $\alpha \leq \beta \leq \gamma$. Let x, y, z be three arbitrary numbers from the interval $[a, b]$ such that $x \leq y \leq z$. Then

$$E(x, y, z) - E(x, z, y) = (\gamma - \alpha)((z - x)^2 - (y - x^2)) \geq 0,$$

and

$$E(a, y, b) = \alpha(y - a)^2 + \beta(y - b)^2 + \gamma(b - a)^2$$
$$E(b, y, a) = \alpha(y - b)^2 + \beta(y - a)^2 + \gamma(b - a)^2.$$

We need to find the maximal values of the functions

$$f_1(y) = \alpha(y - a)^2 + \beta(y - b)^2$$

and

$$f_2(y) = \alpha(y - b)^2 + \beta(y - a)^2$$

on the interval $[a, b]$. Since $f_1(a) = \beta(b - a)^2 \geq \alpha(b - a)^2 = f_1(b)$ and the coefficient of y^2 in f_1 is $\alpha + \beta \geq 0$, it follows that the maximum value of f_1 is obtained for $y = a$. Likewise, $f_2(b) \geq f_2(a)$ and the maximum value of f_2 is obtained for $y = b$.

Therefore

$$\max_{y \in [a,b]} E(a, y, b) = E(a, a, b) = (\beta + \gamma)(b - a)^2,$$

and

$$\max_{y \in [a,b]} E(b, y, a) = E(b, b, a) = (\beta + \gamma)(b - a)^2.$$

It follows that the maximum value of E is $(\beta + \gamma)(b - a)^2$ and is obtained for $x = a$, $y = a$, $z = b$ or $x = b$, $y = b$, $z = a$.

(*Dorin Andrica* and *Ioan Raşa*, Revista Matematică Timişoara (RMT), No. 1(1983), pp. 66, Problem C5:2)

9. For a function $f : \{1, 2, \ldots, n\} \to \{a, b, c\}$ let $M_a = f^{-1}(\{a\})$, $M_b = f^{-1}(\{b\})$, $M_c = f^{-1}(\{c\})$ and let p, q, r be the number of elements of sets M_a, M_b, M_c, respectively. Obviously $p + q + r = n$ and without loss of generality we may assume that $p \geq q \geq r$.

A term $|f(i) - f(j)|$ is different from 0 if the pair (i, j) is in one of the sets $M_a \times M_b$, $M_b \times M_a$, $M_a \times M_c$, $M_c \times M_a$, $M_b \times M_c$ or $M_c \times M_b$. Hence the number of nonzero terms in the sum $\sum_{i,j=1}^{n} |f(i) - f(j)|$ is $2(pq + qr + rp)$.

The problem reduces to finding the maximal value of $2(pq+qr+rp)$ when $p+q+r = n$ and $p, q, r \geq 0$ are integers.

Note that if (p_0, q_0, r_0) is a triplet that maximizes $2(pq+qr+rp)$ then the absolute value of any difference of two numbers from this triplet is at most 1. Indeed, assume that $p_0 - r_0 \geq 2$ and define

$$p_1 = p_0 - 1, \quad q_1 = q_0, \quad r_1 = r_0 + 1.$$

Then $p_1 + q_1 + r_1 = n$ and

$$p_1 q_1 + p_1 r_1 + q_1 r_1 = (p_0 - 1)q_0 + (p_0 - 1)(r_0 + 1) + q_0(r_0 + 1) =$$

$$= p_0 q_0 + p_0 r_0 + q_0 r_0 + p_0 - r_0 - 1 > p_0 q_0 + p_0 r_0 + q_0 r_0,$$

which contradicts the maximality of $2(p_0 q_0 + q_0 r_0 + r_0 p_0)$.

We have the following cases.

1) $n = 3k$. Then $p_0 + q_0 + r_0 = 3k$, $p_0 \geq q_0 \geq r_0 \geq p_0 - 1$, hence $p_0 = k$ and then $q_0 = r_0 = k$.

In this case the maximal value is

$$2(k^2 + k^2 + k^2) = 6k^2 = \frac{2n^2}{3}.$$

2) $n = 3k + 1$. Then $p_0 + q_0 + r_0 = 3k + 1$, $p_0 \geq q_0 \geq r_0 \geq p_0 - 1$, so $3p_0 \geq 3k + 1 \geq 3p_0 - 2$. Hence $p_0 = k + 1$ and then $q_0 = r_0 = k$. In this case the maximal value is

$$2((k+1)k + (k+1)k + k^2) = 2(3k^2 + 2k) = \frac{2}{3}(n^2 - 1).$$

3) $n = 3k+2$. Then $p_0 + q_0 + r_0 = 3k+2$, $p_0 \geq q_0 \geq r_0 \geq p_0 - 1$, so $3p_0 \geq 3k+1 \geq 3p_0 - 2$. It follows that $p_0 = k + 1$ and $q_0 + r_0 = 2k + 1$. Because $k + 1 \geq q_0 \geq r_0 \geq k$, $q_0 = k + 1$ and $r_0 = k$. The maximal value is in this case

$$2[(k+1)(k+1) + (k+1)k + (k+1)k] = 2(k+1)(3k+1) = 2 \cdot \frac{n^2 - 1}{3}$$

Therefore the requested number is $2\dfrac{n^2}{3}$ if 3 divides n and $2\dfrac{n^2 - 1}{3}$ otherwise.

Remark. The problem can be reformulated as follows: Suppose that n points in space are colored by three different colors. Find the maximum number of segments AB such that A and B are different colors.

(*Dorin Andrica* and *Pal Dalyai*, Romanian IMO Selection Test, 1982; Revista Matematică Timișoara (RMT), No. 1(1982), pp. 83, Problem 4917)

10. From the inequality

$$\left(\frac{\sqrt{a_1}}{\sqrt[4]{b_1}} - \sqrt[4]{b_1}\right)^2 + \left(\frac{\sqrt{a_2}}{\sqrt[4]{b_2}} - \sqrt[4]{b_2}\right)^2 + \cdots + \left(\frac{\sqrt{a_n}}{\sqrt[4]{b_n}} - \sqrt[4]{b_n}\right)^2 \geq 0,$$

it follows that

$$\sqrt{a_1} + \sqrt{a_2} + \cdots + \sqrt{a_n} \leq$$

$$\leq \frac{1}{2}\left[\left(\frac{a_1}{\sqrt{b_1}} + \frac{a_2}{\sqrt{b_2}} + \cdots + \frac{a_n}{\sqrt{b_n}}\right) + \left(\sqrt{b_1} + \sqrt{b_2} + \cdots + \sqrt{b_n}\right)\right]$$

We have

$$\frac{a_1}{\sqrt{b_1}} + \frac{a_2}{\sqrt{b_2}} + \cdots + \frac{a_n}{\sqrt{b_n}} = \frac{1}{\sqrt{b_n}}(a_n + a_{n-1} + \cdots + a_1) +$$

$$+ \left(\frac{1}{\sqrt{b_{n-1}}} - \frac{1}{\sqrt{b_n}}\right)(a_{n-1} + a_{n-2} + \cdots + a_1) +$$

$$+ \cdots + \left(\frac{1}{\sqrt{b_2}} - \frac{1}{\sqrt{b_1}}\right)(a_2 + a_1) + \frac{1}{\sqrt{b_1}}a_1 \leq$$

$$\leq \frac{1}{\sqrt{b_n}}(b_n + b_{n-1} + \cdots + b_1) + \left(\frac{1}{\sqrt{b_{n-1}}} - \frac{1}{\sqrt{b_n}}\right)(b_{n-1} + b_{n-2} + \cdots + b_1) +$$

$$+ \cdots + \left(\frac{1}{\sqrt{b_2}} - \frac{1}{\sqrt{b_1}}\right)(b_2 + b_1) + \frac{1}{\sqrt{b_1}}b_1 = \sqrt{b_1} + \sqrt{b_2} + \cdots + \sqrt{b_n},$$

hence

$$\sqrt{a_1} + \sqrt{a_2} + \cdots + \sqrt{a_n} \leq \sqrt{b_1} + \sqrt{b_2} + \cdots + \sqrt{b_n},$$

as claimed.

(*Titu Andreescu*, Revista Matematică Timişoara (RMT), No. 2(1977), pp. 63, Problem 3046)

11. By multiplying the numbers $a_1, a_2, \ldots, a_n$ with a suitable factor $\mu = \dfrac{1}{\sum\limits_{i=1}^{n} a_i^{2p}}$

we may reduce the problem to the case when $\sum\limits_{i=1}^{n} a_i^{2p} = 1$.

Assume without loss of generality that

$$a = a_1 \leq a_2 \leq \cdots \leq a_n.$$

Let $\alpha = \dfrac{2}{\sqrt[2p]{S(n,p)}}$ and suppose by way of contradiction that

$$\min\{a_2 - a_1, a_3 - a_2, \ldots, a_n - a_{n-1}\} > \alpha.$$

Then

$$a_i - a = (a_i - a_{i-1}) + (a_{i-1} - a_{i-2}) + \cdots + (a_2 - a_1) > (i-1)\alpha,$$

hence

$$\sum_{i=1}^{n} a_i^{2p} > \sum_{i=1}^{n}[a + \alpha(i-1)]^{2p}.$$

Consider the function $\varphi : \mathbb{R} \to (0, \infty)$,

$$\varphi(x) = \sum_{i=1}^{n}[x + \alpha(i-1)]^{2p}.$$

Then

$$\varphi'(x) = 2p \sum_{i=1}^{n} [x + \alpha(i-1)]^{2p-1}$$

and

$$\varphi''(x) = 2p(2p-1) \sum_{i=1}^{n} [x + \alpha(i-1)]^{2p-2} > 0.$$

Because $\varphi'(x)$ is a polynomial of odd degree and $\varphi''(x) > 0$ for all real x, it follows that φ' has a unique real zero:

$$x_0 = \frac{(1-n)}{2} \alpha$$

The number x_0 is also a minimum point of the function φ, so

$$\sum_{i=1}^{n} a_i^{2p} > \varphi(x_0) = \sum_{i=1}^{n} \left[\frac{1-n}{2} \alpha + \alpha(i-1) \right]^{2p} = \frac{\alpha^{2p}}{4^p} S(n,p) = 1,$$

a contradiction.

Hence

$$\min_{1 \le i < j \le n} (a_i - a_j)^{2p} \le \frac{4^p}{S(n,p)} \sum_{i=1}^{n} a_i^{2p},$$

as desired.

Remark. For $p = 1$ we obtain the Mitrinović's inequality

$$\min_{1 \le i < j \le n} (a_i - a_j)^2 \le \frac{12}{n(n^2-1)} \sum_{i=1}^{n} a_i^2.$$

(*Dorin Andrica*)

12. Note that

$$(1+x)^n > 1 + \binom{n}{k} x^k$$

for all positive real numbers x.

Setting $x = \sqrt[n]{n} - 1 > 0$, implies

$$(\sqrt[n]{n})^n > 1 + \binom{n}{k} (\sqrt[n]{n} - 1)^k$$

then

$$n - 1 > \binom{n}{k} (\sqrt[n]{n} - 1)^k.$$

It follows that

$$\frac{n-1}{\binom{n}{k}} > (\sqrt[n]{n} - 1)^k,$$

and then

$$\sqrt[k]{\frac{n-1}{\binom{n}{k}}} > \sqrt[n]{n} - 1,$$

as desired.

(*Dorin Andrica*, Romanian Winter Camp, 1984; Revista Matematică Timişoara (RMT), No. 1(1985), pp. 72, Problem 1)

13. a) Clearly,

$$\begin{vmatrix} 1 & 1 & \cdots & 1 & 1 \\ 1 & 1 & \cdots & 1 & 1 \\ a_{11} & a_{12} & \cdots & a_{1,n-1} & a_{1,n} \\ a_{21} & a_{22} & \cdots & a_{2,n-1} & a_{2,n} \\ \cdots & \cdots & \cdots & \cdots & \cdots \\ a_{n-2,1} & a_{n-2,2} & \cdots & a_{n-2,n-1} & a_{n-2,n} \end{vmatrix} = 0$$

Expanding the determinant after the first row yields

$$A_1 - A_2 + A_3 - A_4 + \cdots = 0,$$

hence

$$A_1 + A_3 + A_5 + \cdots = A_2 + A_4 + A_6 + \ldots,$$

as desired.

b) Consider the determinants

$$A_k = \begin{vmatrix} 1 & \cdots & 1 & 1 & \cdots & 1 \\ x_1 & \cdots & x_{k-1} & x_{k+1} & \cdots & x_n \\ \cdots & \cdots & \cdots & \cdots & \cdots & \cdots \\ x_1^{n-2} & \cdots & x_{k-1}^{n-2} & x_{k+1}^{n-2} & \cdots & x_n^{n-2} \end{vmatrix} =$$

$$= \prod_{\substack{i>j \\ i,j \neq k}}^{n} (x_i - x_j) = \frac{\prod_{i>j}^{n}(x_i - x_j)}{p_k q_k}$$

From equality a) we obtain

$$\sum_{k=1}^{n} \frac{(-1)^k}{p_k q_k} = 0.$$

c) Set $x_k = k^2$, $k = 1, 2, \ldots, n$, in the previous equality. After some algebraic manipulations we obtain

$$\sum_{k=1}^{n} \frac{(-1)^k k^2}{(n-k)!(n+k)!} = 0, \quad n \geq 3,$$

as desired.

(*Dorin Andrica*, Romanian Mathematical Regional Contest "Grigore Moisil", 1995)

14. Let $x_1, x_2, \ldots, x_n > 0$ be the zeros of polynomial P. The relations between zeros and coefficients yield

$$\sum x_1 x_2 \ldots x_m = \binom{n}{m} \quad \text{and} \quad \sum x_1 x_2 \ldots x_p = \binom{n}{p}.$$

Then we have the equality case in the Generalized Mac Laurin's Inequality:

$$\sqrt[m]{\frac{\sum x_1 x_2 \ldots x_m}{C_n^m}} \geq \sqrt[p]{\frac{\sum x_1 x_2 \ldots x_p}{C_n^p}}, \quad m \leq p$$

hence $x_1 = x_2 = \cdots = x_n$. From $\sum x_1 x_2 \ldots x_m = \binom{n}{m}$, it follows that $x_i = 1$, $i = 1, 2, \ldots, n$, hence

$$P(x) = (x - 1)^n,$$

as claimed.

(*Titu Andreescu*, Revista Matematică Timişoara (RMT), No. 1(1977), pp. 24, Problem 2300)

15. It is obvious that $\deg p_0 = 0$ and $\deg p_1 = 1$. Assuming that $\deg p_k = k$, from the given relation we obtain $\deg p_{k+1} = k + 1$, hence by induction $\deg p_i = i$ for all $i = 0, 1, \ldots, n$.

Consider the function $f : \mathbb{R} \to \mathbb{R}$, $f(x) = x^n e^x$. It is easy to prove that

$$f^{(k)}(x) = x^{n-k} Q_k(x) e^x,$$

where $Q_k(x)$ is a polynomial with real coefficients of degree k.

We prove that $Q_k(x) = P_k(x)$ for all k.

Note that $Q_0(x) = 1 - P_0(x)$ and

$$x^{n-(k+1)} Q_{k+1}(x) e^x = f^{(k+1)}(x) = (f^{(k)}(x))' = (x^{n-k} Q_k(x) e^x)' =$$
$$= x^{n-(k+1)}[(n - k + x) Q_k(x) + x Q_k'(x)],$$

hence

$$Q_{k+1}(x) = (n - k + x) Q_k(x) + x Q_k'(x).$$

Since $(P_k)_{k=\overline{0,n}}$ and $(Q_k)_{k=\overline{0,n}}$ satisfy the same recursive relation and $P_0 = Q_0$ it follows that $P_k = Q_k$ for all k.

So

$$f^{(n)}(x) = P_n(x) e^x,$$

and, on the other hand,

$$f^{(n)}(x) = (x^n e^x)^{(n)} = \sum_{k=0}^{n} C_n^k (x^n)^{(k)} e^x.$$

It follows that

$$P_n(x) = x^n + \frac{n^2}{1!} x^{n-1} + \frac{n^2(n-1)^2}{2} x^{n-2} + \cdots + n!$$

(*Dorin Andrica*, Revista Matematică Timişoara (RMT), No. 1(1978), pp. 67, Problem 3293)

16. We prove that

$$P_n'(x) = -2nP_{n-1}(x), \quad n \geq 0.$$

Note that

$$P_1'(x) = -2 = -2 \cdot 1 \cdot P_0(x)$$

and assume that

$$P_{n-1}'(x) = -2(n-1)P_{n-2}(x), \quad n \geq 2.$$

Then

$$P_n(x) = -2xP_{n-1}(x) + P_{n-1}'(x) = -2xP_{n-1}(x) - 2(n-1)P_{n-2}(x).$$

Differentiating we obtain

$$P_n'(x) = -2P_{n-1}(x) - 2xP_{n-1}'(x) - 2(n-1)P_{n-2}'(x) =$$
$$= -2P_{n-1}(x) + 4(n-1)xP_{n-2}(x) - 2(n-1)P_{n-2}'(x) =$$
$$= -2P_{n-1}(x) - 2(n-1)[-2xP_{n-2}(x) + P_{n-2}'(x)] =$$
$$= -2P_{n-1}(x) - 2(n-1)P_{n-1}(x) = -2nP_{n-1}(x),$$

as needed.

The initial relation becomes

$$P_n(x) = -2xP_{n-1}(x)_2(n-1)P_{n-2}(x), \quad n \in \mathbb{N}, n \geq 2,$$

so

$$P_n(0) = -2(n-1)P_{n-2}(0), \quad n \geq 2.$$

Hence

$$P_n(0) = \begin{cases} 0 & \text{if } n \text{ is odd} \\ (-1)^{\frac{n}{2}} \dfrac{n!}{\left(\dfrac{n}{2}\right)!} & \text{if } n \text{ is even} \end{cases}$$

Alternative solution. Note that

$$(e^{-x^2})^{(n)} = Q_n(x)e^{-x^2}$$

for a polynomial Q_n. From

$$(e^{-x^2})^{(n+1)} = [(e^{-x^2})^{(n)}]' = (Q_n(x)e^{-x^2})' =$$
$$= [Q_n'(x) - 2xQ_n(x)]e^{-x^2} = Q_{n+1}(x)e^{-x^2},$$

we obtain

$$Q_{n+1}(x) = -2xQ_n(x) - Q_n'(x), \quad n \geq 0.$$

Since $Q_0(x) = 1 = P_0(x)$, we note that

$$Q_n(x) = P_n(x) \text{ for all } n \geq 0,$$

hence

$$(e^{-x^2})^{(n)} = P_n(x)e^{-x^2}.$$

On the other hand,

$$e^{-x^2} = 1 - \frac{x^2}{1!} + \frac{x^4}{2!} - \frac{x^6}{3!} + \cdots + (-1)^n \frac{x^{2n}}{n!} + \cdots \tag{1}$$

If n is odd, then by differentiating the series (1) for an odd number of times, we deduce that $P_n(0) = 0$.

If n is even, set $n = 2m$. Differentiating (1) n times yields

$$(e^{-x^2})^{(2m)} = (-1)^m \frac{(2m)}{m!} + x \left[(-1)^{m+1} \frac{x^{2m+1}}{(m+1)!} + \cdots \right],$$

hence

$$P_n(0) = (-1)^m \frac{(2m)!}{m!}$$

Therefore

$$P_n(0) = \begin{cases} 0 & \text{if } n \text{ is odd} \\ (-1)^{\frac{n}{2}} \dfrac{n!}{\left(\frac{n}{2}\right)!} & \text{if } n \text{ is even} \end{cases}$$

(*Dorin Andrica*, Revista Matematică Timişoara (RMT), No. 2(1978), pp. 76, Problem 3706)

17. Let $P(x) = \displaystyle\sum_{k=0}^n a_k x^k$ be a polynomial with nonnegative real coefficients. By the Cauchy-Schwarz Inequality we derive that

$$P(x) = \left(\sum_{k=0}^n \sqrt{a_k} \cdot \sqrt{a_k} x^k \right)^2 \leq \left(\sum_{k=0}^n a_k \right) \left(\sum_{k=0}^n a_k x^{2k} \right) = P(1)P(x^2).$$

It suffices to prove that $P(1) < 1$. Indeed

$$\sum_{k=0}^n \frac{1}{n+l+1} < 1$$

as needed.

Therefore $P^2(x) < P(x^2)$ for all x, so the equation has no real roots.

(*Dorin Andrica*, Revista Matematică Timişoara (RMT), No. 1-2(1989), pp. 107, Problem C9:8)

18. If $P = 0$, then for $t = 0$ and for any function $f : \mathbb{R} \to \mathbb{R}$ the claim holds. Let

$$P(x) = \sum_{k=0}^n a_k x^k$$

with $a_n \neq 0$, and let $t \in \mathbb{R}^*$. We search for a polynomial

$$Q_t(x) = \sum_{k=1}^{n+1} b_k x^k$$

such that

$$Q_t(x+t) - Q_t(x) = P(x), \quad x \in \mathbb{R}.$$

Identifying the coefficients from both sides yields

$$\begin{cases} \binom{n+1}{1} t b_{n+1} = a_n \\ \\ \binom{n+1}{2} t^2 b_{n+1} + \binom{n}{1} t b_n = a_{n-1} \\ \cdots \\ \binom{n+1}{n+1} t^{n+1} b_{n+1} + \cdots + \binom{1}{1} t b_1 = a_0. \end{cases}$$

Note that the system has unique solution, hence there is a unique polynomial Q_t such that

$$Q_t(x+t) - Q_t(x) = P(x), \quad x \in \mathbb{R}$$
$$Q_t(0) = 0,$$

and

$$\deg Q_t = 1 + \deg P.$$

Set $g(x) = f(x) - Q_t(x)$. Then f satisfies the claim if and only if $g(x+t) - g(x) = 0$ for all real x, i.e. g has period t.

Therefore

$$f(x) = Q_t(x) + g(x),$$

where g is a function of period t.

(*Dorin Andrica*, Revista Matematică Timişoara (RMT), No. 2(1984), pp. 103, Problem C6:10)

19. Because $\frac{1}{2}a, \frac{1}{2}b, \frac{1}{2}c, \frac{1}{2}d, \frac{1}{2}e \in [-1, 1]$, there are real numbers x, y, z, t, u such that

$$a = 2\cos x, \quad b = 2\cos y, \quad c = 2\cos z, \quad d = 2\cos t, \quad e = 2\cos u.$$

Using the identity

$$2\cos 5\alpha = (2\cos\alpha)^5 - 5(2\cos\alpha)^3 + 5(2\cos\alpha),$$

we obtain

$$2\cos 5x = a^5 - 5a^3 + 5a$$

and the analogous relations. Summing them up yields

$$\sum 2\cos 5x = \sum a^5 - 5\sum a^3 + 5\sum a = 10$$

so

$$\sum \cos 5x = 5.$$

Hence

$$\cos 5x = \cos 5y = \cos 5z = \cos 5t = \cos 5u = 1,$$

and therefore $a, b, c, d, e \in \left\{ 2, \dfrac{\sqrt{5}-1}{2}, -\dfrac{\sqrt{5}+1}{2} \right\}$.

From the relation $a + b + c + d + e = 0$, it follows that one of the numbers is 2, two of them $\dfrac{\sqrt{5}-1}{2}$ and the other two $-\dfrac{\sqrt{5}+1}{2}$. It is easy to check that for these numbers $\sum a^3 = 0$.

(*Titu Andreescu*, Romanian Mathematical Olympiad - final round, 2002)

20. We will say that a subset of N is p-progression-free if it does not contain an arithmetic progression of length p. Denote by b_n the number obtained by writing n in base $p - 1$ and reading it in base p. One can easily prove that $a_n = b_n$ for all $n = 0, 1, 2, \ldots$ by induction, using the following properties of the set $B = \{b_0, b_1, \ldots, b_n, \ldots\}$ (whose proofs we postpone):

1° B is p-progression-free;

2° If $b_{n-1} < a < b_n$ for some $n \geq 1$, then the set $\{b_0, b_1, \ldots, b_{n-1}, a\}$ is not p-progression-free.

Indeed, assume 1° and 2° hold. By the definition of a_k and b_k, we have $a_k = b_k$ for $k = 0, 1, \ldots, p - 2$. Let $a_l = b_k$ for all $k \leq n - 1$, where $n \geq p - 1$. By 1°, the set

$$\{a_0, a_1, \ldots, a_{n-1}, b_n\} = \{b_0, b_1, \ldots, b_{n-1}, b_n\}$$

is p-progression-free, so $a_n \leq b_n$. Also, the inequality $a_n < b_n$ is impossible, in view of 2°. Hence $a_n = b_n$ and we are done.

So it suffices to prove 1° and 2°. Let us note first that B consists of all numbers whose base p representation does not contain the digit $p - 1$. Hence 1° follows from the fact that if $a, a + d, \ldots, a + (p-1)d$ is any arithmetic progression of length p, then all base p digits occur in the base p representation of its terms. To see this, represent d in the form $d = p^m k$, where $gcd(k, p) = 1$. Then d ends in m zeros, and the digit δ preceding them is nonzero. It is easy to see that if α is the $(m + 1)$st digit of a (from right to left), then the corresponding digits of $a, a + d, \ldots, a + (p - 1)d$ are the remainders of $\alpha, \alpha + \delta, \ldots, \alpha + (p - 1)\delta$ modulo p, respectively. It remains to note that $\alpha, \alpha + \delta, \ldots, \alpha + (p-1)\delta$ is a complete set of residues modulo p, because δ is relatively prime to p. This finishes the proof of 1°.

We start proving 2° by the remark that $b_{n-1} < a < b_n$ implies $a \notin B$. Since B consists precisely of the numbers whose base p representations do not contain the digit $p - 1$, this very digit must occur in the base p representation of a. Let d be the number obtained from a be replacing each of its digits by 0 if the digit is not $p - 1$, and by 1 if it is $p - 1$. Consider the progression

$$a - (p-1)d, a - (p-2)d, \ldots, a - d, a.$$

As the definition of d implies, the first $p - 1$ terms do not contain $p - 1$ in their base p representation. Hence, being less than a, they must belong to $\{b_0, b_1, \ldots, b_{n-1}\}$. Therefore the set $\{b_0, b_1, \ldots, b_{n-1}, a\}$ is not p-progression-free, and the proof is finished. $\square$

(*Titu Andreescu*, USA Mathematical Olympiad, 1995)

21. i) For a bounded region M of the plane we denote by $n(M)$ the number of points with nonnegative integral coordinates in M.

Function f is increasing and bijective, hence continuous. Consider the sets

$$M_1 = \{(x,y) \in \mathbb{R}^2 \mid a \le x \le b, \ 0 \le y \le f(x)\},$$

$$M_2 = \{(x,y) \in \mathbb{R}^2 \mid c \le y \le d, \ 0 \le x \le f^{-1}(y)\},$$

$$M_3 = \{(x,y) \in \mathbb{R}^2 \mid 0 \le x \le b, \ 0 \le y \le d\},$$

$$M_4 = \{(x,y) \in \mathbb{R}^2 \mid 0 \le x \le a, \ 0 \le y \le c\}.$$

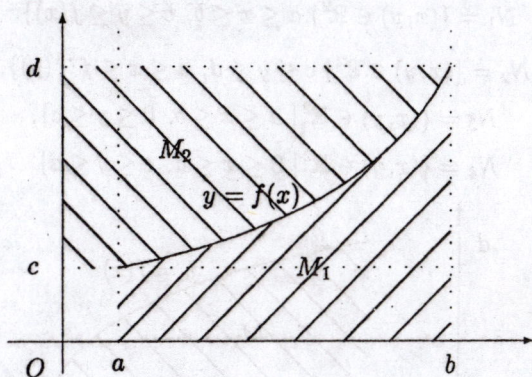

Then

$$n(M_1) = \sum_{a \le k \le b} [f(k)], \quad n(M_2) = \sum_{c \le k \le d} [f^{-1}(k)],$$

$$n(M_3) = [b][d], \quad n(M_4) = \alpha(a)\alpha(c).$$

We have

$$n(m_1) + n(M_2) - n(M_1 \cap M_2) = n(M_1 \cup M_2),$$

hence

$$n(M_1) + n(M_2) - n(G_f) = n(M_3) - n(M_4),$$

and the conclusion follows.

ii) Consider the function $f : [1, n] \to \left[1, \dfrac{n(n+1)}{2}\right]$,

$$f(x) = \frac{x(x+1)}{2}.$$

Function f is increasing and bijective. Note that $n(G_f) = n$ and $f^{-1}(x) = \dfrac{-1 + \sqrt{1 + 8x}}{2}$. Applying formula i) we obtain

$$\sum_{k=1}^{n} \left[\frac{k(k+1)}{2}\right] + \sum_{k=1}^{\frac{n(n+1)}{2}} \left[\frac{-1 + \sqrt{1 + 8k}}{2}\right] - n = \frac{n^2(n+1)}{2},$$

hence

$$\sum_{k=1}^{\frac{n(n+1)}{2}} \left[\frac{-1 + \sqrt{1 + 8k}}{2}\right] = \frac{n^2(n+1)}{2} + n - \frac{1}{2}\sum_{k=1}^{n} k(k+1) =$$

$$= \frac{n^2(n+1)}{2} + n - \frac{n(n+1)}{4} - \frac{n(n+1)(2n+1)}{12} = \frac{n(n^2+2)}{3}.$$

(*Titu Andreescu* and *Dorin Andrica*, "Asupra unor clase de identități", Gazeta Matematică (GM-B), No. 11(1978), pp. 472-475)

22. i) Function f is decreasing and bijective, hence continuous. Consider the sets

$$N_1 = \{(x,y) \in \mathbb{R}^2 \mid a \leq x \leq b,\ c \leq y \leq f(x)\},$$

$$N_2 = \{(x,y) \in \mathbb{R}^2 \mid c \leq y \leq d,\ a \leq x \leq f^{-1}(y)\},$$

$$N_3 = \{(x,y) \in \mathbb{R}^2 \mid a \leq x \leq b,\ 0 \leq y \leq c\},$$

$$N_4 = \{(x,y) \in \mathbb{R}^2 \mid 0 \leq x \leq a,\ c \leq y \leq d\}.$$

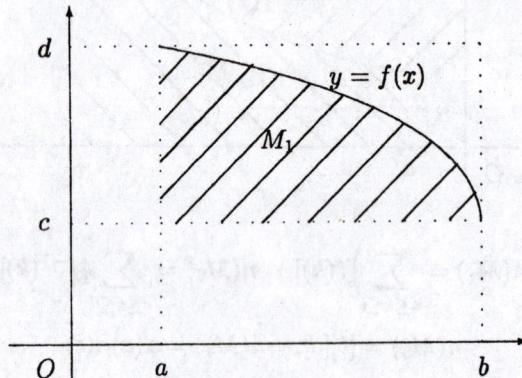

Then

$$\sum_{a \leq k \leq b} [f(k)] = n(N_1) + n(N_3),$$

$$\sum_{c \leq k \leq d} [f^{-1}(k)] = n(N_2) + n(N_4),$$

$n(N_1) = n(N_2)$, and

$$n(N_3) = ([b] - \alpha(a))\alpha(c), \quad n(N_4) = ([d] - \alpha(c))\alpha(a)$$

It follows that

$$\sum_{a \le k \le b} [f(k)] - \sum_{c \le k \le d} [f^{-1}(k)] = n(N_3) - n(N_4) =$$

$$= [b]\alpha(c) - [d]\alpha(a),$$

as desired.

ii) Consider the function $f : [1, n] \to [1, n^2]$,

$$f(x) = \frac{n^2}{x^2}$$

Note that f is decreasing and bijective and

$$f^{-1}(x) = \frac{n}{\sqrt{x}}.$$

Using formula i), we obtain

$$\sum_{k=1}^{n} \left[\frac{n^2}{k^2} \right] - \sum_{k=1}^{n^2} \left[\frac{n}{\sqrt{k}} \right] = n\alpha(1) - n^2\alpha(1) = 0,$$

hence

$$\sum_{k=1}^{n} \left[\frac{n^2}{k^2} \right] = \sum_{k=1}^{n^2} \left[\frac{n}{\sqrt{k}} \right], \quad n \ge 1,$$

as desired.

(*Dorin Andrica* and *Titu Andreescu*, Gazeta Matematică (GM-B), No. 6(1979), pp. 254, Problem O.48)

23. It is easy to prove that between numbers $a > b \ge 0$ such that $\sqrt{a} - \sqrt{b} > 1$ there is a perfect square – take for example $([\sqrt{b}] + 1)^2$.

It suffices to prove that

$$\sqrt{n_1 + \cdots + n_{m+1}} - \sqrt{n_1 + \cdots + n_m} > 1, \quad m \ge 1.$$

This is equivalent to

$$n_1 + \cdots + n_m + n_{m+1} > (1 + \sqrt{n_1 + n_2 + \cdots + n_m})^2$$

and then

$$n_{m+1} > 1 + 2\sqrt{n_1 + n_2 + \cdots + n_m}, \quad m \ge 1.$$

We induct on m. For $m = 1$ we have to prove that $n_2 > 1 + 2\sqrt{n_1}$. Indeed, $n_2 \ge n_1 + 2 = 1 + (1 + n_1) > 1 + 2\sqrt{n_1}$. Assume that the claim holds for some $m \ge 1$. Then

$$n_{m+1} - 1 > 2\sqrt{n_1 + \cdots + n_m}$$

so $(n_{m+1} - 1)^2 > 4(n_1 + \cdots + n_m)$ hence

$$(n_{m+1} + 1)^2 > 4(n_1 + \cdots + n_{m+1}).$$

This implies $n_{m+1} + 1 > 2\sqrt{n_1 + \cdots + n_{m+1}}$, and since $n_{m+2} - n_{m+1} \geq 2$, it follows that

$$n_{m+2} > 1 + 2\sqrt{n_1 + \cdots + n_{m+1}},$$

as desired.

(*Titu Andreescu*, Gazeta Matematică (GM-B), No. 1(1980), pp. 41, Problem O.113)

24. Substituting $x_{n+1} = x_n^2 - 2$ in the relation

$$u_n x_{n+1} - v_n x_n = 1$$

yields

$$u_n x_n^2 - v_n x_n - (2u_n + 1) = 0, \quad n \geq 1. \tag{1}$$

For a given $n \geq 1$ the relation (1) is a quadratic equation with integral coefficient and with an integer root x_n. Hence the discriminant

$$\Delta = v_n^2 + 8u_n^2 + 4u_n = t_n^2,$$

is a square, as desired.

(*Dorin Andrica*)

25. Let $(a_n)_{n \geq 1}$ be a sequence of real numbers. From the equality

$$\frac{x^n}{1 - x^n} = x^n + x^{2n} + \cdots + x^{kn} + \cdots, \quad |x| < 1, \quad n \geq 1$$

we derive

$$\sum_{n=1}^{\infty} \frac{a_n x^n}{1 - x^n} = \sum_{n=1}^{\infty} A_n x^n,$$

where

$$A_n = \sum_{d|n} a_d.$$

Using Gauss' formula $\sum_{d|n} \varphi(d) = n$, yields

$$\sum_{n=1}^{\infty} \frac{\varphi(n) x^n}{1 - x^n} = \sum_{n=1}^{\infty} n x^n = \frac{x}{(1 - x)^2}.$$

Setting $x = \dfrac{1}{2}$ implies $\displaystyle\sum_{n=1}^{\infty} \frac{\varphi(n)}{2^n - 1} = 2.$

(*Dorin Andrica*)

26. We start with a useful lemma.

Lemma. *There are* $\gcd(k,n) - 1$ *integers among*

$$\frac{1\cdot n}{k}, \frac{2\cdot n}{k}, \ldots, \frac{(k-1)n}{k}.$$

Proof. Let $\gcd(k,n) = d$, $k = k_1 d$, $n = n_1 d$ and note that $\gcd(k_1, n_1) = 1$. The numbers are

$$\frac{1\cdot n_1}{k_1}, \frac{2\cdot n_1}{k_1}, \ldots, \frac{(k-1)n_1}{k_1}.$$

The number of multiples of k_1 in the set $1, 2, \ldots, k-1$ is $d-1$, hence among the above numbers there are $d - 1 = \gcd(k,n) - 1$ integers, as desired.

The line OA_k has the equation

$$y = \frac{n}{k}\cdot x.$$

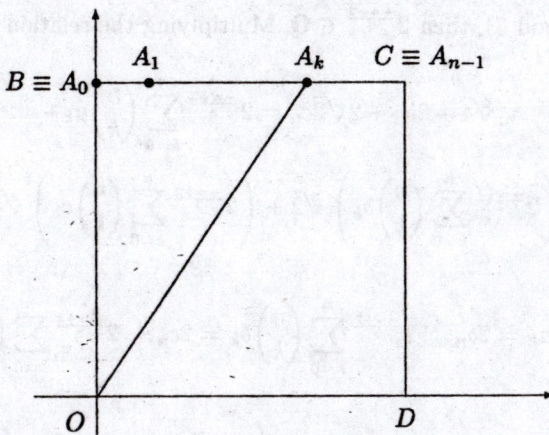

From the lemma it follows that among numbers

$$\frac{1\cdot n}{k}, \frac{2\cdot n}{k}, \ldots, \frac{(k-1)n}{k}$$

there are $\gcd(k,n) - 1$ integers. Hence the open segment OA_k does not contain points with integral coordinates if and only if $\gcd(k,n) = 1$. There are $\varphi(n)$ such numbers and we are done.

Remark. An alternative version of this problem can be: "A hunter stays at the point O in a forest where the trees are placed at points with integral coordinates. Deers stay at points $A_0, A_1, \ldots, A_{n-1}$. How many chances of success has the hunter?"

(*Dorin Andrica*)

27. We have

$$a_n + b_n\sqrt[3]{2} + c_n\sqrt[3]{4} = (1 + \sqrt[3]{2} + \sqrt[3]{4})^n = \frac{(\sqrt[3]{2}(1 + \sqrt[3]{2} + \sqrt[3]{4}))^n}{(\sqrt[3]{2})^n} =$$

$$= 2^{-\frac{n}{3}}(\sqrt[3]{2} + \sqrt[3]{4} + 2)^n = 2^{-\frac{n}{3}}(1 + (1 + \sqrt[3]{2} + \sqrt[3]{4}))^n =$$

$$= 2^{-\frac{n}{3}} \sum_{k=0}^{n} \binom{n}{k}(1 + \sqrt[3]{2} + \sqrt[3]{4})^k = 2^{-\frac{n}{3}} \sum_{k=0}^{n} \binom{n}{k}(a_k + b_k \sqrt[3]{2} + c_k \sqrt[3]{4}),$$

hence

$$a_n + b_n \sqrt[3]{2} + c_n \sqrt[3]{4} = 2^{-\frac{n}{3}} \sum_{k=1}^{n} \binom{n}{k}a_k +$$

$$+ \left(2^{-\frac{n}{3}} \sum_{k=0}^{n} \binom{n}{k}b_k\right)\sqrt[3]{2} + \left(2^{-\frac{n}{3}} \sum_{k=0}^{n} \binom{n}{k}c_k\right)\sqrt[3]{4}. \tag{1}$$

We study three cases.

i) If $n \equiv 0 \pmod 3$, then $2^{-\frac{n}{3}} \in \mathbb{Q}$, hence

$$2^{-\frac{n}{3}} \sum_{k=0}^{n} \binom{n}{k}a_k = a_n, \quad 2^{-\frac{n}{3}} \sum_{k=0}^{n} \binom{n}{k}b_k = b_n, \quad 2^{-\frac{n}{3}} \sum_{k=0}^{n} \binom{n}{k}c_k = c_n. \tag{I}$$

ii) If $n \equiv 2 \pmod 3$, then $2^{\frac{-n+2}{3}} \in \mathbb{Q}$. Multiplying the relation (1) by $2^{\frac{2}{3}} = \sqrt[3]{4}$, we obtain

$$a_n \sqrt[3]{4} + 2b_n + 2\sqrt[3]{2}c_n = 2^{\frac{-n+2}{3}} \sum_{k=0}^{n} \binom{n}{k}a_k +$$

$$+ \left(2^{\frac{-n+2}{3}} \sum_{k=0}^{n} \binom{n}{k}b_k\right)\sqrt[3]{2} + \left(2^{\frac{-n+2}{3}} \sum_{k=0}^{n} \binom{n}{k}c_k\right)\sqrt[3]{4}, \tag{2}$$

then

$$2^{\frac{-n+2}{3}} \sum_{k=0}^{n} \binom{n}{k}a_k = 2b_n, \quad 2^{\frac{-n+2}{3}} \sum_{k=0}^{n} \binom{n}{k}b_k = 2c_n, \quad 2^{\frac{-n+2}{3}} \sum_{k=0}^{n} \binom{n}{k}c_k = 2a_n.$$

Hence

$$2^{-\frac{n}{3}} \sum_{k=0}^{n} \binom{n}{k}a_k = b_n \sqrt[3]{2}, \quad 2^{-\frac{n}{3}} \sum_{k=0}^{n} \binom{n}{k}b_k = c_n \sqrt[3]{2}, \quad 2^{-\frac{n}{3}} \sum_{k=0}^{n} \binom{n}{k}c_k = \frac{a_n}{\sqrt[3]{4}}. \tag{II}$$

iii) if $n \equiv 1 \pmod 3$, then $2^{\frac{-n+1}{3}} \in \mathbb{Q}$. By multiplying the relation (1) by $2^{\frac{1}{3}} = \sqrt[3]{2}$, we obtain

$$a_n \sqrt[3]{2} + b_n \sqrt[3]{4} + 2c_n = 2^{\frac{-n+1}{3}} \sum_{k=0}^{n} \binom{n}{k}a_k +$$

$$+ \left(2^{\frac{-n+1}{3}} \sum_{k=0}^{n} \binom{n}{k}b_k\right)\sqrt[3]{2} + \left(2^{\frac{-n+1}{3}} \sum_{k=0}^{n} \binom{n}{k}c_k\right)\sqrt[3]{4}, \tag{3}$$

then

$$2^{\frac{-n+1}{3}} \sum_{k=0}^{n} \binom{n}{k}a_k = 2c_n, \quad 2^{\frac{-n+1}{3}} \sum_{k=0}^{n} \binom{n}{k}b_k = a_n, \quad 2^{\frac{-n+1}{3}} \sum_{k=0}^{n} \binom{n}{k}c_k = b_n$$

Hence

$$2^{-\frac{n}{3}} \sum_{k=0}^{n} \binom{n}{k}a_k = c_n \sqrt[3]{4}, \quad 2^{-\frac{n}{3}} \sum_{k=0}^{n} \binom{n}{k}b_k = \frac{a_n}{\sqrt[3]{2}}, \quad 2^{-\frac{n}{3}} \sum_{k=0}^{n} \binom{n}{k}c_k = \frac{b_n}{\sqrt[3]{2}}. \tag{III}$$

Relations (I), (II), (III) imply

$$2^{-\frac{n}{3}} \sum_{k=0}^{n} \binom{n}{k} a_k = \begin{cases} a_n, & n \equiv 0 \pmod 3 \\ b_n \sqrt[3]{2}, & n \equiv 2 \pmod 3 \\ c_n \sqrt[3]{4}, & n \equiv 1 \pmod 3 \end{cases}$$

$$2^{-\frac{n}{3}} \sum_{k=0}^{n} \binom{n}{k} b_k = \begin{cases} b_n, & n \equiv 0 \pmod 3 \\ c_n \sqrt[3]{2}, & n \equiv 0 \pmod 3 \\ \dfrac{a_n}{\sqrt[3]{2}}, & n \equiv 1 \pmod 3 \end{cases}$$

and

$$2^{-\frac{n}{3}} \sum_{k=0}^{n} \binom{n}{k} c_k = \begin{cases} c_n, & n \equiv 0 \pmod 3 \\ \dfrac{a_n}{\sqrt[3]{4}}, & n \equiv 0 \pmod 3 \\ \dfrac{b_n}{\sqrt[3]{2}}, & n \equiv 1 \pmod 3 \end{cases}$$

(*Titu Andreescu* and *Dorin Andrica*, Revista Matematică Timişoara (RMT), No. 1(1984), pp. 83, Problem C6:3)

28. Note that $(\sqrt{2} + \sqrt{3})^n = a_n + b_n\sqrt{2} + c_n\sqrt{3} + d_n\sqrt{6}$, $n \geq 1$. Let $n = 2k$ and

$$x_k = \frac{1}{2}[(5 + 2\sqrt{6})^k + (5 - 2\sqrt{6})^k],$$

$$y_k = \frac{1}{2}\sqrt{6}[(5 + 2\sqrt{6})^k - (5 - 2\sqrt{6})^k].$$

Then

$$(\sqrt{2} + \sqrt{3})^{2k} = x_k + y_k\sqrt{6}, \quad k \geq 1,$$

hence

$$a_n = \frac{1}{2}x_{\frac{n}{2}}, \quad b_n = c_n = 0 \text{ and } d_n = y_{\frac{n}{2}}.$$

Let $n = 2k + 1$. Then

$$(\sqrt{2} + \sqrt{3})^{2k+1} = (\sqrt{2} + \sqrt{3})(\sqrt{2} + \sqrt{3})^{2k} = (x_k + 3y_k)\sqrt{2} + (x_k + 2y_k)\sqrt{3},$$

for all $k \geq 1$, hence

$$a_n = 0, \quad b_n = x_{\frac{n-1}{2}} + 3y_{\frac{n-1}{2}},$$

$$c_n = x_{\frac{n-1}{2}} + 2y_{\frac{n-1}{2}}, \quad d_n = 0$$

(*Dorin Andrica*)

29. We have

$$f(p,q) = f(p-1,q) + p - 1 =$$

$$= f(p-2,q) + (p-2) + (p-1) = \cdots = f(1,q) + \frac{p(p-1)}{2} =$$

$$= f(1, q-1) + (q-1) + \frac{p(p-1)}{2} = \cdots =$$

$$= f(1,1) - \frac{q(q-1)}{2} + \frac{p(p-1)}{2} = 2001.$$

Therefore

$$\frac{p(p-1)}{2} - \frac{q(q-1)}{2} = 1999$$

$$(p-q)(p+q-1) = 2 \cdot 1999.$$

Note that 1999 is a prime number and that $p - q < p + q - 1$ for $p, q \in \mathbb{N}^*$. We have the following two cases:

(a) $p - q = 1$ and $p + q - 1 = 3998$. Hence $p = 2000$ and $q = 1999$.

(b) $p - q = 2$ and $p + q - 1 = 1999$. Hence $p = 1001$ and $q = 999$.

Therefore $(p, q) = (2000, 1999)$ or $(1001, 999)$.

(*Titu Andreescu*, Korean Mathematics Competition, 2001)

30. The only solutions are $f(x) = 0$, $f(x) = x$, and $f(x) = -x$. First, it is clear that these three are solutions. Next, setting $x = y = z = 0$, we find $f(0) = 3(f(0))^3$, the only integer solution of which is $f(0) = 0$. Next, with $y = -x$ and $z = 0$, we obtain $f(0) = (f(x))^3 + (f(-x))^3 + (f(0))^3$. This yields $f(-x) = -f(x)$, so f is an odd function. With $(x, y, z) = (1, 0, 0)$, we obtain $f(1) = (f(1))^3 + 2(f(0))^3 = f(1)^3$; thus $f(1) \in \{-1, 0, 1\}$. Continuing with $(x, y, z) = (1, 1, 0)$ and $(x, y, z) = (1, 1, 1)$ yields $f(2) = 2(f(1))^3 = 2f(1)$ and $f(3) = 3(f(1))^3 = 3f(1)$. To continue, we need a lemma.

Lemma. *If x is an integer greater than 3, then x^3 can be written as the sum of five cubes that are smaller in magnitude than x^3.*

Proof. We have $4^3 = 3^3 + 3^3 + 2^3 + 1^3 + 1^3$, $5^3 = 4^3 + 4^3 + (-1)^3 + (-1)^3 + (-1)^3$, $6^3 = 5^3 + 4^3 + 3^3 + 0^3 + 0^3$, and $7^3 = 6^3 + 5^3 + 1^3 + 1^3 + 0^3$. If $x = 2k + 1$ with $k > 3$, then

$$x^3 = (2k+1)^3 = (2k-1)^3 + (k+4)^3 + (4-k)^3 + (-5)^3 + (-1)^3,$$

and all of $\{2k-1, k+3, |4-k|, 5, 1\}$ are less than $2k + 1$. If $x > 3$ is an arbitrary integer, then write $x = my$, where y is 4 or 6 or an odd number greater than 3 and m is a natural number. Express y^3 as $y_1^3 + y_2^3 + y_3^3 + y_4^3 + y_5^3$. The number x^3 can then be expressed as $(my_1)^3 + (my_2)^3 + (my_3)^3 + (my_4)^3 + (my_5)^3$. $\square$

Since f is an odd function and $f(1) \in \{-1, 0, 1\}$, it suffices to prove that $f(x) = xf(1)$ for every integer x. We have proved this for $|x| \leq 3$. For $x \geq 4$, suppose that the claim is true for all values with magnitude smaller than x. By the lemma, $x^3 = x_1^3 + x_2^3 + x_3^3 + x_4^3 + x_5^3$, where $|x_i| < x$ for all i. After writing $x^3 + (-x_4)^3 + (-x_5)^3 = x_1^3 + x_2^3 + x_3^3$, we apply f to both sides. By the stated condition of f and the oddness of f, we have

$$(f(x))^3 - (f(x_4))^3 - (f(x_5))^3 = (f(x_1))^3 + (f(x_2))^3 + (f(x_3))^3.$$

Therefore, the inductive hypothesis yields

$$(f(x))^3 = \sum_{i=1}^{5}(x_i f(1))^3 = (f(1))^3 \sum_{i=1}^{5} x_i^3 = (f(1))^3 x^3.$$

Thus $f(x) = xf(1)$, and the result follows by induction.

(*Titu Andreescu*, The American Mathematical Monthly, Volume 108, No. 4(2001), pp. 372, Problem 10728)

31. Assume by way of contradiction that the distance between any two points is greater than or equal to 1. Then the spheres of radius $1/2$ with centers at these 1981 points have disjoint interiors and are included in the cube of side 10 determined by the six parallel planes to the given cube's faces and situated in the exterior at a distance of $1/2$. It follows that the sum of the volumes of the 1981 spheres is less than the volume of the cube of side 10, hence

$$1981 \cdot \frac{4\pi \cdot \left|\frac{1}{2}\right|^3}{3} = 1981 \cdot \frac{\pi}{6} > 1000,$$

a contradiction. The proof is complete.

Remark. The pigeonhole principle does not help us here. Indeed, dividing each side of the cube in $[\sqrt[3]{1981}] = 12$ congruent segments we obtain $12^3 = 1728$ small cubes of side $\frac{9}{12} = \frac{3}{4}$. In such a cube there will be two points from the initial 1981 points. The distance between them is less than $\frac{3}{4}\sqrt{3}$ which is not enough, since $\frac{3}{4}\sqrt{3} > 1$.

(*Titu Andreescu*, Revista Matematică Timişoara (RMT), No. 2(1981), pp. 68, Problem 4627)

32. Note that

$$\sum_{k=1}^{63} |n_k - k| = \sum_{k=1}^{63} \varepsilon_k(n_k - k), \text{ where } \varepsilon_k \in \{-1, 1\},$$

hence

$$S = \sum_{k=1}^{63} |n_k - k| = \pm 63 \pm 63 \pm 62 \pm 62 \pm \cdots \pm 2 \pm 2 \pm 1 \pm 1,$$

with 63 signs of $+$ and 63 signs of $-$. Then

$$S \leq (63 + 63 + 62 + 62 + \cdots + 33 + 33 + 32) - (32 + 31 + 31 + \cdots + 1 + 1) = 1984,$$

as desired.

Remark. We prove that, for some labeling, $S = 1984$. It is known that a knight can pass through all the 64 squares of the board only once and then come back to the initial square. Now label the squares from 1 to 64 in the order given by these knight moves. The free position can be made successively $64, 1, 2, \ldots, 63, 64, \ldots$ so we can reach the situation $n_1 = 32, n_2 = 33, \ldots, n_{32} = 63, n_{33} = 1, n_{34} = 2, \ldots, n_{63} = 31$. For this diagram we have $S = 1984$.

(*Titu Andreescu*, Revista Matematică Timişoara (RMT), No. 2(1984), pp. 103, Problem C6:6)

33. Note that

$$F_{2n+2} - 3F_{2n} = F_{2n+1} - 2F_{2n} = F_{2n-1} - F_{2n} = -F_{2n-2},$$

hence

$$3F_{2n} - F_{2n+2} - F_{2n-2} = 0 \qquad (1)$$

for all $n \geq 2$. Setting $a = 3F_{2n}$, $b = -F_{2n+2}$, and $c = -F_{2n-2}$ in the algebraic identity

$$a^3 + b^3 + c^3 - 3abc = (a + b + c)(a^2 + b^2 + c^2 - ab - bc - ca)$$

gives

$$27F_{2n}^3 - F_{2n+2}^3 - F_{2n-2}^3 - 9F_{2n+2}F_{2n}F_{2n-2} = 0.$$

Applying (1) twice gives

$$F_{2n+2}F_{2n-2} - F_{2n}^2 = (3F_{2n} - F_{2n-2})F_{2n-2} - F_{2n}^2 =$$

$$= F_{2n}(3F_{2n-2} - F_{2n}) - F_{2n-2}^2 = F_{2n}F_{2n-4} - D_{2n-2}^2 =$$

$$= \cdots = F_6F_2 - F_4^2 = -1.$$

The desired result follows from

$$9F_{2n+2}F_{2n}F_{2n-2} - 9F_{2n}^3 = 9F_{2n}(F_{2n+2}F_{2n-2} - F_{2n}^2) = -9F_{2n}.$$

(*Titu Andreescu*, Korean Mathematics Competition, 2000)

34. Let r be the ratio of an arithmetic progression. We have $1 + r(k-1) \leq n$, so $r \leq \dfrac{n-1}{k-1}$. It follows that the maximum ratio is $q = \left| \dfrac{n-1}{k-1} \right|$.

Let $r \in \{1, 2, \ldots, q\}$ and let $a_r \in \{1, 2, \ldots, n\}$ be the greatest first term of a progression with ratio r. Then

$$a_r + (r-1)k \leq n, \qquad (1)$$

so a_r is equal to the number of arithmetic progressions of ratio r from the set $\{1, 2, \ldots, n\}$. Hence

$$N(n, k) = a_1 + a_2 + \cdots + a_q.$$

Because $a_1 = n - k + 1$, using (1) gives

$$N \leq a_1 + n - k + n - 2k + \cdots + n - (q-1)k =$$

$$= nq - k + 1 - k(1 + 2 + \cdots + (q-1)) = nq - k - \frac{(q-1)qk}{2} + 1 =$$

$$= -\frac{q^2}{2}k + \left(n + \frac{k}{2}\right)q + 1 - k.$$

It suffices to prove that

$$\frac{q^2}{2}k + \left(n + \frac{k}{2}\right)q + 1 - k \leq -\frac{1}{2}q^2 + \left(n + \frac{1}{2}\right)q$$

which is equivalent to $\dfrac{k-1}{2}q \le \dfrac{k-1}{2}q^2$. This inequality is clearly true, so we are done.

Alternative proof. Note that $n \ge k \ge 2$. The arithmetic progressions with k terms and ratio $r = 1$ are

$$1, 2, \ldots, k$$
$$2, 3, \ldots, k+1$$
$$\cdots$$
$$n - (k-1), \ldots, n$$

so there are $n - k + 1$ such progressions.

The arithmetic progressions with k terms and ratio $r = 2$ are

$$1, 3, \ldots, 2k-1$$
$$2, 4, \ldots, 2k$$
$$\cdots$$
$$n - 2(k-1), \ldots, n$$

so a total of $n - 2(k-1)$ progressions.

It follows that

$$N_k = \sum_{d=1}^{q} [n - d(k-1)],$$

where q is the greatest ratio of an arithmetic progression with k terms from the set $\{1, 2, \ldots, n\}$. We have proved that $q = \left[\dfrac{n-1}{k-1}\right]$, hence

$$N_k = \sum_{d=1}^{q} (n - d(k-1)) = nq - \frac{q(q+1)(k-1)}{2}.$$

It suffices to show that

$$(k-2)q^2 + kq + 2 - 2k \ge 0. \tag{1}$$

The roots of the quadratic polynomial from the left-hand side of the inequality are

$$q_1 = \frac{-2(k-1)}{k-2} \quad \text{and} \quad q_2 = 1.$$

Note that $q_1 < 0$ for $k > 2$. Since $q = \left[\dfrac{n-1}{k-1}\right] \ge 1$, the inequality (1) is true for all $k > 2$. If $k = 2$, then is easy to check that the claim holds as well.

(*Titu Andreescu* and *Dorin Andrica*, Revista Matematică Timişoara (RMT), No. 1(1982), pp. 104, Problem C4:2)

35. Denote by $P_n(x)$ the (unique) polynomial of degree n such that

$$P_n(k) = F_k \quad \text{for } k = n+2, n+3, \ldots, 2n+2. \tag{1}$$

We are going to show that $P_n(2n+3) = F_{2n+3} - 1$ for all $n \geq 0$.

Clearly, $P_0(x) = 1$ and the claim is true for $n = 0$. Suppose it holds for $P_{n-1}(x)$, and consider $P_n(x)$. The polynomial

$$Q(x) = P_n(x+2) - P_n(x+1)$$

has degree at most $n - 1$. In view of (1),

$$Q(k) = P_n(k+2) - P_n(k+1) = F_{k+2} - F_{k+1} = F_k$$

for each $k = n+1, n+2, \ldots, 2n$. Therefore $Q(x)$ and $P_{n-1}(x)$ agree at n distinct points, and hence $Q(x) = P_{n-1}(x)$ for all x. In other words, $P_n(x+2) = P_n(x+1) + P_{n-1}(x)$ for all x. Combined with the inductive hypothesis $P_{2n-1}(2n+1) = F_{2n+1} - 1$, this implies

$$P_n(2n+3) = F_{2n+2} + F_{2n+1} - 1 = F_{2n+3} - 1.$$

(*Titu Andreescu*, IMO 1983 Shortlist)

36. For an arbitrary integer n we have

$$\begin{aligned}
x_{n+1} &= \alpha x_n + \beta x_{n-1}, \\
x_n &= \alpha x_{n-1} + \beta x_{n-2}, \quad n \geq 2.
\end{aligned} \tag{1}$$

This is a system of linear equations with unknowns α and β. The solutions are

$$\alpha = \frac{\Delta\alpha}{\Delta} = \frac{x_n x_{n-1} - x_{n+1} x_{n-2}}{x_{n-1}^2 - x_n x_{n-2}}$$

and

$$-\beta = -\frac{\Delta\beta}{\Delta} = \frac{x_n^2 - x_{n-1} x_{n+1}}{x_{n-1}^2 - x_n x_{n-2}}$$

Since α and $-\beta$ are constant, the conclusion follows.

(*Dorin Andrica*)

37. Let $\Delta_n = a_n - a_{n-1}$ for $n \geq 2$. Because

$$a_{n+1} = \frac{1}{k}(b + a_n + a_{n-1}^2 + \cdots + a_{n-k+2}^{k-1})$$

and

$$a_n = \frac{1}{k}(b + a_{n-1} + a_{n-2}^2 + \cdots + a_{n-k+1}^{k-1}),$$

we have

$$\Delta_{n+1} = \frac{1}{k}(\Delta_n + \lambda_1 \Delta_{n-1} + \cdots + \lambda_{k-1} \Delta_{n-k+2}), \tag{1}$$

where

$$\begin{aligned}
\lambda_1 &= a_{n-1} + a_{n-2} \\
\lambda_2 &= a_{n-2}^2 + a_{n-2} a_{n-3} + a_{n-3}^2 \\
&\cdots \\
\lambda_{k-1} &= a_{n-k+2}^{k-2} + \cdots + a_{n-k+2} a_{n-k+1}^{k-3} + a_{n-k+1}^{k-2}.
\end{aligned}$$

Note that $a_1 = a_2 = \cdots = a_{k-1} = 0$ implies $a_n > 0$ for $n \geq k$, so $\lambda_1, \lambda_2, \ldots, \lambda_{k-1} \geq 0$.

On the other hand, $\Delta_1 = \Delta_2 = \ldots, \Delta_{k-1} = 0$ and from relation (1) it follows that $\Delta_n > 0$ for all $n \geq k$. Hence the sequence $(a_n)_{n \geq k}$ is increasing.

We prove that $a_n < 1$ for all $n \geq 1$. Assume that

$$a_{n-k+2}, a_{n-k+3}, \ldots, a_n \leq 1$$

so

$$a_{n+1} \leq \frac{1}{k}(b + k - 1) < 1,$$

since $b < 1$.

Therefore the sequence is upper bounded, so is convergent.

Let $x = \lim_{n \to \infty} a_n$. Then

$$x^{k-1} + x^{k-2} + \cdots + x^2 - (k-1)x + b = 0 \qquad (2)$$

If $b = 0$, then $a_n = 0$ for all $n \geq 1$, hence $x = 0$.

If $b \in (0, 1)$, we prove that the equation (2) has a unique solution in the interval $(0, 1)$.

Let $f : [0, 1] \to \mathbb{R}$,

$$f(x) = x^{k-1} + x^{k-2} + \cdots + x^2 - (k-1)x + b.$$

Then $f(0) = b$, $f(1) = b - 1$,

$$f(0)f(1) = b(b-1) < 0$$

hence the equation (2) has an odd number of solutions in the interval $(0, 1)$. The function f is twice differentiable and since

$$f''(x) - (k-1)(k-2)x^{k-3} + 2 > 0, \quad x \in (0, 1),$$

f is concave up on $(0, 1)$. It follows that equation (2) has at most two solution in $(0, 1)$ therefore the conclusion follows.

Remark. The claim that equation (2) has a unique positive solution it follows from

$$f(0)f(1) = b(b-1) < 0$$

and from the fact that $f(x) = x^{k-1} + x^{k-2} + \cdots + x^2 - (k-1)x + b$ has a unique variation of sign (Descartes).

(*Dorin Andrica*, Revista Matematică Timişoara (RMT), No. 1-2(1979), pp. 56, Problem 3866)

38. From the relation iii) we obtain

$$\frac{a_{n+1} - a_n}{a_n} + \frac{b_{n+1} - b_n}{b_n} = 0, \quad n \geq 1,$$

then
$$\frac{a_{n+1} - a_n}{b_{n+1} - b_n} = -\frac{a_n}{b_n}, \quad n \geq 1.$$

Using ii) yields
$$\lim_{n\to\infty} \left(-\frac{a_n}{b_n}\right) = \lim_{n\to\infty} \frac{a_{n+1} - a_n}{b_{n+1} - b_n} \tag{1}$$

On the other hand, by the Stolz-Cesaro theorem we have
$$\lim_{n\to\infty} \frac{a_{n+1} - a_n}{b_{n+1} - b_n} = \lim_{n\to\infty} \frac{a_n}{b_n} \tag{2}$$

It is easy to see that relations (1) and (2) imply
$$\lim_{n\to\infty} \frac{a_n}{b_n} = 0,$$

as desired.

(*Titu Andreescu*, Revista Matematică Timişoara (RMT), No. 1(1978), pp. 69, Problem 3304)

39. Consider the determinant

$$\Delta(x_1, x_2, \ldots, x_n) = \begin{vmatrix} 0 & x_1 & x_2 & \ldots & x_n \\ x_1 & 0 & x_2 & \ldots & x_n \\ x_1 & x_2 & 0 & \ldots & x_n \\ \ldots & \ldots & \ldots & \ldots & \ldots \\ x_1 & x_2 & x_3 & \ldots & 0 \end{vmatrix}$$

Note that

$$\Delta(0, x_2, \ldots, x_n) = \Delta(x_1, 0, x_3, \ldots, x_n) = \cdots = \Delta(x_1, x_2, \ldots, x_{n-1}, 0) = 0.$$

Moreover, if $x_1 + x_2 + \cdots + x_n = 0$, then $\Delta(x_1, x_2, \ldots, x_n) = 0$, therefore

$$\Delta(x_1, x_2, \ldots, x_n) = a x_1 x_2 \ldots x_n (x_1 + x_2 + \cdots + x_n),$$

for some real number a. By identifying the coefficients of $x_1^2 x_2 \ldots x_n$ from both sides we obtain $a = 1$.

Hence

$$u_{k+1} = u_1 \ldots u_k (u_1 + \cdots + u_k), \quad k \geq 2.$$

We have
$$1 + u_1 \ldots u_k = 1 + \frac{u_{k+1}}{u_1 + \cdots + u_k} = \frac{u_1 + u_2 + \cdots + u_{k+1}}{u_1 + u_2 + \cdots + u_k},$$

then
$$\prod_{k=2}^n (1 + u_1 \ldots u_k) = \frac{u_1 + u_2 + \cdots + u_{n+1}}{u_1 + u_2}$$

Since $u_2 = -u_1^2$, we obtain

$$\frac{1}{n} \prod_{k=2}^n (1 + u_1 \ldots u_k) = \frac{u_1 + \cdots + u_{n+1}}{n u_1 (1 - u_1)}$$

Let $u = \lim\limits_{n \to \infty} u_n$ and note that

$$\lim_{n \to \infty} \frac{u_1 + \cdots + u_{n+1}}{n} = u.$$

It follows that

$$\lim_{n \to \infty} \frac{1}{n} \prod_{k=2}^{n} (1 + u_1 \ldots u_k) = \frac{u}{u_1(1 - u_1)}.$$

(*Titu Andreescu*, Revista Matematică Timişoara (RMT), No. 2(1978), pp. 52, Problem 3533)

40. Let $a = \lim\limits_{n \to \infty} \dfrac{a_n}{b_n}$ and let $\varepsilon > 0$. There is an integer $n(\varepsilon) > 0$ such that

$$a - \varepsilon \frac{k+1}{k-1} < \frac{a_n}{b_n} < a + \varepsilon \frac{k+1}{k-1} \text{ for } n \geq n(\varepsilon)$$

Since $b_n > 0$ it follows that

$$ab_n - \varepsilon \frac{k+1}{k-1} b_n < a_n < ab_n + \varepsilon \frac{k+1}{k-1} b_n \text{ for all } n \geq n(\varepsilon).$$

Then

$$a(b_{n+1} - b_n) - \varepsilon \frac{k+1}{k-1}(b_{n+1} + b_n) < a_{n+1} - a_n <$$

$$< a(b_{n+1} - b_n) + \varepsilon \frac{k+1}{k-1}(b_{n+1} + b_n),$$

and, dividing by $b_{n+1} - b_n > 0$, we obtain

$$a - \varepsilon \frac{k+1}{k-1} \cdot \frac{b_{n+1} + b_n}{b_{n+1} - b_n} < \frac{a_{n+1} - a_n}{b_{n+1} - b_n} < a + \varepsilon \frac{k+1}{k+1} \cdot \frac{b_{n+1} + b_n}{b_{n+1} - b_n},$$

for all $n \geq n(\varepsilon)$.

From relation ii) we deduce

$$\frac{b_{n+1} + b_n}{b_{n+1} - b_n} \leq \frac{k-1}{k+1}, \quad n \geq 1,$$

hence

$$a - \varepsilon < \frac{a_{n+1} - a_n}{b_{n+1} - b_n} < a + \varepsilon \text{ for all } n \geq n(\varepsilon)$$

Therefore

$$\lim_{n \to \infty} \frac{a_{n+1} - a_n}{b_{n+1} - b_n} = a = \lim_{n \to \infty} \frac{a_n}{b_n},$$

as desired.

(*Dorin Andrica*, "O reciprocă a teoremei Stolz-Cesaro şi aplicaţii ale acesteia", Revista Matematică Timişoara (RMT), No. 2(1978), pp. 6-12)

41. Let $x_1 = k + \sqrt{k^2 + 1}$ and $x_2 = k - \sqrt{k^2 + 1}$. We have

$$|x_2| = \frac{1}{x_1} < \frac{1}{2k} \leq \frac{1}{2},$$

so

$$-\left(\frac{1}{2}\right)^n \le x_2^n \le \left(\frac{1}{2}\right)^n.$$

Hence

$$x_1^n + x_2^n - 1 < x_1^n + \left(\frac{1}{2}\right)^n - 1 < a_n < x_1^n - \left(\frac{1}{2}\right)^n + 1 < x_1^n + x_2^n + 1$$

for all $n \ge 1$. The identities

$$x_1^{n+1} + x_2^{n+1} = (x_1 + x_2)(x_1^n + x_2^n) - x_1 x_2(x_1^{n-1} + x_2^{n-1}) =$$

$$= 2k(x_1^n + x_2^n) + (x_1^{n-1} + x_2^{n-1}), \quad n \ge 1$$

show that $x_1^n + x_2^n$ is an integer for all n, and since a_n is an integer, it follows that $a_n = x_1^n + x_2^n$ for all $n \ge 0$, and that $a_{n+1} = 2k a_n + a_{n-1}$ for all $n \ge 1$.

Then

$$\frac{1}{a_{n-1}a_{n+1}} = \frac{1}{2k} \cdot \frac{2k a_n}{a_{n-1}a_n a_{n+1}} = \frac{1}{2k} \cdot \frac{a_{n+1} - a_{n-1}}{a_{n-1}a_n a_{n+1}} =$$

$$= \frac{1}{2k}\left(\frac{1}{a_{n-1}a_n} - \frac{1}{a_n a_{n+1}}\right),$$

and

$$\sum_{n=1}^{N} \frac{1}{a_{n-1}a_{n+1}} = \frac{1}{2k}\left(\frac{1}{a_0 a_1} - \frac{1}{a_N a_{N+1}}\right).$$

Therefore

$$\sum_{n=1}^{\infty} \frac{1}{a_{n-1}a_{n+1}} = \frac{1}{2k a_0 a_1} = \frac{1}{8k^2}.$$

(*Titu Andreescu*)

42. Assume by way of contradiction that $f(x_0) \ne 0$ for all $x \in \mathbb{R}$. Clearly, $f^{(p)}(x) = 0$ for all integers $p > 0$. For $p = 0, 2, 4, \ldots, 2(n-1)$, we obtain

$$\sin a_1 x + \sin a_2 x + \cdots + \sin a_n x = 0$$
$$a_1^2 \sin a_1 x + a_2^2 \sin a_2 x + \cdots + a_n^2 \sin a_n x = 0$$
$$\ldots$$
$$a_1^{2(n-1)} \sin a_1 x + a_2^{2(n-1)} \sin a_2 x + \cdots + a_n^{2(n-1)} \sin a_n x = 0,$$

(1)

for all $x \in \mathbb{R}$.

Consider a number x such that at least one of $\sin a_1 x, \sin a_2 x, \ldots, \sin a_n x$ is not zero. Then the homogeneous system of linear equation (1) has a nontrivial solution, hence the determinant is zero:

$$\Delta_s = \begin{vmatrix} 1 & 1 & \ldots & 1 \\ a_1^2 & a_2^2 & \ldots & a_n^2 \\ \ldots & \ldots & \ldots & \ldots \\ a_1^{2(n-1)} & a_2^{2(n-1)} & \ldots & a_n^{2(n-1)} \end{vmatrix} = \prod_{\substack{i,j=1 \\ i>j}} (a_i^2 - a_j^2) = 0.$$

It follows that $a_k^2 = a_l^2$ for some $k \neq l$ i.e. $|a_k| = |a_l|$, which is a contradiction. The solution is complete.

(*Dorin Andrica*, Revista Matematică Timişoara (RMT), No. 1-2(1980), pp. 69, Problem 4148)

43. Assume by way of contradiction that $g : \mathbb{R} \to \mathbb{R}$, $g(x) = \sin f(x)$, is periodical. We have $g'(x) = f'(x) \cos f(x)$, and since f and f' are continuous then g' is also continuous.

Note that if g is periodical, then g' is periodical. Moreover, g' is continuous, so it is bounded.

Consider the sequence $y_n = (4n + 1)\dfrac{\pi}{2}$, $n \geq 1$. Function f is continuous and $\lim_{n \to \infty} x_n = \infty$, hence $f(x_n) = y_n$ for n sufficiently large.

Then $g'(x_n) = f'(x_n)$ so

$$\lim_{n \to \infty} g'(x_n) = \lim_{n \to \infty} f'(x_n) = \infty$$

which is a contradiction, since g' is bounded. This concludes the proof.

(*Dorin Andrica*, Revista Matematică Timişoara (RMT), No. 2(1978), pp. 54, Problem 3544)

44. i) Let f be injective and assume by way of contradiction that a is rational. Hence there are integers p, q with $a = \dfrac{p}{q}$ and $gcd(p, q) = 1$.

Then $f(q) = f(2q) = 0$ a contradiction. Therefore a is irrational.

Conversely, let a be irrational and assume by way of contradiction that $f(m) = f(n)$ for some integers $m \neq n \geq 0$. Then $\{am\} = \{an\}$ so $am - [am] = an - [an]$. We obtain

$$a = \frac{[am] - [an]}{m - n} \in \mathbb{Q},$$

which is a contradiction, and the conclusion follows.

ii) Let p, q be relatively prime integers such that $a = \dfrac{p}{q}$. We have

$$f(n) = \{an\} = \left\{ \frac{pn}{q} \right\}.$$

By the division algorithm, there are integers q and r such that

$$n = tq + r, \quad r \in \{0, 1, 2, \ldots, q - 1\}.$$

Then

$$f(n) = \left\{ \frac{p(tq + r)}{q} \right\} = \left\{ pt + \frac{rp}{q} \right\} = \left\{ \frac{rp}{q} \right\} = f(r).$$

We prove that $f(0), f(1), \ldots, f(q - 1)$ are all distinct. Indeed, if $f(i) = f(j)$, then

$$\left\{ \frac{ip}{q} \right\} = \left\{ \frac{jp}{q} \right\}$$

It follows that $\dfrac{(i-j)p}{q}$ is an integer. Note that $(p,q) = 1$ and $|i-j| < q$, hence $i - j = 0$, so $i = j$.

Therefore

$$M = \{f(0), f(1), \ldots, f(q-1)\} = \left\{0, \frac{1}{q}, \frac{2}{q}, \ldots, \frac{q-1}{q}\right\}$$

since M has q elements.

(*Dorin Andrica*, Romanian Winter Camp, 1984; Revista Matematică Timişoara (RMT), No. 1(1985), pp. 67, Problem 3)

45. Assume by way of contradiction that there is a number $t > 0$ such that

$$g(x + t) = g(x), \quad x \in \mathbb{R}.$$

Then

$$f(x + t) + f(x\theta + t\theta) = f(x) + f(x\theta), \quad x \in \mathbb{R},$$

hence

$$f(t) + f(t\theta) = 2f(0) = 2M.$$

From the relation iii) it follows that

$$f(t) = f(t\theta) = M$$

and then

$$t = k_1 T \quad \text{and} \quad t\theta = k_2 T,$$

for some integers $k_1, k_2 \neq 0$. This gives

$$\theta = \frac{k_2}{k_1} \in \mathbb{Q},$$

a contradiction.

(*Dorin Andrica*)

46. We start with an useful lemma.

Lemma. *If θ is an irrational number, then the set*

$$M = \{m\theta + n | \ m, n \ integers\}$$

is dense in $\mathbb{R}$.

Proof. We prove that in any open bounded interval $J \subseteq \mathbb{R}\backslash\{0\}$ there is an element of M, i.e. $J \cap M \neq \emptyset$. Let J be such an interval and without loss of generality consider $J \subset (0, \infty)$.

There is an integer $n(J)$ such that

$$\frac{1}{n(J)} J \subset (0, 1).$$

We consider two cases:

1. $J_1 = \dfrac{1}{n(J)} J = (0, \varepsilon)$, with $0 < \varepsilon < 1$.

Let N be an integer such that $\dfrac{1}{N} < \varepsilon$ and consider the numbers

$$\{\theta\}, \{2\theta\}, \dots, \{N\theta\}.$$

There are $p, q \in \{1, 2, \dots, N, N+1\}$ such that

$$0 < \{p\theta\} - \{q\theta\} \le \frac{1}{N}$$

On the other hand,

$$\{p\theta\} - \{q\theta\} = [q\theta] - [p\theta] + (p-q)\theta \in M,$$

hence $J_1 \cap M \ne \emptyset$. It follows that $n(J)(\{p\theta\} - \{q\theta\}) \in J \cap M$, as desired.

2. $J_1 = \dfrac{1}{n(J)} J = (a, b)$ with $0 < a < b < 1$.

Then $0 < b - a < 1$ and by case 1), there is $c \in M$ such that $0 < c < b - a$.

Let

$$n_0 = \left[\frac{a}{c}\right] + 1.$$

Then $a < n_0 c < b$ and $n_0 c \in M \cap J_1$. Likewise, $J \cap M \ne \emptyset$, as desired.

The lemma is now proved.

a) Let $\lambda \in \left[\min\limits_{x \in \mathbb{R}} f(x), \max\limits_{x \in \mathbb{R}} f(x)\right]$: Hence there is $x_0 \in \mathbb{R}$ such that $f(x_0) = \lambda$.
From the lemma we deduce that there are sequences $(x_n)_{n \ge 1}$ and $(y_n)_{n \ge 1}$ such that

$$\lim_{n \to \infty} (x_n + y_n T) = x_0.$$

The function f is continuous, so

$$\lim_{n \to \infty} f(x_n + y_n T) = f(x_0) = \lambda.$$

Note that $f(x_n + y_n T) = f(x_n)$, therefore

$$\lim_{n \to \infty} f(x_n) = \lambda,$$

as desired.

b) Let θ be an irrational number and consider the function $g(x) = f(x\theta)$, $x \in \mathbb{R}$.
The number $\dfrac{T}{\theta}$ is irrational and a period for the function g. Using the result from a),
there is a sequence $(x_n)_{n \ge 1}$ of integers such that

$$\lambda = \lim_{n \to \infty} g(x_n) = \lim_{n \to \infty} f(\theta x_n),$$

as desired.

(*Dorin Andrica*, "Asupra unor şiruri care au mulţimea punctelor limită intervale",
Gazeta Matematică (GM-B), No. 11(1979), pp. 404-406)

47. i) Let $u = x + y = z + v$ and assume that $x < y$ and $z < v$. Then we have
$x < \dfrac{u}{2}$, $z < \dfrac{u}{2}$, $y = u - x$ and $v = u - z$.

Suppose, by way of contradiction, that there is a number $\lambda > 1$ such that

$$x^\lambda + y^\lambda = z^\lambda + v^\lambda.$$

Consider the function $f : (0, u) \to (0, \infty)$,

$$f(t) = t^\lambda + (u - t)^\lambda,$$

and note that f is differentiable. We have

$$f'(t) = \lambda[t^{\lambda-1} - (u - t)^{\lambda-1}], \quad t \in (0, u),$$

and since $\lambda > 1$, it follows that f is increasing on $\left(0, \frac{u}{2}\right)$. Both x, z are in $\left(0, \frac{u}{2}\right)$, so $f(x) \neq f(z)$, because $x \neq z$. This implies $x^\lambda + y^\lambda \neq z^\lambda + v^\lambda$, which is a contradiction.

ii) Because p is a prime, by Little Fermat's Theorem we have

$$a^p - a \equiv b^p - b \equiv c^p - c \equiv d^p - d \equiv 0 \pmod{p},$$

hence

$$-(a^p - a) + (b^p - b) - (c^p - c) + (d^p - d) \equiv 0 \pmod{p}.$$

From $a^p + b^p = c^p + d^p$, we deduce that

$$a - c + b - d \equiv 0 \pmod{p} \tag{1}$$

By i) we note that $a + b \neq c + d$, therefore

$$|a - c + b - d| \geq p,$$

and then

$$|a - c| + |b - d| \geq p,$$

as desired.

(*Titu Andreescu*, Revista Matematică Timişoara (RMT), No. 2(1978), pp. 55, Problem 3550)

48. i) Consider the function $\varphi : (0, \infty) \to \mathbb{R}$,

$$\varphi(t) = t \ln t - t.$$

The Mean Value Theorem yields

$$\frac{\varphi(x) - \varphi(y)}{x - y} = \varphi'(\theta)$$

for some $\theta \in (y, x)$, then

$$\frac{x \ln x - y \ln y - x + y}{x - y} = \ln \theta.$$

It follows that

$$\ln \frac{x^x}{y^y e^{x-y}} = \ln \theta^{x-y}$$

and so
$$\frac{x^x}{y^y} = (e\theta)^{x-y}.$$

The inequalities $y < \theta < x$, imply
$$(ey)^{x-y} \le \frac{x^x}{y^y} \le (ex)^{x-y},$$

as desired.

ii) Setting $x = k + 1$ and $y = k$ yields
$$\frac{ek}{k+1} < \frac{(k+1)^k}{k^k} < e, \quad k > 0.$$

Multiplying these inequalities from $k = 1$ to $k = n$ gives
$$\frac{e^n}{n+1} < \frac{2 \cdot 3^2 \cdot 4^3 \ldots (n+1)^n}{1 \cdot 2^2 \cdot 3^3 \ldots n^n} < e^n,$$

and then
$$\frac{e^n}{(n+1)^{n+1}} < \frac{1}{n!} < \frac{e^n}{(n+1)^n}.$$

Hence
$$\frac{(n+1)^n}{e^n} < n! < \frac{(n+1)^{n+1}}{e^n},$$

as claimed.

(*Dorin Andrica*, Gazeta Matematică (GM-B), No. 8(1977), pp. 327, Problem 16820; Revista Matematică Timişoara (RMT), No. 1-2(1980), pp. 70, Problem 4153)

49. i) Note that f is bijective and increasing, therefore f is continuous.

In this diagram, we have
$$S_1 = \int_a^b f(t)dt, \quad S_2 = \int_c^d f^{-1}(t)dt,$$

hence
$$S_1 + S_2 = bd - ac,$$

as desired.

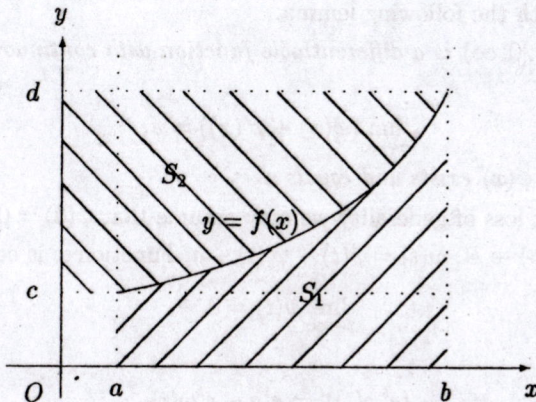

ii) Again, f is continuous and the diagram shows that

$$S_1 - S_2 = (b-a)c - (d-c)a = bc - ad,$$

as desired.

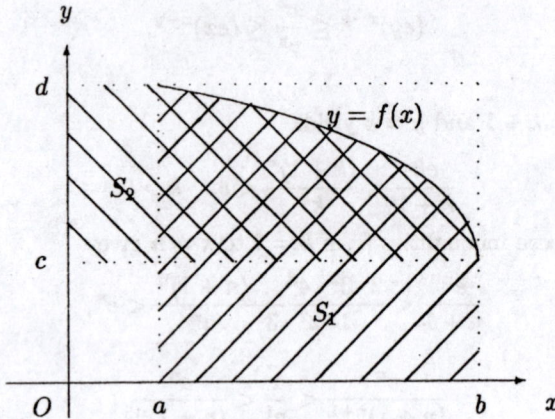

(*Dorin Andrica*, Revista Matematică Timişoara (RMT), No. 1(1981), pp. 62, Problem 4363)

50. i) Let $\varepsilon > 0$. There is $\delta_1 > 0$ such that $|\mu(t)| < \varepsilon$ for all $t > \delta_1$ and there is $\delta_2 > 0$ such that

$$e^{-x} < \varepsilon \frac{1}{\displaystyle\int_0^{\delta_1} e^t |\mu(t)| dt}, \quad x > \delta_2.$$

For $x > \delta = \max(\delta_1, \delta_2)$, we have

$$\left| e^{-x} \int_0^x e^t \mu(t) dt \right| \leq e^{-x} \int_0^{\delta_1} e^t |\mu(t)| dt + e^{-x} \int_{\delta_1}^x e^t |\mu(t)| dt <$$

$$< \varepsilon + \varepsilon e^{-x}(e^x - e^{\delta_1}) < 2\varepsilon,$$

and the conclusion follows.

ii) We start with the following lemma.

Lemma. *If $\varphi : [0, \infty)$ is a differentiable function with continuous derivative such that*

$$\lim_{x \to \infty} (\varphi(x) + \varphi'(x)) = a,$$

then the limit $\lim_{x \to \infty} \varphi(x)$ *exists and equals* a.

Proof. Without loss of generality we may assume that $\varphi(0) = 0$.

Define $\omega : [0, \infty) \to \mathbb{R}$, $\omega(t) = \varphi(t) + \varphi'(t) - a$. Function ω is continuous and

$$\lim_{t \to \infty} \omega(t) = 0.$$

Note that

$$(e^t \varphi(t))' = e^t a + e^t \omega(t),$$

then

$$e^x \varphi(x) = e^x a - a + \int_0^x e^t \omega(t)dt,$$

by integrating on $[0, x]$.

It follows that

$$\varphi(x) = a - \frac{a}{e^x} + e^{-x} \int_0^x e^t \omega(t)dt,$$

and from i) we obtain

$$\lim_{x \to \infty} \varphi(x) = a.$$

Denote

$$f_m(x) = \sum_{k=0}^{m} \binom{m}{k} f^{(k)}(x)$$

and note that

$$f_m(x) = f_{m-1}(x) + f'_{m-1}(x), \quad m > 0.$$

Using the lemma, $\lim_{x \to \infty} f_n(x) = A$ implies

$$\lim_{x \to \infty} f_{n-1}(x) = A.$$

Applying the same argument, we finally obtain

$$\lim_{x \to \infty} f_0(x) = \lim_{x \to \infty} f(x) = A,$$

as desired.

(*Dorin Andrica*)

51. Note that

$$(f(x) - c)(f(x) - d) \le 0$$

so

$$f^2(x) + cd \le (c + d)f(x), \quad x \in [a, b].$$

Then

$$\int_a^b f^2(x)dx + (b - a)cd \le (c + d)\int_a^b f(x)dx,$$

and, since the left-hand side is 0, by hypothesis we obtain

$$0 \le (c + d)\int_a^b f(x)dx,$$

and then

$$0 \le \frac{1}{c + d}\int_a^b f(x)dx. \tag{1}$$

On the other hand,

$$\left(f(x) - \frac{c + d}{2}\right)^2 = f^2(x) - (c + d)f(x) + \frac{(c + d)^2}{4} \ge 0, \quad x \in [a, b]$$

Then

$$\int_a^b f^2(x)dx + (b - a)\frac{(c + d)^2}{4} \ge (c + d)\int_a^b f(x)dx,$$

so

$$\frac{1}{(c+d)^2}\left[-(b-a)cd+(b-a)\frac{(c+d)^2}{4}\right]\geq \frac{1}{c+d}\int_a^b f(x)dx.$$

Hence

$$\frac{b-a}{4}\left(\frac{c-d}{c+d}\right)^2 \geq \frac{1}{c+d}\int_a^b f(x)dx. \qquad (2)$$

From (1) and (2) the conclusion follows.

(*Titu Andreescu*, Revista Matematică Timişoara (RMT), No. 2(1986), pp. 76, Problem 6004)

52. By the Mean Value Theorem there are numbers $c_x \in (x,b)$ and $c_x' \in (a,x)$ such that

$$F(x) = (x-a)(b-x)f(c_x) + (x-b)(x-a)f(c_x') =$$
$$= (x-a)(b-x)[f(c_x)-f(c_x')].$$

We have $c_x' < c_x$ for all $x \in [a,b]$. Since f is monotonic $f(c_x)-f(c_x')$ has constant sign on $[a,b]$. Moreover, $(x-a)(b-x) \geq 0$ for all $x \in [a,b]$ and the conclusion follows.

(*Titu Andreescu*, Revista Matematică Timişoara (RMT), No. 1(1985), pp. 63, Problem 5505)

53. a) The function h is continuous, hence it is a derivative. Let F be an antiderivative of h. By the Mean Value Theorem we have

$$F(k+1) - F(k) = h(c_k) \text{ for some } c_k \in (k,k+1).$$

Since h is nonincreasing,

$$h(k+1) \leq h(c_k) \leq h(k)$$

so

$$h(k+1) \leq F(k+1) - F(k) \leq h(k).$$

Summing these inequalities from $k=1$ to $k=n$ yields

$$a_{n+1} - h(1) \leq F(n+1) - F(1) \leq a_n,$$

hence

$$a_{n+1} - h(1) \leq \int_1^{n+1} g'(x)f(g(x))dx \leq a_n, \quad n \geq 1.$$

Because

$$\int_1^{n+1} g'(x)f(g(x))dx = \int_{g(1)}^{g(n+1)} f(x)dx,$$

the conclusion follows.

b) Setting $f:\left(0,\frac{\pi}{2}\right)\to\mathbb{R}$, $f(x)=-\cot x$ and $g:[1,\infty)\to\mathbb{R}$, $g(x)=\frac{1}{x}$, we obtain $h(x)=\frac{1}{x^2}\cot\frac{1}{x}$, which is decreasing on the interval $[1,\infty)$.

We have

$$\int_{g(1)}^{g(n+1)} f(x)dx = -\int_{1}^{\frac{1}{n+1}} \cot x \, dx =$$

$$= -\ln(\sin x)\Big|_{1}^{\frac{1}{n+1}} = -\ln\left(\sin\frac{1}{n+1}\right) + \ln(\sin 1).$$

Hence

$$\lim_{n\to\infty} \int_{g(1)}^{g(n+1)} f(x)dx = \lim_{n\to\infty}\left[-\ln\left(\sin\frac{1}{n+1}\right) + \ln(\sin 1)\right] = +\infty$$

Using the left-hand side inequality from a) it follows that

$$\lim_{n\to\infty} a_n = \lim_{n\to\infty} \sum_{k=1}^{n} \frac{1}{k^2}\cot\frac{1}{k} = \infty.$$

(*Dorin Andrica*)

54. Recall that

$$\lim_{t\to 0} \frac{a^t - 1}{t} = \ln a.$$

For $\varepsilon > 0$ there is $\delta > 0$ such that

$$\ln a - \varepsilon < \frac{a^t - 1}{t} < \ln a + \varepsilon, \quad |t| < \delta \qquad (1)$$

Function f is integrable on $[0,1]$ hence is bounded. Let $M > 0$ such that $f(x) \le M$ for all $x \in [0,1]$. There is an integer n_0 such that

$$\frac{1}{n}f\left(\frac{k}{n}\right) < \delta \text{ for all } n \ge n_0 \text{ and } k = 0, 1, \ldots, n.$$

The inequality (1) gives

$$\ln a - \varepsilon < \frac{a^{\frac{1}{n}f\left(\frac{k}{n}\right)} - 1}{\frac{1}{n}f\left(\frac{k}{n}\right)} < \ln a + \varepsilon, \quad k = 0, 1, \ldots, n$$

then

$$\ln a - \varepsilon < \frac{\displaystyle\sum_{k=1}^{n}\left(a^{\frac{1}{n}f\left(\frac{k}{n}\right)} - 1\right)}{\displaystyle\sum_{k=1}^{n}\frac{1}{n}\left(\frac{k}{n}\right)} < \ln a + \varepsilon.$$

It follows that

$$\lim_{n\to\infty} \frac{\displaystyle\sum_{k=1}^{n}\left(a^{\frac{1}{n}f\left(\frac{k}{n}\right)} - 1\right)}{\displaystyle\sum_{k=1}^{n}\frac{1}{n}\left(\frac{k}{n}\right)} = \ln a.$$

On the other hand

$$\lim_{n\to\infty}\sum_{k=1}^{n}\frac{1}{n}f\left(\frac{k}{n}\right)=\int_{0}^{1}f(x)dx,$$

therefore

$$\lim_{n\to\infty}\left(\sum_{k=1}^{n}a^{\frac{1}{a}f(\frac{k}{n})}-n\right)=\left(\int_{0}^{1}f(x)dx\right)\ln a.$$

(*Dorin Andrica*, Romanian Mathematical Regional Contest "Grigore Moisil", 1997)

55. 1) We have

$$\lim_{x\to\frac{1}{k\pi}}f_n(x)=\lim_{t\to1}\left(\frac{\sin nk\pi t}{\sin k\pi t}\right)^2=\left(\lim_{t\to1}\frac{\sin nk\pi t}{\sin k\pi t}\right)^2=$$

$$=\left(\lim_{t\to1}\frac{nk\pi\cos nk\pi t}{k\pi\cos k\pi t}\right)^2=n^2[(-1)^{nk-k}]^2=n^2.$$

Hence f_n is continuous on $\mathbb{R}^*$ if and only if $a_{n,k}=n^2$ for all $k\in\mathbb{Z}^*$.

2) It is known that $h_\alpha:\mathbb{R}\to\mathbb{R}$,

$$h_\alpha(x)=\begin{cases}\cos\dfrac{\alpha}{a}, & x\neq0\\ 0, & x=0\end{cases}$$

is a derivative. Recall the identity

$$\left(\frac{\sin nx}{\sin x}\right)^2=n+2\sum_{1\leq l<k\leq n}\cos2(k-l)x,\quad x\in\mathbb{R}\setminus\{m\pi,m\in\mathbb{Z}\}.$$

Then

$$f_n(\dot{x})=\begin{cases}n, & x\neq0\\ a_n, & x=0\end{cases}+2\sum_{1\leq l<k\leq n}h_{2(k-l)}(x),$$

so f_n is a derivative function if and only if $a_n=n$ and $a_{n,k}=n^2$ for all $k\in\mathbb{Z}^*$.

(*Dorin Andrica*, Romanian Mathematical Regional Contest "Grigore Moisil", 1995)

56. We have

$$f_{0,0}(x)=\begin{cases}1, & \text{if } x\neq0\\ c_{0,0}, & \text{if } x=0\end{cases}$$

so $f_{0,0}$ is a derivative if $c_{0,0}=1$.

Functions

$$u(x)=\begin{cases}\sin\dfrac{1}{x}, & x\neq0\\ 0, & x=0\end{cases}\quad\text{and}\quad v(x)=\begin{cases}\cos\dfrac{1}{x}, & x\neq0\\ 0, & x=0\end{cases}$$

are derivatives, so $c_{1,0}=c_{0,1}=0$.

The function

$$f_{1,1}(x) = \begin{cases} \sin\dfrac{1}{x}\cos\dfrac{1}{x}, & x \neq 0 \\ c_{1,1}, & x = 0 \end{cases} = \dfrac{1}{2}\begin{cases} \sin\dfrac{2}{x}, & x \neq 0 \\ 2c_{1,1}, & x = 0 \end{cases} =$$

$$= \dfrac{1}{2}u(2x) + \dfrac{1}{2}\begin{cases} 0, & x \neq 0 \\ 2c_{1,1}, & x = 0 \end{cases}$$

is a derivative if $c_{1,1} = 0$.

For $p, q > 1$ consider the differentiable function $G : \mathbb{R} \to \mathbb{R}$,

$$G(x) = \begin{cases} x^2 \sin^p\dfrac{1}{x}\cos^q\dfrac{1}{x}, & x \neq 0 \\ 0, & x = 0 \end{cases}$$

with

$$G'(x) = \begin{cases} 2x\sin^p\dfrac{1}{x}\cos^q\dfrac{1}{x} \quad -p\sin^{p-1}\dfrac{1}{x}\cos^{q+1}\dfrac{1}{x}+ \\ \qquad\qquad +q\sin^{p+1}\dfrac{1}{x}\cos^{q-1}\dfrac{1}{x}, & x \neq 0 \\ 0, & x = 0 \end{cases}$$

Function

$$x \mapsto \begin{cases} 2x\sin^p\dfrac{1}{x}\cos^q\dfrac{1}{x}, & x \neq 0 \\ 0, & x = 0 \end{cases}$$

is continuous, hence a derivative. Therefore

$$g(x) = \begin{cases} -p\sin^{p-1}\dfrac{1}{x}\cos^{q+1}\dfrac{1}{x} + q\sin^{p+1}\dfrac{1}{x}\cos^{q-1}\dfrac{1}{x}, & x \neq 0 \\ 0, & x = 0 \end{cases}$$

is a derivative. Using the fact that $\sin^2 t = 1 - \cos^2 t$ and $\cos^2 t = 1 - \sin^2 t$, we obtain

$$g(x) = \begin{cases} -p\sin^{p-1}\dfrac{1}{x}\cos^{q-1}\dfrac{1}{x} + (p+q)\sin^{p+1}\dfrac{1}{x}\cos^{q-1}\dfrac{1}{x}, & x \neq 0 \\ 0, & x = 0 \end{cases}$$

Hence

$$g(x) = -pf_{p-1,q-1}(x) + (p+q)f_{p+1,q-1}(x)+$$

$$+ \begin{cases} 0, & x \neq 0 \\ pc_{p-1,q-1} - (p+q)c_{p+1,q-1}, & x \neq 0 \end{cases} =$$

$$= \begin{cases} 0, & x \neq 0 \\ (p+q)c_{p-1,q+1} - qc_{p-1,q-1}, & x = 0 \end{cases}$$

Therefore

$$pc_{p-1,q-1} = (p+q)c_{p+1,q-1}$$

$$qc_{p-1,q-1} = (p+q)c_{p-1,q+1},$$

and so

$$c_{p+1,q-1} = \frac{p}{p+q} c_{p-1,q-1}$$

$$c_{p-1,q+1} = \frac{q}{p+q} c_{p-1,q-1}.$$

For $k, l \geq 1$ we obtain

$$c_{2k,2l} = \frac{2k-1}{2k+2l} c_{2k-2,2l} = \frac{2k-1}{2k+2l} \cdot \frac{2k-3}{2k+2l-2} c_{2k-4,2l} = \cdots =$$

$$= \frac{2k-1}{2k+2l} \cdot \frac{2k-3}{2k+2l-2} \cdots \frac{1}{2l+2} c_{0,2l} =$$

$$= \frac{2k-1}{2k+2l} \cdot \frac{2k-3}{2k+2l-2} \cdots \frac{1}{2l+2} \cdot \frac{2l-1}{2l} c_{0,2l-2} = \cdots =$$

$$= \frac{2k-1}{2k+2l} \cdot \frac{2k-3}{2k+2l-2} \cdots \frac{1}{2l+2} \cdot \frac{2l-1}{2l} \cdot \frac{2l-3}{2l-2} \cdots \frac{1}{2} c_{0,0} =$$

$$= \frac{1 \cdot 3 \ldots (2l-1) \cdot 1 \cdot 3 \ldots (2k-1)}{2^{k+1}(k+l)!}$$

Note that $c_{2k,2l+1} = A \cdot c_{0,1}$, $c_{2k+1,2l} = B \cdot c_{1,0}$ and $c_{2k+1,2l+1} = C \cdot c_{1,1}$, where A, B, C are rational numbers and $c_{0,1} = c_{1,0} = c_{1,1} = 0$, therefore

$$c_{2k,2l+1} = c_{2k+1,2l} = c_{2k+1,2l+1} = 0, \text{ for all } k, l \geq 0.$$

To conclude,

$$c_{p,q} = \begin{cases} \dfrac{(2k-1)!!(2l-1)!!}{2^{k+1}(k+l)!}, & \text{if } p = 2k \text{ and } q = 2l \\ 0, & \text{otherwise} \end{cases}$$

(*Dorin Andrica*, Revista Matematică Timişoara (RMT), No. 1(1986), pp. 78, Problem 5773)

57. We start with a useful lemma.

Lemma. *For any real numbers $x_1, x_2, \ldots, x_n$, we have*

$$\cos x_1 \cdot \cos x_2 \ldots \cos x_n = \frac{1}{2^n} \sum \cos(\pm x_1 \pm x_2 \pm \cdots \pm x_n)$$

where the sum is taken over all 2^n possible choices of signs.

The proof can be made by induction on n.

On the other hand recall that function $g_\alpha : \mathbb{R} \to \mathbb{R}$,

$$g_\alpha(x) = \begin{cases} \cos \dfrac{\alpha}{x}, & x \neq 0 \\ 0, & x = 0 \end{cases}$$

is a derivative.

We have two cases.

Case 1. If $q \geq 2$, set $x_1 = \dfrac{1}{x}$, $x_2 = \dfrac{q}{x}, \ldots, x_n = \dfrac{q^{n-1}}{x}$, $x \neq 0$. From the lemma we obtain

$$\cos \frac{1}{x} \cdot \cos \frac{q}{x} \ldots \cos \frac{q^{n-1}}{x} = \frac{1}{2^n} \sum \cos(\pm 1 \pm q \pm \cdots \pm q^{n-1}) \frac{1}{x}$$

hence

$$f_n(x) = \frac{1}{2^n} \sum g_{\pm 1 \pm q \pm \cdots \pm q^{n-1}}(x) + \begin{cases} \frac{1}{2^n} \dot{a}_n(q), & x \neq 0 \\ a_n(q), & x = 0 \end{cases}$$

where $\alpha_n(q)$ is the number of choices of signs $+, -$ such that $\pm 1 \pm q \pm q^2 \pm \cdots \pm q^{n-1} = 0$, because in the sum are considered only the choices of signs such that $\pm 1 \pm q \pm q^2 \pm \cdots \pm q^{n-1} \neq 0$.

Note that if $\pm 1 \pm q \pm q^2 \pm \cdots \pm q^{n-1} = 0$, then $q < 1$, which is false. Hence $\alpha_n(q) = 0$ and therefore f_n is derivative if and only if $a_n(q) = 0$.

Case 2. If $q = 1$ then for n odd we have $\alpha_n(1) = 0$ because $\pm 1 \pm 1 \pm \cdots \pm 1$ cannot be 0, having an odd number of terms. If n is even, let $n = 2m$. There are $\binom{2m}{m}$ choices of m signs $-$ and m signs $+$ so

$$\alpha_n(1) = \binom{2m}{m} = \binom{n}{\frac{n}{2}}.$$

To conclude, we have

$$\alpha_n(q) = \begin{cases} 0, & \text{if } q \geq 2 \\ 0, & \text{if } q = 1 \text{ and } n \text{ odd} \\ \frac{1}{2^n}\binom{n}{\frac{n}{2}}, & \text{if } q = 1 \text{ and } n \text{ even} \end{cases}$$

(*Dorin Andrica*, Romanian Mathematical Regional Contest "Grigore Moisil", 1999)

58. 1) Function f is continuous, so it is a derivative. Let F be an antiderivative of f. For $x \neq 0$ we have

$$\left(x^2 F\left(\frac{1}{x}\right) \right)' = 2xF\left(\frac{1}{x}\right) - f\left(\frac{1}{x}\right)$$

therefore

$$f\left(\frac{1}{x}\right) = 2xF\left(\frac{1}{x}\right) - \left(x^2 F\left(\frac{1}{x}\right) \right)' \text{ for all } x \neq 0.$$

Consider the function $h : \mathbb{R} \to \mathbb{R}$,

$$h(x) = \begin{cases} 2xF(1/x), & x \neq 0 \\ 2M(f), & x = 0. \end{cases}$$

and note that

$$\lim_{\substack{x \to 0 \\ x > 0}} h(x) = \lim_{\substack{x \to 0 \\ x > 0}} 2xF\left(\frac{1}{x}\right) = \lim_{y \to \infty} \frac{2}{y} \int_0^y f(s)ds = 2M(f).$$

Hence h is continuous so it is a derivative function. Let H be an antiderivative of h.

We have

$$g(x) = \begin{cases} 2xF(1/x) - (x^2 F(1/x))', & x \neq 0 \\ M(f), & x = 0 \end{cases}$$

$$h(x) = \begin{cases} (x^2 F(1/x))', & x \neq 0 \\ M(f), & x = 0. \end{cases}$$

The function $u : \mathbb{R} \to \mathbb{R}$,

$$u(x) = \begin{cases} (x^2 F(1/x))', & x \neq 0 \\ M(f), & x = 0 \end{cases}$$

is a derivative since $U : \mathbb{R} \to \mathbb{R}$,

$$U(x) = \begin{cases} x^2 F(1/x), & x \neq 0 \\ 0, & x = 0. \end{cases}$$

is differentiable and $U' = u$.

It follows that function $G = H - U$ is an antiderivative of g, as desired.

2) We prove that

$$\lim_{t \to \infty} \frac{1}{t} \int_0^t f(x)dx = M(f).$$

For $t > 0$ there is an integer $n = n(t)$ and a number $a = a(t) \in [0, T]$ such that $t = nT + a$.

Then

$$\int_0^t f(x)dx = \int_0^{nT} f(x)dx + \int_{nT}^t f(x)dx \tag{1}$$

On the other hand

$$\int_0^{nT} f(x)dx = \sum_{k=0}^{n-1} \int_{kT}^{(k+1)T} f(x)dx. \tag{2}$$

Setting $x = \theta + kT$ yields

$$\int_{kT}^{(k+1)T} f(x)dx = \int_0^T f(\theta + kT)d\theta = \int_0^T f(\theta)d\theta$$

so relation (2) gives

$$\int_0^{nT} f(x)dx = n \int_0^T f(x)dx$$

Setting $\theta = x - nT$ yields

$$\int_{nT}^t f(x)dx = \int_0^{t-nT} f(\theta + nT)d\theta = \int_0^{a(t)} f(\theta)d\theta$$

The relation (1) becomes

$$\int_0^t f(x)dx = n \int_0^T f(x)dx + \int_0^{a(t)} f(x)dx \tag{3}$$

and hence

$$\frac{1}{t} \int_0^t f(x)dx = \frac{n(t)}{t} \int_0^T f(x)dx + \frac{1}{t} \int_0^{a(t)} f(x)dx \text{ for all } t > 0.$$

We have

$$0 \le \left| \frac{1}{t} \int_0^{a(t)} f(x)dx \right| \le \frac{1}{t} \int_0^{a(t)} |f(x)|dx \le \frac{1}{t} \int_0^T |f(x)|dx \overset{t\to\infty}{\to} 0$$

hence

$$\lim_{t\to\infty} \frac{1}{t} \int_0^{a(t)} f(x)dx = 0.$$

Moreover

$$\lim_{t\to\infty} \frac{n(t)}{t} = \lim_{t\to\infty} \frac{n(t)}{n(t)T + a(t)} =$$

$$= \lim_{t\to\infty} \frac{1}{T + \dfrac{a(t)}{n(t)}} = \frac{1}{T},$$

therefore

$$M(f) = \lim_{t\to\infty} \frac{1}{t} \int_0^t f(x)dx = \frac{1}{T} \int_0^T f(x)dx,$$

as claimed.

The proof is similar for the case $t \to -\infty$.

(*Dorin Andrica*)

59. The answer is negative. Indeed, consider the derivative function $f : \mathbb{R} \to \mathbb{R}$,

$$f(x) = \begin{cases} \cos \dfrac{1}{x}, & x \ne 0 \\ 0, & x = 0 \end{cases}$$

Using the previous problem, the function

$$g(x) = \begin{cases} \left| \cos \dfrac{1}{x} \right|, & x \ne 0 \\ \dfrac{2}{\pi}, & x = 0 \end{cases}$$

is also a derivative. Therefore the function

$$|f(x)| = \begin{cases} \left| \cos \dfrac{1}{x} \right|, & x \ne 0 \\ 0, & x = 0 \end{cases}$$

is not a derivative and we are done.

(*Dorin Andrica*, Romanian Mathematical Regional Contest "Grigore Moisil", 1992)

60. The answer is negative. For example, consider the derivative functions $f_1, f_2 : \mathbb{R} \to \mathbb{R}$,

$$f_1(x) = \begin{cases} -\cos \dfrac{1}{x}, & x \ne 0 \\ 0, & x = 0 \end{cases}, \quad f_2(x) = \begin{cases} \cos \dfrac{1}{x}, & x \ne 0 \\ 0, & x = 0 \end{cases}$$

Then

$$f(x) = \max(f_1(x), f_2(x)) = \begin{cases} \left|\cos \dfrac{1}{x}\right|, & x \neq 0 \\ 0, & x = 0 \end{cases}$$

which is not a derivative function (see problem 59).

Alternative proof. Consider the derivative functions

$$f_1(x) = \begin{cases} \cos \dfrac{1}{x}, & x \neq 0 \\ 0, & x = 0 \end{cases}$$

$$f_2(x) = \begin{cases} -\cos \dfrac{1}{x}, & x \neq 0 \\ 0, & x = 0 \end{cases}$$

$$f_3(x) = \begin{cases} \cos^2 \dfrac{1}{x}, & x \neq 0 \\ \dfrac{1}{2}, & x = 0 \end{cases}$$

Assume for the sake of contradiction that the statement is valid. Then

$$g = \max(f_1, f_2, f_3) - \max(f_1, f_2)$$

is a derivative function, which is a contradiction, since

$$g(x) = \begin{cases} 0, & x \neq 0 \\ \dfrac{1}{2}, & x = 0 \end{cases}$$

Therefore the answer is negative.

(*Dorin Andrica*, Romanian Mathematical Regional Contest "Grigore Moisil", 1997)